THE WILEY BICENTENNIAL—KNOWLEDGE FOR GENERATIONS

Each generation has its unique needs and aspirations. When Charles Wiley first opened his small printing shop in lower Manhattan in 1807, it was a generation of boundless potential searching for an identity. And we were there, helping to define a new American literary tradition. Over half a century later, in the midst of the Second Industrial Revolution, it was a generation focused on building the future. Once again, we were there, supplying the critical scientific, technical, and engineering knowledge that helped frame the world. Throughout the 20th Century, and into the new millennium, nations began to reach out beyond their own borders and a new international community was born. Wiley was there, expanding its operations around the world to enable a global exchange of ideas, opinions, and know-how.

For 200 years, Wiley has been an integral part of each generation's journey, enabling the flow of information and understanding necessary to meet their needs and fulfill their aspirations. Today, bold new technologies are changing the way we live and learn. Wiley will be there, providing you the must-have knowledge you need to imagine new worlds, new possibilities, and new opportunities.

Generations come and go, but you can always count on Wiley to provide you the knowledge you need, when and where you need it!

WILLIAM J. PESCE
PRESIDENT AND CHIEF EXECUTIVE OFFICER

PETER BOOTH WILEY
CHAIRMAN OF THE BOARD

INSTRUCTOR'S MANUAL

Functions Modeling Change
A Preparation for Calculus
Third Edition

by
Eric Connally
Harvard University Extension

Deborah Hughes-Hallett
University of Arizona

Andrew M. Gleason
Harvard University

et al.

Compiled by:
Carl Swenson, Seattle University and
Brigitte Lahme, Sonoma State University

Contributors:
Christopher Bergerson, General Douglas MacArthur High School
Mike Brilleslyper, U.S. Air Force Academy
Kevin Cambria, General Douglas MacArthur High School
Debra Clark, General Douglas MacArthur High School
Ann Davidian, General Douglas MacArthur High School
Brigitte Lahme, Sonoma State University
Jerry Morris, Sonoma State University
Karen Rhea, University of Michigan
Dale Winter, University of Michigan

John Wiley & Sons, Inc.

COVER PHOTO   © Scott Berner / Picture Quest

To order books or for customer service please, call 1-800-CALL WILEY (225-5945).

This material is based upon work supported by the National Science Foundation under Grant No. DUE-9352905. Opinions expressed are those of the authors and not necessarily those of the Foundation.

ISBN-13   978-0-470-10819-2

Printed in the United States of America

10 9 8 7 6 5 4 3 2 1

Printed and bound by Bind-Rite Robbinsville

TABLE OF CONTENTS

Part I   Introduction   1

Part II   Lesson Guidance by Section   11

Part III   Outline Form Lesson Plan   109

Part IV   Directed Lesson Plans   193

Part V   Syllabi   195

Part VI   Worksheets and Transparencies   201

Part VII   Sample Gateway Tests   271

PART I

INTRODUCTION

The introduction is designed to provide tips for successful teaching and to promote the effective use of this instructor's manual. Additional items available at:

http://www.wiley.com/college/

LESSON PLANS

Lesson plans promote organization. They help the instructor focus on the essential aspects of the material, they provide a framework for class time, and they insure thoughtful homework assignments.

Structure of Suggested Lesson Plans

Key Points

These identify essential topics in each section. You could use these:
- to decide what content to test.

- as a guide to your own instruction. The key points are a starting point for developing your own lesson plans, or customizing the suggested lesson plans to meet the specific needs of your course.

- as a guide to reading the lesson plans. One way to read each suggested lesson plan is to ask yourself how it communicates and illustrates each of the key points. Your answers to these questions are worth communicating to the people in your class. You ideas have the potential to:
  1. Help students understand how the different parts of the lesson deal with the key points.
  2. Help students understand how the discussion in class relates to the discussion in the text book.

- to introduce what you hope to achieve in class that day, and, at the end of the class, to summarize what you actually achieved in class that day.

Suggested Lesson Plan

This is a concrete guide to creating and conducting successful and effective lessons. It contains a mixture of different materials including:
- Aspects of the subject matter typically requiring very thorough explanation, and ideas for formulating explanations.

- Ideas for supporting explanations with visual and numerical representations of the mathematics (such as tables and graphs).

- Pedagogical insights. Warnings about material that students often find challenging or mysterious, and advice on dealing with the (usually inappropriate) preconceived notions that some students may bring to their studies.

- Illustrative examples, which are substantially different from those treated in the text. These provide alternative perspectives on the subject matter, and link the mathematics to other fields.

- Ideas for involving students in the class and having them engage the subject matter; many lesson plans suggest problems from the text that students could work on in class.

Suggested Homework Assignment

These homework assignments for the section are merely suggestions. They have been compiled by consulting with instructors who used previous versions of this material. The list is intended to be a core of problems for the central material of the section. Such a list provides a starting point for consideration of your homework assignments. The list should be freely tailored to meet your needs.

Alternate In-Class Assignment

These are suggestions for creating interactive group work by students. They normally give a section's exercise that lends itself to group work. In some cases a more elaborate suggestion is made. These can be used occasionally or as part of each class. This is a springboard for instructors wishing to include classroom activities that are not in the lecture mode.

What the Lesson Plans Are Not

- They are not a schedule or timetable for running a class.
- They are not a recipe or script to read from while conducting class.
- They are not a sequence of steps to work through.
- They are not a substitute for careful and thoughtful reading of the text.
- They are not a substitute for working through and thinking through problems or activities assigned to students in class.
- They are not a substitute for careful planning and attentive conduct of a class.
- They are not a substitute for common sense.
- They are not just a Homework Assignment.

Using the Suggested Lesson Plans When Teaching

One format for a lesson is:
- Introduction
- The Body of the Lesson
- Conclusion/Summary/Wrap-up
- Homework Assignment

The Introduction

The beginning of the lesson could be used to:
- Tie up loose ends from the previous lesson.
- Announce any administrative items (upcoming exams or quizzes, due dates for homework, etc.)
- Address problems from the last day's homework. A warning: if you make a habit of spending some time during each class clarifying or working through homework problems, be careful to keep a tight cap on the amount of time you spend. Solving homework problems can easily eat up the time reserved for the body of your lesson, leaving you scrambling to fit everything in.
- Announce what you plan to do in the lesson, and what you hope that students will get out the lesson. This could be a deeper understanding of each of the key points, or problem-solving skills or an appreciation of how the subject matter of the lesson relates to other sections in the text. Some instructors omit this kind of information, perhaps because they feel that the point of the lesson will be implicitly clear to students. It is true that the point of the lesson will usually become clear if students have the opportunity and inclination to reread their notes. By pointing out, right from the start, what you think your lesson will communicate and illustrate, you can give your students a head start in the process of understanding the subject matter.

The Body of the Lesson

This is where you actually communicate the subject matter knowledge and understanding announced in the introduction.

It is sometimes helpful to regard the body of your lesson not as one big lesson, but as a collection of several mini-lessons, each devoted to communicating and illustrating a specific point.

From the point of view of the student trying to organize his or her notes, and still keep pace with the class discussion, it is helpful for you to give each mini-lesson its own mini-introduction and mini-summary. These need not be elaborate; their function is to landmark what is about to be discussed, or indicate the close of the discussion of a particular point. For example, simply writing the heading, "The Vertical Line Test," on the board, or saying, "OK, next we are going to look at the vertical line test," could be perfectly good mini-introductions. Similarly, saying something like, "Well, that was the vertical line test in all its glory," could be a perfectly good mini-summary. The idea is to provide landmarks and signposts, so that students can navigate your lesson, and, ultimately, the subject matter of your course.

When creating the body of a specific lesson, reading both the section of the text and the suggested lesson plan will help to focus attention key points and issues. Reading the suggested lesson plan before class will help you to see how the key points can be communicated and illustrated. This understanding will contribute both to your own experience as an instructor, and to students understanding of the mathematics.

The Summary or Wrap-Up

This is where you indicate what has been communicated through the body of the lesson. This is also an opportunity to relate the subject matter treated in your lesson to other topics in the book, and to re-state how your lesson has communicated and illustrated the key points. Some instructors overlook the summary, perhaps feeling that the body of the lesson stands alone; the ways in which the keys points are communicated being implicitly clear. This can be the case. However, even when you feel that your modes of communication are implicitly clear, no harm is done by re-capping the subject matter of the lesson.

The summary can also serve as a check for students, giving them the opportunity to ensure that they have recognized the key points, and have made some progress toward understanding them fully.

Managing class time is difficult. Sooner or later, every instructor finds one self having to rush to finish a topic before the end of the lesson. In such a situation, it is easy to to sacrifice the summary in the interests of completing the treatment of the subject matter. However, some summary is better than none. Thirty seconds spent restating each of the key points can be a valid way to wrap up, especially if you have taken the time to spell out how each part of the lesson relates to the key points. Another idea is to begin the next lesson with a summary of the lesson where you had to rush. If the two lessons treat closely related subject matter, this can be a good way to warm up the class for the new material.

Homework Assignment

Suggestions are made for homework assignments. These are not meant to be complete; they will form a core of problems from which you can build and create your own flavor. The suggested problems are relatively straight forward and reinforce section's topics. Problems in this text are sometimes deceptively difficult, and it may be wise to work out a problem or check the complete solutions manual before assigning it. In general, the problem sets are not *template* problems where the even problems from 1 to 30 can be assigned. Therefore, the number of assigned problems may be fewer than that of more traditional texts.

Creating a Lesson Plan from the Suggested Lesson Plan

As mentioned, the suggested lesson plans are not simply scripts to read to your class. Each is a mixture of procedural and pedagogical information intended to supply ideas for framing and illustrating explanations, ideas for engaging students' interest in the subject matter, and insights into what students may find difficult or unfamiliar.

If there is one quality that distinguishes coherent, meaningful lessons from confusing lessons, it is, arguably, planning. The suggested lesson plans are not substitutes for planning what you will actually do in your lessons. The suggested lesson plans are intended to help you plan your lessons.

One methodology for planning lessons:

1. Read the section of the textbook. As you do so, try to identify the important points, ideas, formulas/working and skills that the text relates. Writing brief notes on your observations may help with step 2 below.

2. Read the key points and suggested lesson plans. Compare the key points and subject matter related in the suggested lesson plan to your own observations, and try to decide what you are going to do if points that you consider critical have not been identified or discussed in the suggested lesson plan. Decide which parts of the suggested lesson plan communicate and illustrate particular key points. You could even number the key points and write the numbers beside sections of the suggested lesson plan dealing with particular key points.

3. Design the body of your lesson. At this stage, it may be helpful to decide:

   - Which key points, ideas, formulas/writing and skills you will communicate
   - How you will communicate each key point. If your key points coincide with the key points identified in the suggested lesson plan, then you could use the ways of communicating described in the suggested lesson plan.
   - Decide on a ball-park figure for how much time you plan to devote to each mini-lesson. Consistently making accurate predictions of exactly how much time you will need is very difficult, even for experienced instructors. However, in the interests of accomplishing everything that you want in your lesson, it is helpful to give yourself some kind of approximate schedule.

   At this point, it can also be helpful to review your understanding of how each mini-lesson communicates a key point. It will help your lesson to ensure that you can explain how each part of the lesson communicates and illustrates the key points you have decided upon.

4. Write a plan for your lesson. Steps 1 to 3 will probably have given you a clear idea of what you are going to do, and how you are going to do it. In creating your lesson plan, you may need only to list:

   - each key point
   - the amount of time for each part of the lesson.
   - the essentials of your mini-lessons for each point. This might include a note to yourself on what to do along with the data you need to do it (tables of values, graphs, answers to problems)

   The idea is to create a prompt sheet that you can refer to if you get distracted or lose your place. If you have drawn heavily on the material in the suggested lesson plan, you might like to keep a copy of the suggested lesson plan handy when teaching. If you have devised your own mini-lessons, then you might find it helpful (and reassuring) to write down a more detailed description of these mini-lesson in your lesson plan.

5. Using the pedagogical comments in the suggested lesson plans, common sense and insights you have developed yourself, try to identify potential trouble spots in your lesson plan. Some people draw symbols beside the descriptions of potentially problematic mini-lessons so that they can see at a the glance the places where they may have to take special care.

IN-CLASS ACTIVITIES

The descriptions of in-class activities are included to complement the suggested lesson plans. In most cases these are references to an exercise problem that is suitable for group activity. These suggestions could be used to:

- teach concepts and skills in an alternative way to the approach used in the suggested lesson plan.
- deepen students' experience and facility with the concepts and skill developed in the suggested lesson plan.
- include an active component in class.
- provide ideas for instructors who wish to devise and run their own in-class activities.

Suggestions for Using In-Class Activities

It is usually important for the instructor to do some preparatory work before assigning the activity to the class. At a minimum, this would involve reading the description given, and perhaps highlighting unusual or important points. If you have time, it is often very helpful to actually work through the activity yourself. Often, the problem is selected from the text. In many cases parts can be added to some of these problems to deepen understanding or suggest alternative ways of looking at the subject matter. Introduce the activity to students, alerting them to some of the major points treated in the activity. The amount of time that should be devoted to different parts of an activity is always difficult to ascertain. The suggested schedule for each activity is included to suggest ideas to keep students occupied for the duration of the activity, and to prevent the activity from dragging. Naturally, each individual instructor and each class will have their own ideas for appropriate pacing. Instructors who are developing their sense of the rhythm of in-class activities may find it helpful to use the timing suggestions as a schedule for conducting activities. Instructors with a well developed sense of the rhythm of in-class work may find the timing suggestions helpful as indications of how much class time to reserve for activities when planning lessons.

Classroom Activities and Worksheets:

In addition to in-class activities that are described after the suggested lesson plans, over 30 classroom activities and worksheets are available on page 201 of this manual. Many of them accompany specific sections, others combine topics covered in several sections. The activities were designed to be used during class to give students a chance to practice newly learned material with their peers or for the instructor to introduce a topic in a way that actively involves students in the development of a concept. All activities and worksheets have been successfully tested in various college precalculus classes.

Issues of Class Management

Some issues of class management that frequently present difficulties are:
1. Maintaining a tempo or pace, and completing the activity in a timely fashion.
2. Ensuring that no teams get left behind (especially on long activities with multiple parts).
3. Having students participate by reporting answers.
4. Formulating and giving clear explanations of the answers, and how the activity relates to the subject matter of the text.
5. Anticipating where students may get stuck.
6. Ideas for helping students who do get stuck, beyond simply telling them how to work the problem.

7. Opening and closing the activity in a meaningful way; in particular, alerting students to what they might get out of the activity, and relating the activity to the subject matter discussed in the text.

8. Helping to ensure that students work productively for the duration of the activity.

Ideas for Forming Teams

Most activities assume that students will work on the activities in pairs, or teams of three or four. It is certainly not required that students must work together. However, many instructors find it easier to manage, say, 7 or 8 teams than to manage 30 individuals. For examples, students in teams can ask each other relatively mundane questions ("How do you input formulas into the calculator again?") leaving you free to concentrate on teaching mathematics.

It is usually important for the instructor to form the class into teams. If students are left to form teams on their own initiative, several disagreeable effects can occur. Firstly, students are usually not very efficient at selecting group members, lengthening the amount of class time spent on forming teams. Secondly, students may team up with their friends. Teams of close friends are not usually desirable because often the mathematical activity is quickly shelved in favor of more compelling common interests. Lastly, there will almost inevitably be students in the class who are shy or reticent. It can be very difficult to approach a group of people and ask to join the team. Often, people will simply present themselves to you, and ask to be organized anyway. Several ideas that instructors have successfully used:

- Have the students count off. For example, if you have 28 students and want 7 groups with 4 members each, then you could have the students count off: 1-2-3-4-5-6-7-1-2-3-etc. Have all the people who counted "1" move together and form a team of four, all the people who counted "2" to move together and form a team of four, etc.

- Have a deck of cards that can be shuffled and dealt to the students. (To work in groups of three remove a suit.) Have students form groups of all aces, all twos, etc.. This system has the benefit that you can ask for reporting from say the diamond suit in each group. By delaying the announcement of the reporting suit all the group members must be preparing to report.

    These methods have the advantage that teams will be reasonably mixed in their composition, and will usually avoid the teams-of- friends. You could encourage students to at least get to know each others' names, in the interests of facilitating communication between team members. The disadvantage of this method is the difficulty of having an entire class moving around in cramped quarters.

- Divide by location. Have students who are sitting near one another form teams. One disadvantage of using this method regularly is that students will often sit with their friends in class, producing the
    teams-of-friends.

- Divide using a class list. Assign the first four people to the first group, the next four people to the next group, etc.

In any case, it is rare for the number of people in class to be perfectly divisible by the number of people you wish to be in each team. Slightly over or under strength teams are inevitable and perfectly acceptable, so long as they don't involve the same people every time.

Observing Teams

Observing teams should includes:

- Observing progress with the mathematical aspects of the activity. In particular, looking for teams that have become stuck, or have gone off on tangents that are not contributing to the assigned activity. Once identified, there is the difficult problem of deciding what to do to help the team progress toward completion of the activity. Sometimes, especially if time is pressing, or if the stuck team lags far behind others, it is appropriate to give the team a jump-start by simply telling them what to do. This is not always appropriate. One reason for engaging students with activities is to give them the mathematical experience of grappling with problems and figuring out what to do in order to solve them. By being very directive on a regular basis, an instructor runs the risk of diminishing this mathematical experience.

- Observing social interactions within the teams. One of the goals of having students work in teams is having them work with one another, rather than being four individual workers who happen to be sitting together. The kind of social interactions taking place between team members can serve as an indicator of whether or not this goal is being achieved. Just as good interactions with the math are worthy of praise, good interactions with other team members are also worthy of praise.

Some examples of social interactions that do not contribute to fruitful teamwork:
- People not communicating at all.
- Bullying, ridicule or other personal abuse. (Mercifully rare, but not unknown).
- One or two workers (who may or may not be communicating) and many spectators.
- Domination by experts or born managers.
- Other activities, instead of the one that you have assigned, going on.

Ideas for Handling "Problem Teams"

It is sometimes necessary (especially when working with others is a new experience for the students) to encourage team members to work together. Part of this involves looking for and praising positive, fruitful interactions between team members. It is sometimes necessary to address problematic conduct directly, especially if you witness any of the non-productive interactions listed above. Some ideas for addressing a problematic team:
- You could approach the team and ask them which parts of the activity they have managed to work out, and have them explain their answers to you.
- You could tell them that you will be calling on a person from their team to supply and explain an answer when wrapping up.
- If you notice that they are not working on the assigned activity, you could ask the team to explain their answer to the last part of the activity to you. If they have not completed the activity, you could simply tell them to get to work on the problem at hand.
- If you see one or two members of the team uninvolved, you could ask them to explain the team's answers to you.
- If it seems that you have a collection of individual workers, rather than a team, you could have people compare their answers and methods for doing the problem.

Tips for Handling Teams in Class

The following are tactics that instructors have used to run successful activities in class:
- The instructor gives clear directions on what he or she expects the people in the class to do during the activity.
- The instructor gives very clear directions on how and where teams should form, and what problem they should work on.

- The instructor sets a definite pace for the activity - gives the teams a definite time frame to work in.
- As the teams work on their problem, the instructor visits each team, and gives suggestions on what approaches they might try.
- When wrapping up the group exercise, the instructor has people from the class describe the answers they obtained, rather than listing the answers him or herself.
- When you concluding an activity, the instructor briefly lists the vital points that were touched on in the activity.

TIPS ON TEACHING

Explanations

When explaining, you succeed by having the students understand what you are talking about. Usually, complicated and abstract ideas are difficult to explain quickly and clearly. One strategy to cope with this is to try and break explanations up into important points. You can treat the less complicated points one at a time, and then show how the points all come together to explain the idea or solve the problem. Sometimes, it helps to try and find ways to communicate points besides verbal explanations. Sometimes a graph, a table, or a carefully drawn diagram will communicate a point very clearly. Another alternative is to have the students work on a problem that is relatively simple, but involves some of the subject matter that you wish to explain. This can establish a common ground; it is usually easier to explain an idea when the students have encountered something similar before.

Some problems that instructors have experienced when giving explanations:

Problem:

When the instructor explains at the board for a long time, the energy and attentiveness of the class decreases.

Ideas:

- Try to avoid situations which involve you talking for more than 10 minutes at a time. Asking a couple of questions does not count as breaking up your lecture.
- When you are planning your lesson, try to plan what you are going to say in 10 minute blocks.
- One way to break up lecture blocks is to include activities between blocks. These activities could be designed to reinforce the explanation that you have just given, or to establish common ground for the next explanation.

Problem:

A few people in the class do not understand, yet the instructor keeps explaining.

Ideas:

- If only one or two people do not understand the point you are trying to make, you could encourage them to see you after class, come to your office hours or speak with their classmates.
- If you have the sense that the class has already mastered a concept, or knows how to work a problem, it may not be necessary to explain as thoroughly or do as many examples as you planned. Retain some flexibility in the execution of your lesson.

Using Questions

One way to involve students in class is to ask them questions, or ask them to explain concepts or working in their own words.

Some techniques that instructors can use to increase the effectiveness of questions:

1. When you ask a question, ask it for a reason. Make sure that you have some idea of how you will use the responses to further the class discussion.

2. Learn and use students' names when asking questions. One of the scenarios that many instructors dread is the situation where a question is asked, but nobody responds. If you ask the question of a particular student, then at least one person will have to answer your question. Addressing questions to individual students can also allow you prevent domineering students from monopolizing class time. You can ask questions of visibly inattentive students to try and get their attention back on the class, and you can give more reticent students the opportunity to participate in class more fully.

3. Never ridicule or demean responses, or allow other students to ridicule or demean responses. Ridicule will undermine any efforts that you make to create a positive climate in your class.

4. Wait a long time for responses. It is difficult to endure the uncomfortable silence that follows your question. Many instructors cannot tolerate this for more than about 1 second. The problem is that if people realize that you will supply the answer after a second or two, then they will simply wait for it. Wait at least 5-10 seconds (counting in your head helps) before giving the answer.

Some behaviors which discourage students from participating in class through asking and answering questions include:

1. Not waiting long enough for the answer. As mentioned, many instructors wait for as little as one second before answering their own questions. Students are usually quite happy to wait for the instructor to answer the question, and a second or two is not very long to wait. Beyond this, one or two seconds is not really long enough for students to hear the question, and formulate a satisfactory response.

2. Rapid-fire strings of questions. Eager to clarify the question to help students answer, some instructors turn one question into a rapid string of restatements and reductions of the original question. The problem is that because they are trying to keep track of what the instructor is asking them, students have little opportunity to think of an answer.

3. Low-level questions. Questions which require students to simply remember and recite memorized information have their place, and are often a valuable tool for recalling facts, or setting the scene for a class discussion. However, if all that the instructor requires is that students be able to recite memorized information, development of more complex intellectual and analytical skills may be discouraged.

PART II

LESSON GUIDANCE BY SECTION

This section includes suggested lesson plans for the sections of the text. For each section the instructor will find ideas about creating a lesson plan, an alternate in-class activity that is usually meant to be used as a group activity if desired, and a set of suggested homework problems that can serve as the core of a homework assignment.

1.1   WHAT IS A FUNCTION?

Key Points

- The definition of a function
- Numerical, graphical and symbolic examples
- The vertical line test
- Basic function concepts and language

Suggested Lesson Plan

Start with the definition of a function as a rule that assigns to each input a unique output. This can be done without reference to variables or formulas. Students have difficulty understanding the precise meaning of the word unique in this definition. Give an example of the numeric squaring function that takes an input and gives its square as an output. Note that 4 and -4 both have the same output. Ask the students if this violates the given definition. Have the students try to re-phrase the definition of a function without using the word *unique*. The goal is to get the students to understand that each input yields only one output, but the same output can be associated to several inputs. Discuss an extreme example such as the function that assigns every integer to the number three.

Introduce the idea of a variable representing the input and a variable to represent the output of a function. Note that the text uses the letters t and Q. This is a good idea since many students have preconceived notions concerning x and y. Take a moment to discuss the phrase: *is a function of B*. Make sure the students know that B is the input. It is important to get the students to say things correctly and to know the precise meaning of what they say. Have students frequently speak in class.

Introduce a numerical table such as the following:

Table 1.1

Month	1	2	3	4	5	6
Milk	$1.65	$1.72	$1.78	$1.81	$1.75	$1.72
Gas	$1.13	$1.16	$1.26	$1.29	$1.41	$1.48

The table shows the average price of a gallon of milk and the average price of a gallon of gasoline during the first six months of the year. Lead a discussion (or have the students work in groups) to determine which of the three variables (month, milk or gas) are functions of one of the other variables. Pay particular attention to the cases where the month is a function of the price of gasoline, and the case where gasoline is not a function of the price of milk. This is also a good time to mention that functions do not have to be defined by formulas.

Next present the idea of a function represented graphically. Use the example of a ball being thrown straight up to represent height as a function of time. This is a good example because some students confuse the graph (a parabola) with the actual motion of the ball. You can display the graph on a calculator by using the following function and window size: $Y_1 = -16x^2 + 32x, 0 \le x \le 2, 0 \le y \le 25$. Once the graph is displayed, you can discuss how the definition of a function is satisfied when height is viewed as a function of time, but not when time is viewed as depending on height. Given any graph the vertical line test can be used to determine if the variable on the vertical axis is a function of the variable on the horizontal axis. If drawing a graph directly from an equation is still a difficult procedure for students, you might consider making a table of input and output values from the function, and then using these to plot points on the graph. This would be a good opportunity to point out to students that a function does not have to be defined by a formula–tables of values and graphs can define functions, too.

Another option for introducing the notion of a function's graph is to consider problems involving distance as a function of time. There are many interesting examples such as Problems 28 and 33. To get the students even more involved you might have one student graph another student's distance from a fixed point in the room as that student moves around. Make sure the student who is moving also stands still for a few seconds and that the student who is graphing includes the appropriate horizontal segment on the graph (it is also interesting to have the moving student circle the reference point at a fixed distance).

The introduction of the graph of the function also provides an opportunity to note the graphical interpretation of the definition of a function–namely, the vertical line test. (See also the alternate in–class activity.)

In conclusion, introduce a symbolic representation of a function through an example such as $Q = 4t + 9$. Note that because the equation is solved for Q, we interpret this formula as giving Q as a function of t. You can have the students find a formula for a function that models a given situation as in Problems 30 and 34.

Suggested Homework Assignment

Problems 6, 7, 8, 10, 18, 26, 28, 34 and some of your choice.

Alternate In-Class Activity

Problem:

The instructor draws several (four to six) graphs on the board. The graphs can be as complicated as you like (discontinuities, asymptotes, pictures of cartoon characters, etc.) Make sure that at least one of the graphs is not the graph of a function. The problem is to decide which of the graphs represent the graph of a function, and which do not.

Goals

- To have people recognize what *each input has a unique output* means for the graph.
- To show people how the Vertical Line Test is related to the definition of a function.

Activity

1. Draw the graphs on the board. Tell the people in the class what you want them to do, and tell them what you hope that they will get out of this exercise (you could just rephrase the goals if you like).
2. Break the class into teams with three or four members, and have them start on the problem.
3. As the teams work on the assigned problem, circulate and observe their progress. It is often helpful to watch teams who are stuck, listening to what point they are stuck on. Taking a moment to see how the team is trying to approach the problem can help you phrase your hints and suggestions in the terms that they are using. It is sometimes tempting to jump into the middle of teams who are working very well. If the team is working well, and getting correct answers, a word of praise might be all the help that they need.

4. When you see the majority of teams working on or completing their analysis of the last graph, you could call for everyone's attention. When you have it, begin your wrap up of the problem.

5. One way to wrap this activity up is to treat each of the graphs on the board in turn. You could ask representatives from different teams to say what their team thinks of the graph in question, and to explain how they reached their conclusion. If the representative does not mention it, you could also explain why their answer is (or is not) correct using the vertical line test.

6. End the activity by quickly using the graphs on the board to reiterate what the definition of a function means for the appearance of the graph of the function, and how the vertical line test is related.

Time: 15-20 minutes. The activity could be broken down as follows:

- 2-3 minutes Draw graphs and introduce problem.
- 2-3 minutes Form teams
- 5-6 minutes Working on problems
- 4-5 minutes Analyzing graphs on board
- 2-3 minutes Reiterate definition of function, relate to vertical line

1.2 RATE OF CHANGE

Key Points

- The average rate of change of a function over an interval
- Increasing and decreasing functions
- Rate of change in function notation

Suggested Lesson Plan

This is an important section. It lays the foundation for a basic concept in calculus: use of the difference quotient to represent rate of change. It is possible to discuss most of the key concepts of this section through one example. The following works well.

The table below shows the populations (in thousands) of three towns as functions of the year. In each case the population is determined at the end of the year.

Table 1.2

Town	1980	1981	1982	1983	1984	1985
P	10	14	18	22	26	30
Q	10	17	23	27	29	30
S	10	12	15	19	24	30

Have students determine the average rate of change of each function over the entire interval. Note that the process involves computing the differences of the outputs divided by the differences of the inputs; in this case $(30 - 10)/(1985 - 1980) = 4$ thousand people per year.

All three functions are increasing; however, they are increasing in different ways. By looking at the table, students should observe that town P's population is actually growing at the average rate of 4000 people per year. On the other hand, if they look at how town Q's population is changing, they see that the differences in successive years are (in thousands) 7, 6, 4, 2, 1. Thus the rate of change is decreasing, even though the function is increasing. This deserves repeating a few times! (The text has chosen to delay the use of the term *concavity* until chapter 2.) You could ask students to draw a fresh graph with the only criteria that the graph must be the graph of an increasing function. Be sure to point out that there are many possibilities here – the graph might be increasing and the rate of change increasing, or increasing and rate of change decreasing, or a straight line, or increasing and some combination of all of these. The important point to make is that rate of change and increasing/decreasing are independent of each other. Looking at how town S's population is changing reveals an increasing sequence of successive differences: 2, 3, 4, 5, 6. Thus the rate of change is increasing.

Have the students plot the three functions from the table on the same set of axes. Ask them to predict the shapes before plotting. Finally note that all three curves pass through the points $(1980, 10)$ and $(1985, 30)$ and hence all have exactly the same average rate of change over the entire time interval. Have the students note that on any sub-interval of length 3 years, the average rate of change of each of the three populations is different.

It is important to make the connection between speeding up and slowing down with rate of change. Have the students sketch a graph of distance versus time for a car starting from a standstill, reaching a certain speed, slowing down and then stopping for a red light.

A harder example is to plot the height of the water as a function of time while an inverted cone is filled at a constant rate. Conversely, you can start with the cone full and allow the water to drain out at a constant rate. These make good group projects, but be sure to require full explanations for the resulting graphs.

Lastly, you should introduce the general notion of average rate of change for a function on a given interval. For example you might have the students compute the average rate of change of $f(x) = x^2 + 2x$ over the interval $-5 \leq x \leq -1$. The use of negative numbers is intentional and impresses the point that you are dividing by the change in the inputs which is positive. A graph of this function reveals that the computation gives the same value as the slope of the secant line connecting the points $(-5, f(-5))$ and $(-1, f(-1))$. This is a very key idea that plays a major role in calculus.

Students are often confused by functional notation, especially when it is used in an apparently complicated calculation such as the average rate of change. Students often prefer to describe a rate of change as a rise-over-run instead of using functional notation. While this is fine as a memory aid, this may be a good opportunity to show students how the version of the average rate of change that includes functional notation is used to calculate the rate, rather than using the functional notation to calculate some y values and then doing rise-over-run. This appears to be a trivial point here, but will be important when students have to come to grips with the difference quotient (expressed using functional notation) in calculus.

Finally, a cautionary point to be aware of–make sure that all of your students know to read graphs from left to right when making decisions about whether the graph is increasing or decreasing. Some students may have picked up the habit of reading graphs from the origin outward. That is, they might describe a function like $f(x) = x^2$ as an everywhere increasing function, because as you move out from the origin, the function goes up. This is an important point to catch and correct if you notice students reading graphs in this way.

Suggested Homework Assignment

Problems 4, 10, 12, 16, 17, 18, 24, and some of your choice.

Alternate In-Class Activity

Problem: 17. **Time:** 20 minutes.

1.3 LINEAR FUNCTIONS

Key Points

- Functions with a constant rate of change
- Construction of linear models
- Slope and the general form of a linear function

Suggested Lesson Plan

The length and depth of this section indicates the importance that linear functions and their applications play throughout mathematics.

Many students associate the mention of lines or linear functions with the equation $y = mx + b$. Though this is correct in some sense, we want students to know linear functions as those functions that have a constant average rate of change. In particular, some students may believe that a linear function *is* the formula $y = mx + b$. Emphasize that the function is a special kind of relationship between two quantities; the formula (when it exists) is a convenient way of describing that relationship. Begin with an example of a linear function given numerically:

Table 1.3

t	0	4	8	12	16
Q	50	150	250	350	450

Note that the average rate of change over any interval is always 25. This is the property that characterizes linear functions. Contrast this example with a nonlinear function.

Next, move onto simple linear modeling problems such as in Example 1. Emphasize that linear functions have the form

$$\text{dependent variable} = \text{initial value} + (\text{rate of change})(\text{independent variable})$$

This formulation is the one that arises more naturally in applications and thus we will not write $y = mx + b$ but $y = b + mx$. Although either form is correct we will write the initial value first. For example, we might know that a population was 40,000 in 1970 and increased by 2000 per year. We can write $P = 40{,}000 + 2000t$, where t is the number of years since 1970. Note that often, students who are expert at quoting $y = mx + b$ are confused when letters other than x and y are used to denote quantities. Try to get the students using the version of the equation with words, and have students identify what the independent and dependent variables are in each example. Also note that students sometimes have trouble interpreting the practical meaning of the slope and intercept of linear equations. Whenever an example affords the opportunity of practical interpretation, it is usually helpful to spend a little time doing this. If the quantities in question have tangible units (such as kg, years, $, etc.), then the units can also help to guide students in making practical interpretations.

Next, have the students find the equation of a linear function from two data points. For example, again let t be the number of years since 1970 and suppose the population of a city was known to be 23,000 in 1982 and 21,000 in 1986. Assuming the population has been declining at a constant rate since 1970, find a formula for the population as a function of t.

You can also ask when the population will be zero. Stress the idea of creating equations that are solved to answer relevant questions. Emphasize the difference between a function and an equation to be solved. It is also important to note that the domain is $t \geq 0$ even though the formula defining the function makes sense for all real values of t (in fact there is an upper limit for the domain as well since the population cannot be negative).

Students should recognize a linear function from its graph. Use simple examples and note that increasing linear functions have positive slopes and decreasing ones have negative slopes. Have students compare the magnitude of the slopes of different lines. For example present the graphs of $y = -3x$ and $y = -2x$. Which one has a larger slope? (Students often confuse larger with larger in magnitude.)

Finally, a function may appear to be linear when only a portion of its graph is shown. Have the students graph $f(x) = (1.1)^x$ on $0 < x < 5$. Compute a table of values for the function:

Table 1.4

x	0	1	2	3	4
$f(x)$	1	1.1	1.21	1.331	1.4641

The table reveals that the rate of change is increasing, that is, the difference between consecutive $f(x)$ values is actually increasing. Graphing on a larger viewing window, say $0 \leq x \leq 20$, shows the nonlinear exponential shape. The exponential function will be formally introduced later, but the graphing calculator allows you to use it as an example at this early stage.

When you are finished with this section, the students should know what a linear function is, what general form its equation takes, how to find the equation of a linear function from two data points and how to use linear models to make predictions or find certain information (evaluation and equation solving). Stress the conceptualization that a linear function can be viewed graphically as a line, algebraically as an equation ($y = b + mx$), and numerically as a table that exhibits a constant rate of change.

This is a good point to make sure all students can use a graphing calculator and graph a simple linear function in a suitable window.

Suggested Homework Assignment

Problems 1–6, 7, 8, 15, 16, 20, 23, 27, and some of your choice.

Problems Requiring Graphing Calculator or Computer

Problems 26–30.

Alternate In-Class Activity

Problems: 26–30 to build graphing calculator skills. **Time:** 30 minutes.

> Note: Some graphing calculator companies will provide free overhead projection devices for instructors.

1.4 FORMULAS FOR LINEAR FUNCTIONS

Key Points

- Interpreting the effects of different rates of change and the initial values on the graphs of linear functions
- Finding the formula representing a linear function from numerical data, the graph of a function or a verbal description.

Suggested Lesson Plan

The point of this section is to make all the important connections between the concept of a linear function and the general equation of a line: $y = b + mx$. Note that the y-intercept is written first. This is in keeping with the idea of a linear function as a model starting from some initial value and having a constant change of change.

Begin by comparing the following two linear functions: $y = 2 + 0.3x$ and $y = 4 + 0.25x$. Do not graph them. Have the students explain the significance of the y-intercepts and the slopes. Students should understand the slope in two ways: (1) it measures the steepness of the line by telling you how much the line rises for each unit you move in the positive x-direction, and (2) it gives the average rate of change of the function over any interval on the x-axis. This explains why the slope can be computed from any two points on the line.

Still before graphing the lines have the students decide if the lines will intersect. Now graph them. The point is for the students to realize that the linear function with the larger slope must eventually *catch* the other function. This is true despite the initial values. You can ask similar questions with negative slopes.

A good abstract exercise is to present the class with two abstract linear functions: $y = Mx + P$ and $y = Nx + Q$. You can now ask questions such as the following: If $N < M < 0$ and $P < Q$, then what are the relative positions of the lines (which line is above the other) as x tends toward either positive infinity or negative infinity? Questions involving parameters are often difficult for students who are just learning to deal with abstraction. With the students working in groups, you can allow one group to make up the conditions on M, N, P and Q and then have a different group answer the question about the relative position of the two lines. Another stumbling block that students may encounter when they are just learning to deal with abstraction is that they do not view the parameters M, N, P and Q as representing numbers. If groups of students are stuck, you might encourage them to select some numbers for M, N, P and Q that are consistent with $N < M < 0$ and $P < Q$, and see what happens. You can encourage students to repeat their investigation for other values of these parameters, and then make conjectures based on their observations. If the students get as far as making conjectures, ask them to try to justify their conjectures using just the letters M, N, P and Q, not concrete numbers.

It is important for students to find the equations of linear functions from numerical or graphical information. This is not difficult, but be sure to give an example of a numerical table that does not include $x = 0$. Once the students find the slope, have them discover that they get the same y-intercept no matter which data point they use to find it.

Finally, you should do an example of finding a linear function from a verbal description. Consider the following example: The stock of company ZYX costs \$28 per share and the stock of company ABC costs \$20 per share. You have decided to buy a total of \$600 worth of stock in the two companies. Let z be the amount of ZYX stock that you buy and let a be the amount of ABC stock that you buy. Find a linear equation relating the values of z and a. This is a fairly straight forward question. It does not take students long to arrive at the equation $28z + 20a = 600$. However, when they solve for a they get $a = (-7/5)z + 30$. Have the class interpret the intercepts of this function with the axes. It is interesting to impose the restriction that you cannot purchase a fraction of a share of stock. If you must spend all $600, how many shares of each company can you actually purchase? As in the above example, keep changing the variable names so that x and y are not used exclusively.

Note that the text presents three versions of the equation for a line. This may be confusing for some students (for example, the *standard form* is probably something that students will not have run across before). Be prepared to show students that all of these equations really just boil down to the slope–intercept form.

Suggested Homework Assignment

Problems 1, 4, 12, 13, 17, 18, 24, 30, 31, 34, 38, 40, and some of your choice.

Alternate In-Class Activity

Problem: 42. **Time:** 20 minutes.

1.5 GEOMETRIC PROPERTIES OF LINEAR FUNCTIONS

Key Points

- Parallel and perpendicular lines
- Horizontal and vertical lines
- The intersection of two lines

Suggested Lesson Plan

Quickly go over the idea that parallel lines have identical slopes. Next, motivate the slope relationship between perpendicular lines by drawing a set of axes on the board and placing the corner of a sheet of notebook paper at the origin. Rotate the paper and ask the students to estimate the slopes of lines determined by the two adjacent edges of the paper. If one line has a large positive slope, then any line perpendicular to it must clearly have a negative slope that is close to zero. State that the slopes of perpendicular lines must be negative reciprocals of each other. A few examples clarifies the terminology: 3 and $-1/3$, -1.5 and $2/3$, etc.

Next discuss linear functions whose rate of change is zero. By comparison with the general equation of a line, students should easily arrive at the form $y = b + 0x$. Hence a constant function is simply a linear function with slope zero. Constant functions are often confusing for students. Although many students readily recognize that a graph with constant height will be a horizontal line, the formula $y = constant$ confuses many (perhaps because there is no x present, as in the prescription $y = mx + b$). Some students will be confused because there is nowhere to put the x. Define $f(x) = 8$ and ask your students to evaluate $f(5)$, $f(0)$, $f(\pi + 1)$, etc. Point out to the students that this equation means that the height of the function will be the same no matter what x is, which is exactly what you expect if you are dealing with a horizontal line.

Vertical lines are more problematic. First note that a vertical line is not the graph of a function. Therefore y is not a function of x and students should not expect to be able to get a formula for this case. Discuss that any graph is simply a set of ordered pairs that satisfy a particular condition.

Have the students determine what that condition is for a vertical line. You can then explain that an equation such as $x = 4$ really represents the set of all points in the plane whose first coordinate is 4.

Finding the point of intersection for two non-parallel lines is straightforward. However, be careful to ensure that students are not just mindlessly replicating the steps that they can find in some of the examples from the text. For example, you should confirm that students recognize that the reason for equating the linear functions is because the x and y coordinates of the two functions are the same–this is, after all, what it means for the lines to intersect in the first place. You should have the students solve for the intersection points both algebraically and graphically. Use the graphical method of solution to justify the steps that the students carry out in the algebraic method for finding the intersection. It is also good to look at one or two examples where one of the lines is horizontal or vertical.

Finally, have the students work out a problem that requires them to correctly interpret the points of intersection of various pairs of lines. The text deals with a car rental problem. Another good question is the following: A power company offers residents of a certain area the following options for supplying electric power.

- Option 1: A flat fee of $180 per month regardless of how much power you use.
- Option 2: A flat fee of $50 per month plus $0.12 per KWh.
- Option 3: $0.21 per KWh with no flat fee imposed.

Have the students determine which option is best. Of course, it depends on your power usage, but the students should provide this in their solution. See if the students can find viewing windows that clearly show the points of intersection and the relative slopes of the lines.

Suggested Homework Assignment

Problems 2, 6, 10, 11, 12, 16, 22, 25, 30, 32 and some of your choice.

Problems Requiring Graphing Calculator or Computer

Problems 19–21.

Alternate In-Class Activity

Problem: 35. **Time:** 15 minutes.

1.6 FITTING LINEAR FUNCTIONS TO DATA

Key Points

- Regression line
- Interpolation and extrapolation
- Correlation and causation

Suggested Lesson Plan

Consider a set of data points that are almost linear. For example, you might use $\{(3, 1), (4, 3), (6, 6), (8, 12)\}$. Have the students plot these points (either by hand or on a calculator). Have the students sketch the line that seems to fit to the given data. Did any students try to get the data points to fall directly on the line? Did any students try to minimize the distance from points to the line? If students seem to be using different criteria for fitting their lines, you could facilitate a discussion by having students describe their methods, and as they do so, briefly note the steps or criteria of each method on the board. For example, some students may just connect the first and last points, others may try to find a line that has about half the data points above the line, and half the data points below the line.

Next, mention that there are standard ways of picking a line that has some attribute that makes it a best-fit. It is a simple matter on most graphing calculators to enter data points and have the machine calculate the regression line. Have the students perform the regression for this data on their own calculators and compare their result to the line they constructed by hand. Avoid the discussion of how the calculator actually finds the regression line. If asked make it an assignment for strong students.

Next, consider data given below:

Table 1.5

t	1983	1985	1986	1988	1991
D	1047	1212	1547	1939	2634

For this function, t represents the year and D is the closing value of the Dow-Jones average. Have the students work in groups to determine the equation of the regression line. Based on their equation, they can predict the value of the Dow in 1984 and 1987. The actual values were 1259 and 1896 respectively. Explain that this is called interpolation and is a reasonable method for making predictions.

Point out the danger in using the regression line to extrapolate (make predictions beyond the extreme data points). Ask the students to use their linear equation to predict what the value of the Dow-Jones average is now (have someone check the current value in the newspaper). One important lesson here is that data may appear to be linear over relatively small time intervals, when in fact its long-term behavior can be far from linear.

Finally, you may want to briefly explain how regression works. Do not spend too much time here. It is best to avoid the formula. (The text does not give a formula for the slope and intercept of the least squares regression line, although these formulas are readily available in elementary statistics texts for students who might be interested.) It is hard to motivate exactly why it would occur to someone to minimize the sum of the squares of the vertical distances from the data to the line. However, it is perhaps worthwhile to spend some time discussing the basic idea with the students. Two carefully drawn diagrams will beautifully illustrate why a good fit line will have a low sum of squares, and a poorly chosen line will have a rather large sum of squares.

Introduce the students to the idea of assessing the *goodness of fit*. One measure of this fit is known as correlation and it is given by a value between -1 and 1 (most calculators find the correlation coefficient). A value near -1 or 1 indicates a strong linear relation between the variables, whereas a value near zero indicates almost no linear relationship. Have the students look carefully at the scatter plots in Figure 1.58.

End with a discussion of the fallacy that correlation is causation. Think of examples where there is correlation between two variables, but causation clearly does not exist. For example there is a positive correlation between car sales and boat sales. However, one does not cause the other.

Suggested Homework Assignment

Problems 1, 2, 3, 5 and some of your choice.

Problems Requiring Graphing Calculator or Computer

Problems 3–6, 8.

Alternate In-Class Activity

Problem: 6. **Time:** 30 minutes.

Chapter 1 Review Problems Requiring Graphing Calculator or Computer

Problems 44.

2.1 INPUT AND OUTPUT

Key points

- Basic function interpretation and manipulation using standard function notation
- The effect on a function of changing the input variable versus changing the output variable

Suggested Lesson Plan

Start by defining the terms independent and dependent. Emphasize that the *independent variable* is the *input* into the function, and that the *dependent variable* is the *output* from the function. Students are often confused about which way around these go. Illustrative examples (where the variables have a practical meaning such as temperature) can help the students keep track. Consider the example of the function which expresses degrees Celsius in terms of degrees Fahrenheit: $C = 5/9(F - 32)$. Since the equation is solved for C, we interpret F as the independent variable and C as the dependent variable. This example points out that the roles are not fixed. Solving for F yields $F = (9/5)C + 32$ and now C is the independent variable.

Since a function may take many different forms, it is convenient to have names for different functions. If we name a function f for example then there is a convenient notation: $Q = f(t)$. Explain that this is read "Q equals f of t." Emphasize that one does not need a formula in order to use this notation. For example, let $f(t)$ be the total number of reported cases of the flu at your school by the tth day of the year. Have the students explain carefully what $f(103)$ means. You might further ask about the relative sizes of say $f(103)$ and $f(147)$. Since $f(t)$ records the cumulative number of flu cases, then $f(103)$ is less than or equal to $f(147)$. Students may be uncomfortable about assigning meaning to the symbols such as $f(103)$ and $f(147)$, perhaps because they are so accustomed to identifying a function with a formula describing the function. In this view, symbols like $f(103)$ are not a final, interpretable quantity, but instead an intermediate calculation resulting in a number that can be interpreted. For example, if a student is asked to interpret $f(103) = 56$, he or she might say, "By day 103, there were 56 cases of the flu." However, when asked to interpret $f(103)$, the same student might be completely confused as to what we are looking for. This is a subtle point, but one that you need to address. Remind students that functions may be described by formulas, but functions are not formulas. If necessary, repeat the point that symbols like $f(103)$ have intrinsic meaning–they are not just simply cues to evaluate formulas.

That said, note with students that we often do have formulas that describe functions. Explain that in these cases we find the output value by substituting an input value, and that this process is referred to as *evaluating* the function. Use an example where the input variable occurs more than once in the formula, such as $c(y) = y^2 - 3y$. Evaluate several inputs such as $y = 1, 0, -2, 3/4$, etc. Highlight the correspondence between an input and an output and a point on the graph of the function. For instance $c(5) = 10$, so the point $(5, 10)$ is on the graph of c and vice versa.

Formulas from geometry also make nice examples; however, there is a potential point of confusion here. Typically the formula for the area of a circle is written $A = \pi r^2$. But when we wish to emphasize the idea that the area is a function of the radius, we might write $A(r) = \pi r^2$. We have now changed the role of A from representing the output variable to being the name of the function. Since we want students to be careful in their use of notation and language, we must be consistent in our own use of mathematical notation. It is correct to write $A = g(r) = \pi r^2$.

The students will have the most trouble with Example 9. They are used to seeing distance on the vertical axis. Ask several questions about the graph to be sure they understand it:

- When is the car stopped? ($t = 0$, 4.5–6, 16–19, 30)

- How long was he in the store? (Probably 3 minutes, from 16 to 19 minutes. We don't know about the stop from 4.5 to 6.)

- When was he going the fastest? (A wrong answer will be 8–15 minutes; note the speed of return is greater from $t = 20$ to 27.)

Remember the key to this section is understanding simple functional notation.

Suggested Homework Assignment

Problems 3, 6, 12, 18, 20, 22, 25, 30, 32, 33, 34 and some of your choice.

Alternate In-Class Activity

Problem: 36. **Time:** 20 minutes.

2.2 DOMAIN AND RANGE

Key Points

- Domain and range of a function
- Using a graph to find the domain and range
- Finding domain and range algebraically

Suggested Lesson Plan

Introduce the idea of the domain and range of a function. Stress the idea that the domain is the set of all allowable inputs for the function and the range is then determined by those inputs. A good example of the subtlety involved is to consider the function $n = f(A)$ (Example 1), where n is the number of gallons of paint to be bought to cover a surface of A square meters. In this context the range is the set $\{1, 2, 3, \ldots\}$; whereas if n instead represents simply the amount of paint needed, then the range is $\{n | n > 0\}$ (since now a fraction of a gallon is allowed).

Graphical examples are also good. Have the students find the range of a piecewise function that omits an interval such as $3 \le y < 6$. We have intentionally avoided the use of the bracket notation in expressing an interval. The use of the inequality symbols is unambiguous.

Explain the typical convention that if the domain of a function is not stated, then it is determined to include as many inputs as possible. Start with simple examples such as $f(x) = \sqrt{x + 3}$, progressing quickly to the more difficult $g(x) = \sqrt{x+3} + 1/(x-4)$. Have the students try to write down functions that have specified domains. For example, find a function whose domain is the set $-3 < x < 5$. This is not easy. Be sure to point out the difference between strict inequalities and allowing the endpoints to be included. You may have to work up to this type of problem considering examples such as $h(x) = 1/\sqrt{5-x}$.

Initially, it may be helpful to have students graph functions whose domains they have just found. By finding the domain first, they can then set their viewing windows to see the particular behavior near boundary points of the domain. For example in the function $f(x) = x/(x-6)$, students can view the graph near $x = 6$ to observe the behavior. A more interesting example from the point of view of technology is to discuss the difference between the functions $f(x) = (x^2-1)/(x+1)$ and $g(x) = x - 1$. Graphing f on most calculators does not show a hole at $x = -1$. However, on some calculators it is possible to choose an appropriate window so that the value $x = -1$ is sampled for evaluation. In this case the point will not be shown and the visual effect of a hole is produced at the point $(-1, -2)$. This points out the danger in simplifying functions while ignoring their domains. You can note that f can be written as $f(x) = x - 1, x \neq -1$ (which is not quite the same as the function g).

At this point, students will probably be reasonably comfortable with the procedures of finding domains algebraically by inspecting formulas and deducing which inputs are not allowed. However, finding ranges is still probably more of an art than a science at this point. Point out to students that they can always get a rough idea of what the range is by graphing the function over its entire domain, and checking the range of output values that they get. Graphing calculators are a tremendous aid for this. Finding ranges using algebra is usually quite difficult for students until they realize that they are usually calculating the *forbidden* outputs. Motivate the algebraic method by noting with students that although the graphical methods can give you a good idea of what the range is, these methods are (at best) approximations.

Finally, you can discuss the problem of finding the range of a function algebraically. This amounts to solving for the dependent variable and noting what values are excluded. You should point out you are actually finding the outputs that are not allowed. Hence the range of the function consists of everything else. These problems are good for reviewing algebraic manipulation. This section is designed to strengthen algebraic skills.

Suggested Homework Assignment

Problems 1, 4, 6, 11, 16, 29, 30, 35 and some of your choice.

Problems Requiring Graphing Calculator or Computer

Problem 1–12.

Alternate In-Class Activity

Problems: 22 and 31. **Time:** 25 minutes.

2.3 PIECEWISE DEFINED FUNCTIONS

Key Points

- Piecewise functions
- Absolute value functions

Suggested Lesson Plan

A function may or may not have a formula giving its rule. In the same manner, there is no reason that one function cannot have a rule that requires more than one formula. Start with an example such as the following.

A wholesale carpet company sells a certain brand of carpet for $9 per square yard for the first 100 square yards purchased. The price drops to $7 per square yard after the first 100 square yards have been purchased. Let x be the number of square yards of carpet to purchased. Find a formula in terms of x for the function that gives the cost of purchasing up to 200 square yards of carpet. The hardest part of this problem is getting the correct formula when $x > 100$. In this case the students should think of it as $9 \cdot 100$ for the first 100 square yards plus 7 multiplied by the amount in excess of 100 square yards, which gives $900 + 7(x - 100)$. It should be clear that this formula does not give the correct cost if you are purchasing less than 100 square yards. Students may have trouble deriving these equations. You might encourage them to calculate the prices for different purchases of carpet, and then using these points to calculate each of the equations of the linear functions involved. If you have students do this, be aware that there are a lot of ways that students can go wrong here–for example, if they calculated the line between a point where $x < 100$ and a point where $x > 100$. If you can afford the class time, these failures are highly illustrative of a basic principle of formulas for piecewise functions–that the given formulas only apply over a limited range of input values, not over the entire domain of the function.

From here, you can introduce the standard notation for representing piecewise functions and their domains. Be sure to emphasize that this is one function that just happens to use two different formulas in its rule. You can now have the students graph this function, paying close attention to how the restrictions effect the graph. It may be helpful to have the students generate a table of values prior to graphing. Caution: many students interpret the restriction $x > 100$ as meaning that the graph begins at $x = 101$.

Step functions are common types of piecewise functions and you should have the students graph an example such as $f(x) = 3$ if $x > 2$, $f(x) = 5$ if $x \leq 2$. It is also instructive to give an example of a piecewise formula that does not define a function. Consider the formula $g(x) = 2$ if $x < 1$ and $g(x) = 4$ if $x > 0$. See if the students can explain why this does not define function without graphing it. Once it is graphed, the students can easily see that it fails the vertical line test.

Introduce the absolute value function as giving distance from a point on the number line to zero (distance must be non-negative). Students have some difficulty understanding the piecewise definition of the absolute value function. The problem is defining $|x| = -x$ when $x < 0$. Since the absolute value function must give positive outputs, the use of $-x$ bothers some students. Several specific examples may help. Have students sketch the graph of the $y = |x|$. It is a graph they should memorize.

Suggested Homework Assignments

Problems 2, 8, 9, 14, 19, 20 and some of your choice.

Problems Requiring Graphing Calculator or Computer

Problem 12 and 13.

Alternate In-Class Activity

Problem: 18. **Time:** 30 minutes.

2.4 COMPOSITE AND INVERSE FUNCTIONS

Key Points

- The concept of composite functions
- The concept of inverse functions
- Finding the composition of function algebraically
- Finding the formula for an inverse function

Suggested Lesson Plan

To introduce the idea of a composite function, consider the following example. A rock dropped into a pond creates a circular ripple whose radius, r, increases at a steady rate of 10 cm per second. Therefore, $r = f(t)$, where t measures the time, in seconds, after the pebble has been dropped into the pond. As a review of linear functions, you could ask students to find a formula for r as a function of time, t, in seconds. After it has been established that $f(t) = 10t$, you can ask the students how we would come up with a formula for the area, A, of the ripple as a function of time. Many students will remember that $A = g(r) = r^2$ is the formula for the area of a circle as a function of its radius, r, so we can find the area of the ripple as a function of time as follows:

$$A = g(r) = g(f(t)) = (10t)^2 = 100t \text{ square centimeters}$$

Therefore, $A = h(t) = 100t$. Point out that to construct the composite function h, we substituted the output of the function f into the function g.

To treat inverses of functions, note that many students may have encountered inverses before, but it is probably unlikely that students connect practical meaning with calculating inverses. More likely, students may know and verbalize a procedure like, 'Swap x and y and then solve for y," but have no conceptual understanding of what they are doing. In this section, the functional notation should be stressed and not the procedure for finding general inverse formulas. The book covers inverses in more detail in Chapter 8.

Start with an example where the independent and dependent variables have practical meaning. Such an example could be the population of the town Jonesville, that has a population of 15,000 people in 1980 and grows by 200 citizens every year. Look at the population, P as a function of time, t (in years since 1980), in terms of a table.

Table 2.6

t	0	1	2	5	10
$P = f(t)$	15,000	15,200	15,400	16,000	17,000

Have students come up with the formula $P = f(t) = 15{,}000 + 200t$ for the population. Ask the students if they could tell you in what year the population of Jonesville reaches 30,000. Continue by generalizing the question to any population size. Point out that no matter what P is, we can always find the corresponding value of t

Introduce the students to the concept of the inverse by noting that you can form another relationship by swapping the roles of the independent and dependent variable. The table of the new function for t in terms of P looks like:

Table 2.7

P	15,000	15,200	15,400	16,000	17,000	30,000
$t = f^{(-1)}(P)$	0	1	2	5	10	75

You might like to point out that in this example, town planners would actually be very interested in predictions for when the population of the town would reach certain levels, so the inverse is not merely a mathematical abstraction; inverses frequently have important practical meanings, too. Finally, have the students compute the formula for the inverse function. Situate this in the context of solving an equation–i.e. you are now making the independent variable the subject of the equation.

Do a problem like number 30 where students have to find and interpret function values and inverse function values. Stress the units of the input and output variables in each case.

Suggested Homework Assignment

Problems 2, 3, 8, 9, 14, 15, 20, 26, 30, 36, 39 and some of your choice.

Alternate In-Class Activity

Problem: 39. Have students work in groups on the different parts of the problems and put the solutions on the board. **Time:** 15 minutes.

2.5 CONCAVITY

Key Points

- The relationship between the behavior of the rate of change of a function and the concavity of the function's graph

Suggested Lesson Plan

Lines are functions with constant rates of change. In this section we describe functions with increasing or decreasing rates of change to introduce the concept of concavity.

Consider the distances (in miles) traveled by two cyclists, Mike and Colby, as a function of time (t in hours).

Table 2.8

t, time (hours)	d, Mike's distance (miles)	Average speed, $\Delta d / \Delta t$ (mph)
0	0	
		16 (mph)
1	16	
		19 (mph)
2	35	
		23 (mph)
3	58	
		27 (mph)
4	85	

Table 2.9

t, time (hours)	d, Colby's distance (miles)	Average speed, $\Delta d/\Delta t$ (mph)
0	0	
		30 (mph)
1	30	
		22 (mph)
2	52	
		20 (mph)
3	72	
		19 (mph)
4	91	

Show the students only the first two columns of the tables and have them describe how the two data sets differ in terms of the movement of the cyclists. Mike rides faster with time; his average speed is increasing. Colby slows down with time; his average speed is decreasing. Recall that average speed is the average rate of change of distance with respect to time and fill in the third column of each table.

Continue by having the students graph the distance of each cyclist. Have them describe the shape of each graph and explain the shape using average rates of change. Mike's distance graph bends upward – we say the graph is *concave up*. Colby's distance graph bends downward – we say the graph is *concave down*. Point out that the shape of Mike's distance graph – *concave up* – results from the increasing rates of change, and the shape of Colby's distance graph – *concave down* – results from the decreasing rates of change.

Summarize the four different shapes concave functions can have: increasing and concave down, decreasing and concave down, decreasing and concave up, and increasing and concave up.

Suggested Homework Assignment

Problems 2, 4, 7, 8, 10, 12, 14, 18, 21 and some of your choice.

Alternate In-Class Assignment

Problem: 19. **Time:** 15 minutes.

2.6 QUADRATIC FUNCTIONS

Key Points

- The general formula for quadratic functions
- Finding the zeros of a quadratic function
- Concavity of quadratic functions

Suggested Lesson Plan

In this section we will have a first look at quadratic functions. For now we will concentrate on the general shape and the zeros of a quadratic. After the book has introduced transformations of functions in Chapter 5 we will have a closer look at the vertex form of a quadratic function.

Students are generally familiar with quadratic functions, so it is possible to move through some of this material quickly. Start with the basic graph of $y = x^2$.

Observe that a quadratic function may have two, one or no real zeros.

Take an example of a quadratic function that easily factors such as $y = 3x^2 + 5x - 2 = (3x - 1)(x + 2)$. Have the students also find the zeros using the quadratic formula, which is covered in the tools section at the end of this chapter.

The study of quadratic functions has many applications to physics. It is important to consider an example of an object falling under the effect of gravity. Consider a ball which is thrown upward from a bridge and is allowed to fall past the bridge all the way to the ground. For example let $h(t) = -16t^2 + 48t + 120$ denote the height of the ball in feet above the ground t seconds after being released. Make sure the students understand that the shape does not physically represent the path of the ball, which is straight up and down. Have the students work in groups to answer the following questions:

1. How high is the ball when it is released? How high is the bridge?

2. When does the ball hit the ground? (Do this by using the answer from question 2 and by using the quadratic formula.) There are two answers. Are they both valid?

3. Sketch a graph of the function h, showing the domain and range. (Note that the physical constraints impose a domain of $t \geq 0$ and a range $h(t) > 0$.) Find a window on your graphing calculator that shows the height of the ball from the time it is thrown until it hits the ground.

Point out that an important characteristic of a quadratic function is that the average rate of change over equal intervals is not constant (as in the case of a linear function), but is itself changing linearly. This can be illustrated by considering an object falling under the influence of gravity. Let $d(t) = 16t^2$ be the distance in feet that an object has fallen after t seconds. Have the students compute the average speed of the object over each of the time intervals $0 \leq t \leq 1$, $1 \leq t \leq 2$, $2 \leq t \leq 3$ and $3 \leq t \leq 4$. Observe that the average speed over each interval is 16, 48, 80 and 112 respectively. Since it the average rate of change is increasing, the graph is concave up.

Suggested Homework Assignment

Problems 2, 8, 10, 15, 22, 26, 30, 34, and some of your choice.

Problems Requiring Graphing Calculator or Computer

Problem 33, 35.

Alternate In-Class Activity

Problem: 34 **Time:** 20 minutes.

3.1 INTRODUCTION TO THE FAMILY OF EXPONENTIAL FUNCTIONS

Key Points

- Growth factors and growth rates
- Decay factors and decay rates
- The definition of an exponential function

Suggested Lesson Plan

Start with a review of how you increase or decrease a number by a given percentage. For example, ask the students to increase 60 by 20%. It is easy for the students to arrive at the expression $60 + (60)(0.20)$. Note that you can factor out the 60 to obtain $60(1 + 0.20)$. From here you can obtain the general statement: to increase A by R percent, multiply A by $1 + R/100$. Let $r = R/100$. You can note that $1 + r$ is called the growth factor, since it is what you multiply by to increase the initial amount by $R\%$. You should also derive the general form for decreasing a number by a given percentage: to decrease A by R percent, multiply A by $1 - r$.

If your students are weak on concepts relating to percentages, have them complete a table showing the percentage, its decimal equivalent and the corresponding growth factor.

Table 3.10

Percentage	Decimal representation	Growth factor
15	0.15	1.15
2	0.02	1.02
-30	-0.30	0.7
1/2		
78		
100		
150		

Now, go back to the first example and have the students increase the result by 20% again. Point out that they get $60(1 + 0.2)(1 + 0.2) = 60(1 + 0.2)^2 = 86.4$. Point out that this is not the same thing as increasing 60 by 40%, which gives 84.

Next, consider the example of an investment earning a fixed return of 8% per year. Suppose you start with $500. Have the students derive a general formula for how much money you have after t years. Students are usually able to easily calculate how much the investment will be worth after a specified number of years, but some have difficulty understanding how this corresponds to the formula, $A(t) = 500(1.08)^t$. Part of the difficulty may arise from the fact that exponential functions are often quite new to students (for example, some students are unable to distinguish between the formula for an exponential function and a power function). Another part of the difficulty may arise from the fact that some students do not immediately recognize that multiplying 500 by 1.08 a total of five times is actually the same as multiplying 500 by 1.08^5. Pointing out substituting $t = 5$ into $A(t) = 500(1.08)^t$ boils down to multiplying 500 by 1.08 a total of five times may help students to make the connection between the numerical results and the algebraic description.

Have them graph this function and note some of its characteristics (increasing/decreasing, intercepts, etc.). This is a good place to state that this is an example of an exponential function (note that the variable occurs in the exponent). In fact, this example is typical of all exponential functions and we call any function of the form $f(x) = ab^x$ an exponential function. (Note that b can written as $1 + r$.) More will be said about the graphs of exponential functions in the following sections. This may also be a good place to point out to students that what distinguishes the formula for an exponential function from many of the other formulas that they are familiar with is the fact that the independent variable appears in the *exponent* of the formula.

Using the above example, have the students determine how long it would take for the amount of money in the account to reach $1000 (the doubling time).

It is important for the students to identify growth or decay rates and initial values from a given exponential function. Consider the example of a population of bacteria given by the function $P(t) = 4.3(0.76)^t$ (in millions of bacteria present after t hours). Have the students determine the initial population (4.3 million) and the percent decrease per hour (24%). Have the students graph the function, noting the differences between this graph and the preceding investment graph.

Finally, you can state the defining property of all exponential functions: A function is exponential if it has a constant percentage change. This should be sharply contrasted with the definition of a linear function which is defined as having a constant rate of change.

End the class by having the students make several connections between percent changes and the value of the growth factor. For example if a quantity increases by 200%, then $b = 1 + 2$, so the quantity is tripling. Problem 38 uses the idea of a quantity tripling to illustrate just how rapidly an exponential function can grow.

Suggested Homework Assignment

Problems 2, 8, 12, 16, 21, 24, 26, 33, 37, and some of your choice.

Problems Requiring Graphing Calculator or Computer

Problems 23, 31.

Alternate In-Class Activity

Problem: 38. You may want to start with a double fold example on a single sheet of paper.
Time: 15-20 minutes.

3.2   COMPARING EXPONENTIAL AND LINEAR FUNCTIONS

Key Points

- How to determine when a function is linear
- How to determine when a function is exponential
- Finding formulas for exponential functions

Suggested Lesson Plan

The purpose of this section is to introduce students to exponential functions defined by data and to find formulas for exponential functions that describe data. The use of logarithms to solve exponential equations is postponed until the following chapter.

You could begin by presenting students with a table of data and asking them how they could tell what sort of function would do a good job of describing the data. For example, the table in Problem 5 would work well here. Students often recognize that the data would not be well described by a linear function. You could use this as an opportunity to remind students of the defining characteristic of linear functions–that the slope is always the same no matter which two points are used for the calculation. Students often neglect to make a scatter plot of data, and this is something that you could suggest to them. Alternatively, you could proceed directly to a calculation of the ratios of successive terms and note that (a) these are constant, and (b) constant ratios between successive terms is the defining property of exponential functions. Having determined that an exponential function would be a good representation of the data in the table, you could use two points from the table to derive a formula that describes the data in the table.

Have the students determine the domain and range of the function that you have derived. Be sure they understand that even when negative input values are used for t, the output is still positive. Discuss the idea that exponential functions have horizontal asymptotes. This is an opportunity to reinforce the connection between the algebraic formula for an exponential function and the appearance of the graph. Make sure, for example, that the students appreciate that if the growth factor is between zero and one, then substituting large values of x into the formula is like multiplying by the growth factor over and over again. The net result of multiplying by a number $0 < b < 1$ is that you get closer and closer to zero, which is why the height of the exponential function gets closer and closer to zero as x increases.

Next, move on to finding the formula for an exponential function and a linear function given two points (see Example 1). You may wish to demonstrate this for the class a second time, as it comes up in many problems.

You might like to have students work on some similar problems themselves to confirm that they have comprehended the material presented to them. Problem 17 is suitable for this purpose.

Compare the rate of growth of exponential functions with that of linear functions. Even the most slow-growing exponential function will eventually catch and far surpass any linear function. You can illustrate this by having the students graph the following two functions: $f(x) = 5x + 20$ and $g(x) = 3(1.08)^x$. First have them use a window with $0 \le x \le 10$ and $0 \le y \le 80$. It appears that g is hopelessly behind f, but redraw the graphs using the window $0 \le x \le 80$ and $0 \le y \le 600$ to see a very different picture.

Suggested Homework Assignment

Problems 2, 6, 9, 12, 20, 31, 34 and some of your choice.

Problems Requiring Graphing Calculator or Computer

Problems 1, 30, 40, 41.

Alternate In-Class Assignment

Problem: 41. **Time:** 15 minutes.

3.3 GRAPHS OF EXPONENTIAL FUNCTIONS

Key Points

- The possible appearances of the graphs of exponential functions

- The effect of the initial value on the appearance of the graph of an exponential function
- The effect of the growth factor on the appearance of the graph of an exponential function
- Why exponential functions have horizontal asymptotes
- Understanding limit notation and limits to infinity

Suggested Lesson Plan

Start by developing the general characteristics of the graphs of $Q = ab^t$. Have the students work in groups to quickly graph several exponential functions on the same screen: $f(t) = 20(1.4)^t$, $g(t) = 28(1.2)^t$, $h(t) = 15(0.6)^t$ and $k(t) = 10(0.8)^t$. Use a window with $-5 \leq x \leq 5$ and $0 \leq y \leq 70$. They should note that the value of a gives the y-intercept and that whether the function is increasing or decreasing depends on whether $b > 1$ or $0 < b < 1$ respectively. Observe that the graphs in this example are all concave up.

Have the students determine the domain and range of any of the functions given above. Discuss the idea that exponential functions have horizontal asymptotes. Discuss what it means to say $f(x) \to k$ when $x \to \infty$. Introduce the limit notation $\lim_{x \to \infty} f(x) = k$, and have students investigate

$$\lim_{x \to \infty} (3 + 2^{-x})$$

by plugging in larger and larger values for x, and then by looking at a graph of the function.

This is an opportunity to build on students' understanding of the connection between the algebraic formula for an exponential function and the appearance of the graph. Make sure, for example, that the students appreciate that if the growth factor is between zero and one, then substituting large values of x into the formula is like multiplying by the growth factor over and over again. The net result of multiplying by a number $0 < b < 1$ is that you get closer and closer to zero, which is why the height of the exponential function gets closer and closer to zero as x increases.

Next, consider several examples of functions with the same growth factor ($b > 1$) but different initial values. Have students graph these functions on their calculators (if available) and note that the effect of the initial value is to increase both the y–intercept and the rate at which the graph rises.

Next, remind the students how to test a table of data to check whether or not an exponential function could represent the given data. This can also serve as a second chance to illustrate the calculations for finding the formula for an exponential function. Consider the following data:

Table 3.11

t	9	12	15	18	21
$h(t)$	120	216	389	700	1260

Observe that whenever t increases by 3, the value of $h(t)$ increases by a factor of 1.8. Hence the ratio of successive terms is constant, so this is an exponential function. Emphasize that it is only the ratio of $h(t)$-values for equally spaced inputs that is constant. Caution: 1.8 is not the growth factor. The growth factor is the ratio of two outputs whose inputs differ by one unit. To find the formula for $h(t)$, note that it must be of the form $h(t) = ab^t$. Since there are two values to be determined, we need two equations. Use any two data points to obtain the equations: $ab^9 = 120$ and $ab^{12} = 216$. Have several students solve this system of equations by substitution. Have other students solve it by taking the ratio of the two equations to obtain $b^3 = 1.8$. Hence $b = 1.216$. The value of a can then be found easily: $a(1.216)^9 = 120$; so $a = 20.57$. Thus $h(t) = 20.57(1.216)^t$. Aside from taking square roots and possibly cube roots, students are often inexperienced in solving equations like $b^9 = 5.832$. Be ready for this, especially if your students have trouble with algebra.

If there is class time available, you might like to ask students how they would use the formula for an exponential function to decide when the function value reaches 1000. Although the students may not have encountered logarithms by this point, they can graph the function on a calculator and trace the graph to locate the approximate solution of the equation $1000 = 3(1.08)^x$. They can also graph both g and the constant function $y = 1000$ then look for the intersection.

Suggested Homework Assignment

Problems 1, 4, 10, 16, 19, 24, 28, 33, 38 and some of your choice.

Problems Requiring Graphing Calculator or Computer

Problems 9–12, 17, 18, 26, 35, 36, 38– 40,42 –44.

Alternate In-Class Assignment

Problem: 17. **Time:** 15 minutes.

3.4   CONTINUOUS GROWTH AND THE NUMBER e

Key Points

- Basic facts about the number e
- Continuous growth rates

Suggested Lesson Plan

It is difficult to motivate the existence of the number e in a precalculus course. Nevertheless, the function $f(x) = e^x$ will probably play a prominent role in any calculus course that students are likely to take.

Now take a few minutes to introduce the number e. Pragmatically, the relevance of e to this section is that if k is the continuous growth rate, then e^k gives the growth factor. This is one way (although perhaps not the most mathematically satisfying) of defining the number e. First note that e is an irrational number, like π with no repeating decimal representation, which is why a letter is used instead of a number. Even though e cannot be written down exactly as a decimal number, it is approximately given by $e = 2.71828\ldots$ (just like $\pi = 3.14159\ldots$). Hence $2 < e < 3$. Mention that e may be the most important number in mathematics and that they will spend a good deal of their calculus studies working with it.

Observe that we have written Q in the form $Q(t) = ab^t$ and in the form $Q(t) = ae^{kt}$. The two expressions are connected by the equation $e^k = b$. Summarize that e raised to the growth rate gives the annual effective growth factor.

Introduce the general formula for any quantity that is growing or decaying at a continuous rate k. In this case $Q(t) = ae^{kt}$. This works even when k is negative. For example, suppose that a lake is evaporating at a continuous rate of 3.5% per month. Find a formula that gives the amount of water remaining after t months. Also determine by what percentage the amount of water decreases each month. Since the water is evaporating the quantity of water is decreasing and hence the growth rate must be negative. Thus, $k = -0.035$. Therefore, $Q(t) = ae^{-0.035t}$. To see the monthly growth factor let $e^{-0.035} = 0.9656$. Thus, this function can also be written as $Q(t) = a(0.9656)^t$ or $Q(t) = a(1 - 0.0344)^t$. Hence a continuous rate of evaporation of 3.5% is equivalent to 3.44% each month. Most students initially think that the monthly rate should be greater than 3.5%. A simple example may clarify that an effective decay rate is less than the nominal decay rate. If 100 is decreased by 40% the result is $100(0.6) = 60$. But if 100 is decreased by 20% twice the result is $100(0.8)(0.8) = 100(0.64) = 64$.

At this point, you might like to have students try some problems for themselves. Problem 1 could be useful here.

Now introduce the exponential function $f(x) = e^x$ as a member of the family $f(x) = b^x$. Emphasize that this function is very similar to other exponential functions already studied such as $g(x) = 2^x$, where $b = 2$ or $h(x) = 10^x$, where $b = 10$. Have the students graph $y = e^x$ on their calculators and compare these functions.

Suggested Homework Assignment

Problems 2, 3, 7, 16, 20, 21, 24.

Problems Requiring Graphing Calculator or Computer

Problems 21–23, 25–28.

Alternate In-Class Assignment

Problem: 23. **Time:** 15 minutes.

3.5 COMPOUND INTEREST

Key Points

- Compound interest

Suggested Lesson Plan

You might like to begin by asking students if any of them have investments, and what kinds of interest rates they are getting. If students do have investments, you may want to follow up by asking how often the interest is compounded. Ask the students if they know how to use this information to calculate the value of the investment as it grows with time. Show students how to use the compound interest formula to do these calculations. Point out to students that the compound interest formula is an example of an exponential formula, with initial value P_0 and growth factor $(1 + r/n)^n$. At this point, it might be useful to have students work on several problems using the compound interest formula. Problems 7–10 may be useful here.

To connect the use of the number e and the ideas of continuous growth with compound interest, begin by considering the example of a nominal interest rate of 20% being compounded many times per year. Have the students determine the growth factor if the interest is compounded 10 times per year, 100 times per year and 1000 times per year. They should generate the following table:

Table 3.12

Number of compounding periods	Growth factor
10	1.2190
100	1.2212
1000	1.2214
10000	1.2214

It appears that compounding more often only increases the growth factor up to a point. After 1000, the fourth decimal digit will no longer change for larger numbers of compounding periods. It seems that the maximum possible effective rate for a nominal rate of 20% is about 22.14%. We say that 22.14% is the effective rate if the nominal rate of 20% is compounded continuously (that is, there are an unlimited number of compounding periods). Now, have the students observe that $e^{0.2} = 1.2214$. Hence e raised to the nominal rate gives the effective growth factor if the nominal rate is compounded continuously. Note that the students should use the built-in exponential function from their calculators when using e in calculations.

Consider the following example: Suppose that $500 is invested in an account earning 8% compounded continuously. What is the effective annual rate? Find a formula that gives the amount of money in the account after t years. Since $e^{0.08} = 1.0833$, we see that the effective annual rate is about 8.33%. Hence, the amount of money in the account after t years is given by $Q(t) = 500(1.0833)^t$. Observe that this can also be written as $Q(t) = 500(e^{0.08})^t$, which by properties of exponents can be written as $Q(t) = 500e^{0.08t}$. Hence we have two ways of expressing the same exponential function. The first $Q(t) = 500(1.0833)^t$ shows the annual effective rate; the second $Q(t) = 500e^{0.08t}$ shows the continuous growth rate. If you feel that it is important for students to understand that e^r is the limit of $(1 + r/n)^n$ as $n \to \infty$, then you could have students use their calculators to verify the approximate equality between these two quantities when very large values of n are substituted into the growth factor, $(1 + r/n)^n$, from the compound interest formula.

Observe that, in the previous example, we have written Q in the form $Q(t) = ab^t$ and in the form $Q(t) = ae^{kt}$. This is a good time to remind the students that these two expressions are connected by the equation $e^k = b$. Summarize that e raised to the growth rate gives the annual effective growth factor.

Note with students that the formula $(P = P_0 e^{rt})$ for calculating compound interest is an example of the general formula for any quantity that is growing or decaying at a continuous rate k. In this case $Q(t) = ae^{kt}$. This works even when k is negative.

Suggested Homework Assignment

Problems 6, 7, 14, 16, 20, 22.

Alternate In-Class Assignment

Problem: 18. **Time:** 20 minutes.

Chapter 3 Review Problems Requiring Graphing Calculator or Computer

Problems 12, 59–61.

4.1   LOGARITHMS AND THEIR PROPERTIES

Key Points

- Using logarithms to solve exponential equations
- The definition of the logarithm function
- The equivalence of exponential and logarithmic expressions
- The inverse relationship between the $y = \log(x)$ and $y = 10^x$

Suggested Lesson Plan

Begin by reviewing the definition of the common logarithmic function. Make sure that students understand that $\log(x)$ is a function, but it can be viewed as the solution to an exponential equation. Spend a few minutes having the students convert logarithmic expressions to their equivalent exponential expression. For example $\log(10{,}000) = 4$, since $10^4 = 10{,}000$. Or $\log(342) \approx 2.53$, since $10^{2.53} \approx 342$.

The idea that the common log function is the inverse of the exponential function with base 10 is very important. Ensure that it is clear to students by now that there is some relationship between the two functions. Clarify the relationship by looking at the following types of function statements: The function $f(x) = 10^x$ passes the horizontal line test and hence it has an inverse. Observe, for example, that if $x = 4$, then $f(4) = 10^4 = 10{,}000$. So, for the inverse function if 10,000 is used as the input, then 4 must be the output. Note that $\log(10{,}000) = 4$. Doing this for several other x-values indicates that $y = \log(x)$ is the inverse function for $f(x) = 10^x$. Point out that composing the two functions in either order must be the identity function. That is $\log(10^N) = N$ for all N, and $10^{\log(N)} = N$ for $N > 0$. It is worth having the students use the definition to explain why $10^{\log(N)} = N$. The goal is to get them to state that since $\log(N)$ is the exponent to which 10 must be raised to get N, then raising 10 to that exponent must equal N. (This is not as easy as it sounds; you may need to lead them to the correct statement.)

Students can see the inverse relationship by graphing the functions $y = 10^x$ and $y = \log(x)$ on the same set of axes. The graph of $y = \log(x)$ is important. Students should note the characteristic properties and shape of the graph.

Use the properties of exponents to motivate the algebraic properties of logarithms:

1. $\log(a^b) = b \cdot \log(a)$
2. $\log(ab) = \log(a) + \log(b)$
3. $\log(a/b) = \log(a) - \log(b)$

Most students are familiar with these properties, but do not really know why they are true. Although students are often aware that these properties hold, some students suffer from misconceptions. (See the end of this lesson plan.)

You can assign the proofs as required reading, or if time permits you can do one of them in class.

One of the main applications of the logarithm properties is in solving exponential equations. Later sections will deal with many applied problems involving exponential models, but for now we focus on the mechanical techniques required to solve such equations.

Consider an example such as $3^x = 6$. One approach to such an equation is to graph $y = 3^x - 6$ and to find the x-intercept. Alternatively, they can graph both $y = 3^x$ and $y = 6$ and find the intersection. On the other hand, observe that property (1) above gives a way of getting the exponent "down" out of the exponent. Applying the log function to both sides of the equation and using property (1) gives $x \log(3) = \log(6)$; so $x = \log(6)/\log(3)$. Note that this is not the same as

$\log(2)$.

Students have a difficult time working with expressions such as $\log(4)$ as constants. Consider solving $3^{(2x-1)} = 4^{(3x)}$. The solution of this equation is full of potential pitfalls. When applying property (1), the use of parentheses is essential. We get $(2x-1)\log(3) = (3x)\log(4)$. Require them to solve for x before computing any logarithms. The answer is $x = \log(3)/(2\log(3) - 3\log(4))$. Tell them to enter this expression in a calculator. Do not do intermediate calculations. These multi-step problems are difficult for students. Here, applying the $\log$ function resulted in a not so obvious linear equation that requires further manipulation.

Introduce the natural logarithm as a variation on the theme of the logarithm, except using the number e (rather than 10) as the base. It is probably worthwhile to recount the definition of the natural logarithm, but it may be sufficient to simply remark that the properties of the natural logarithm are largely the same as the common logarithm. From here, you can advance through progressively more difficult examples such as Examples 5 and 6.

Finally, wrap up this section by discussing common misconceptions about logarithms. For example, students can see that $\log(a+b) \neq \log(a) + \log(b)$ by graphing $y = \log(x+3)$ and $y = \log(x) + \log(3)$ on the same set of axes. Another way to challenge this misconception is to have the students solve some equations like the ones in Problem 48 and then check their answers. You will be amazed how many students incorrectly simplify the equation $e^{2x} + e^{2x} = 1$ to $2x + 2x = \ln 1$ because they think they are "multiplying" both sides of the equation by $\ln$. Of course, this does not make sense, but some students will need to be reminded of this repeatedly. Have students construct numerical examples to challenge each misconception.

Suggested Homework Assignment

Problems 19, and 20 should be assigned or done out loud in class. Some problems from the list 11-18 and from the list 34-47 involving exact solutions of equations using logarithms should be assigned according to the needs of your students. Problems 4, 5, 10, 26, 28, 32, 51 and some of your choice. If you assign 29 or 30 then it would be best to show an example in class.

Alternate In-Class Activity

Problems: 34, 41, and 42. Discuss the similarities. **Time:** 20 minutes.

4.2 LOGARITHMS AND EXPONENTIAL MODELS

Key Points

- Using logarithms to determine doubling time and half-life for exponential growth and decay models
- Conversion between different bases in exponential functions

Suggested Lesson Plan

We suggest an application illustrating doubling time and an application illustrating half life. This can help students to recognize that logarithms are not simply mathematical abstractions, but are highly relevant to quantities that students already know about.

Begin by explaining that the *half–life* is the amount of time that it takes for a decreasing exponential function reduce to half its previous level. Similarly, the *doubling time* is the amount of time that it takes for an increasing exponential function to grow to twice its previous level. These are usually easy ideas for students to comprehend, although students often have difficulty working with formulas. You might like to divide the class into groups and have them work on Problems 48, 51, and 52.

Then, spend some time emphasizing how to convert back and forth between the $Q = ab^t$ and $Q = ae^{kt}$ form of an exponential function. This is a surprisingly difficult skill for students to master. An activity that allows students to practice this in the context of exponential growth and decay is to give them a table like the one below, with all but one entry in each row hidden.

Table 4.13

$Q = ab^t$	$Q = ae^{kt}$	Annual growth rate	Annual decay rate
$5(1.2)^t$	$5e^{(\ln 1.2)t}$	20%	18.23%
$10(0.91)^t$	$10e^{(\ln .91)t}$	−9%	−9.43%
$6(e^{-.04})^t$	$6e^{-0.04t}$	−3.92%	−4%

Then, ask the students to fill in the three missing entries in each row. You could also follow up by asking them to explain why the annual and continuous growth rates are different for each function. If time permits, try to work in an example of an applied growth or decay problem which asks them about both the annual and continuous growth rates.

Conclude this lesson by summarizing that exponential functions arise naturally in many applications. These functions are used to model quantities that grow or decay at a constant percentage rate. Once a function model is constructed, questions about the model frequently become equations to be solved either algebraically or by using technology.

Suggested Homework Assignment

Problems 3, 4, 9, 14, 22, 27, 32, 34, 40, 46, 52, 58 and some of your choice.

Problems Requiring Graphing Calculator or Computer

Problem 49.

Alternate In-Class Activity

Problem: 50. **Time:** 20 minutes.

4.3 THE LOGARITHMIC FUNCTION

Key Points

- Definition of the common logarithmic function
- Domain and range of the common logarithm function
- Asymptotes of the common logarithm function
- Using limit notation to understand asymptotes
- The graph of the common logarithm function
- Applications of logarithms to sound and pH levels

Suggested Lesson Plan

The point of this section is to have students work with the ideas involved in defining the common logarithm function, to have the students work with the definition so that they can understand the shape and features of the graph of the common logarithm function, and finally, to see how logarithms are used to model physical quantities such as sound and pH levels. Even though all calculators have a log button, the students should understand what the output value means and they should be able to estimate logarithm values without a calculator. For example, students should understand the definition of the common logarithm well enough so that they can explain why $\log(0.45)$ is between -1 and 0.

Begin by reminding students of the definition of the common logarithm function. Ask students to draw a set of axes, and use the following set of questions to guide them in using the definition of the common logarithm and the axes they have drawn to construct a graph of the common logarithm function.

- How is the equation $x = 10^y$ related to the graph of $y = \log(x)$?
- If $x = 1$, then what does the equation $x = 10^y$ say that y has to be?
- If $x < 1$, then according to the equation $x = 10^y$, what has to happen to y?
- If $x > 1$, then according to the equation $x = 10^y$, what has to happen to y?
- If x is close to zero, then 10^y has to be close to zero, too. What does y have to do in order to make 10^y close to zero?
- If $x < 0$, then according to the equation $x = 10^y$, what has to happen to y?

If students are really struggling with these questions, you might consider giving them some hints until they can see how to use their responses to the questions to decide on the shape of the graph of $y = \log(x)$.

You might wrap up the activity by leading a class–wide discussion to list all of the important features of the graph of $y = \log(x)$. In particular, students should recognize that the x–intercept is located at $(1, 0)$, and that the graph has a vertical asymptote at $x = 0$. You might use this as an opportunity to review the precise meanings of *horizontal* and *vertical* asymptotes with the students.

Next, indicate to students how the similarities between the definitions of the common logarithm and natural logarithm lead to the graph of $y = \ln(x)$ being practically identical to the graph of $y = \log(x)$. Although this is a somewhat subtle use of exponents and logarithms, you might like students to try to figure out exactly how the graphs of the natural and common logarithms are related. One way to explain this (that involves only the Laws of Exponents and the definitions of the logarithms) is to note that: $e^{\ln(x)} = x = 10^{\log(x)} = (e^{\ln(10)})^{\log(x)} = e^{\ln(10)\cdot\log(x)}$. So, the natural logarithm is a vertical stretch (stretch factor $= \ln(10)$) of the common logarithm.

Explain the meaning of $f(x) \to \infty$ as $x \to a$, and introduce the limit notation $\lim_{x \to a} f(x) = \infty$. Discuss limits from the left and from the right and both, and illustrate the ideas with graphs.

As time permits, spend some time discussing logarithmic models. The reason for choosing chemical acidity or sound intensity is that it introduces students to a quantity (either pH or dB) that they are familiar with, and uses common logarithms in the formula. This can help students to recognize that logarithms are not simply mathematical abstractions, but are highly relevant to quantities that students already know about.

Explain that sound intensity is measured in watts/cm^2. Intense sound hurts your ears when too much energy is applied over the surface of your eardrum. The softest audible sound intensity is approximately 10^{-16} watts/cm^2; we denote this by I_0. Give the class some different sound intensities such as 10^{-12}, 10^{-5}, etc. Have the students determine how many orders of magnitudes these intensities are greater than I_0. The negative exponents cause confusion, so have the students write out statements such as $10^{-16} \cdot 10^{11} = 10^{-5}$. Hence an intensity of 10^{-5} watts/cm^2 is 11 orders of magnitude greater than I_0. Note that once you have the term 10^{11}, the orders of magnitude are obtained by taking the exponent. This is the same as computing $\log(10^{11}) = 11$. From here it is easy to define the number of decibels for any sound intensity: $f(I) = 10 \log(I/I_0)$. The ten in front is simply for convenience. It causes typical sound intensities to have nice values. Students should recognize that the term $\log(I/I_0)$ gives the number of orders of magnitude that I is greater than I_0.

For lengthy applications it works well to divide the class into groups. Have the students work in groups to solve several problems involving decibels. Begin by having them compute the decibel level for several different sound intensities. After this, move on to harder questions such as comparing sound intensities for different decibel levels. For instance, if one sound measures 50 dB and another measures 65 dB, how many times more intense is the second sound? This type of problem is very difficult for most students. Guide them toward the correct solution by letting I_A and I_B be the sound intensities of the first and second sound respectively. Ask the students what expression they need to find in order to answer the question. Once the students see that I_B/I_A is the required expression, have them write down equations involving the two intensities: $50 = 10 \log(I_A/I_0)$ and $65 = 10 \log(I_B/I_0)$. Is there any way to combine the two equations to obtain an equation involving the term I_B/I_A? Subtracting the two equations and using properties of logarithms yields $15 = 10 \log(I_B/I_A)$; hence, $I_B/I_A = 10^{1.5} = 31.6$. Most students will try to tackle this problem by actually finding I_A and I_B (using the fact that $I_0 = 10^{-16}$) and then comparing them. Other good questions involve asking how much the decibel level increases by if sound intensity is doubled or tripled.

Suggested Homework Assignment

Problems 4, 6, 7, 11, 14, 19, 25, 28, 30 and some of your choice. You could also choose some application problems from 32–37 to assign according to what was covered in class.

Problems Requiring Graphing Calculator or Computer

Problems 7–12.

Alternate In-Class Activity

Problem: 20. Focus on the justification. **Time:** 10 minutes.

4.4 LOGARITHMIC SCALES

Key Points

- Linear scale
- Logarithmic scale
- Definition of the common logarithmic function
- Using logarithmic scales and linear regression to model data with exponential functions

Suggested Lesson Plan

This section is a nice introduction to the ideas involved in defining the logarithmic functions. By the time that students reach this section, they will probably be familiar with logarithms (or at least their use in solving exponential equations). However, students are not usually familiar with the ways in which the logarithm function can transform data. Log–linear and log–log plots and scales are important in many of the science–based courses that students might be interested in.

The students should be able to see that linear scales are not adequate for displaying data sets that involve a large range of values. Begin by considering a table of astronomical distances from the sun (see Table 4.4). Explain that a linear scale requires that the tick marks represent equal increments. Consider a few different linear scales and demonstrate how it is impossible to display the entire data set.

Now, draw a number line with equally spaced tick marks, but label the tick marks by powers of ten: 10^0, 10^1, 10^2, 10^3, 10^4, $10^5 \cdots$ Next ask the students to plot the data on this new scale. A handy technique is to use powers of ten shown as tick marks labeled below the line, and plotted points shown as dots labeled above the line. To plot a point requires the students to write each distance as a power of ten. Some students are confused by the difference between writing a number as a power of ten and writing a number in scientific notation. For example, consider Neptune which is 4495 million km from the sun. In scientific notation this is $4.495 \cdot 10^3$. This is useful in that it shows $10^3 < 4.495 \cdot 10^3 < 10 \cdot 10^3 = 10^4$. To write 4495 as a power of ten requires that the equation $10^t = 4495$ be solved for t. The above comment shows that $3 < t < 4$. Students should try to find the approximate values of t by substituting values such as $t = 3.5$. They can use a calculator to see the graph of $y = 10^x$ and find x when $y = 4495$. In this case $3.6 < x < 3.7$.

Next, have the students convert the rest of the distances to powers of ten. Note that the distances for Proxima Centauri and the Andromeda Galaxy are already a power of ten. The Proxima Centauri distance is $4.1 \cdot 10^7$. Hence this number is between 10^7 and 10^8. If we write $4.1 \cdot 10^7 = 10^t$, then we see that $7 < t < 8$. Substituting some values for t shows that $7.6 < t < 7.7$. The astronomical distances can now be plotted on the axis using the logarithmic scale.

At this point, you can remind students of the definition of the common logarithm function, and relate this definition to the plots that the students have constructed. Remind students that the fundamental definition of the common logarithm is: If a number x, is written in the form $x = 10^t$, then t is called the logarithm of x and is denoted by $\log(x)$. It is very important that students understand the exact meaning of the expression "$\log(x)$". Require the students to know the following definition: $\log(x)$ is the exponent to which 10 must be raised to get x. Use some of the computations from the above example to illustrate the definition. For instance, we computed that $10^{3.65} \leq 4495$. Hence, $\log(4495) \leq 3.65$.

The remainder of this section revisits the topic of linear regression and shows how to use logarithmic scales to linearize data. This is a topic that all students eventually master, although some have difficulties with the details of reconstructing the exponential function from the slope and intercept of the transformed data. Start by reminding the students of the basic shapes of exponential graphs. Consider both exponential growth and decay. Also recall the basic shapes of some simple power functions such as $y = x^2$, $y = x^3$, etc.

Consider a table of data such as the following:

Table 4.14

x	1	2	3	4	5	6
y	210	405	833	1590	3245	6510

Plotting the data shows that y appears to be an exponential function of x. Hence, it is reasonable to try to fit a curve to the data that has the form $y = Ae^{kx}$. Since we do not know that any of our data points actually lie on the curve, we cannot solve for A and k by using the data points. Observe that if $y = Ae^{kx}$, then taking the natural log of both sides gives $\ln(y) = \ln(A) + kx$. Since $\ln(A)$ is a constant, this shows that $\ln(y)$ is a linear function of x. This is a good test to see if an exponential model of the data is reasonable. Computing the natural log of the y-values gives the following table:

Table 4.15

x	1	2	3	4	5	6
$\ln(y)$	5.34	6.00	6.72	7.37	8.08	8.78

Plotting this data reveals a linear relationship between x and $\ln(y)$. Using the linear regression program on a calculator gives the equation $\ln(y) = 4.64 + 0.7x$. You may wish to define a dummy variable such as $z = \ln(y)$ since treating $\ln(y)$ as single variable is often confusing for students. Hence, we have $z = 4.64 + 0.7x$. However, this expresses z as a function of x. To get y as a function of x, we must solve for y in the above equation. We get $y = e^{(4.64+0.7x)} = e^{4.64}e^{(0.7x)} = 103.5e^{0.7x}$. Plotting this exponential function reveals an excellent fit to the given data. This can also be checked numerically by substituting in x-values. For instance, when $x = 3$, $y = 103.5e^{(0.7)(3)} = 845$. The original data shows that when $x = 3$, then $y = 833$. Note that if the linear fit is poor, then the corresponding exponential curve will also be a poor fit. Be sure that the students understand that y can be modeled as an exponential function of x, if $\ln(y)$ can be modeled as a linear function of x.

At this point, you might like to have students try to apply the ideas that they have encountered to try to make sense of some of the data sets given in the problems. Useful problems to ask students to try include Problems 12 and 15.

Suggested Homework Assignment

Problems 1, 5, 11, 12, 13 and some of your choice.

Problems Requiring Graphing Calculator or Computer

Problems 6–8, 18–22 .

Alternate In-Class Activity

Problem: 14. **Time:** 15 minutes.

5.1 VERTICAL AND HORIZONTAL SHIFTS

Key points

- Horizontal and vertical graphical shifts
- Finding a formula for a shifted graph in terms of the formula for the original graph

Suggested Lesson Plan

This section begins material on how changing a given function produces a new function, complete with its own domain, range and graph. It is important that students understand this numerically, graphically, symbolically and verbally.

Begin with the following function and have the students work in groups to fill in the next four rows of the table:

Table 5.16

x	1	2	3	4	5	6
$f(x)$	-5	-3	0	3	7	12
$f(x+2)$						
$f(x-2)$						
$f(x)+2$						
$f(x)-2$						

They should observe that each row gives a new function. Hence, each new function could be given a name such as letting $g(x) = f(x+2)$. Any abstract expression involving function notation is a potential source of confusion for students. To help clarify the situation you might note for example that since $f(2) = -3$, then the point $(2, -3)$ is on the graph of f. On the other hand, what input must be used for g to obtain the same output of -3? Since $g(x) = f(x+2) = -3$, we see that x must be 0. Hence $g(0) = -3$, so the point $(0, -3)$ is on the graph of g. Thus, the point $(2, -3)$ was moved to the left two units. The common student error is to assume that the $x+2$ term causes a shift to the *right* two units. It will shift to the *left* two units.

The global behavior of shifting left two units can best be seen by graphing the two functions f and g on the same set of axes (smoothly connect the points of each function). Using two different colors to draw the two different graphs can also help students to distinguish between them. Another idea is to make two overhead transparencies, one with the original graph and the coordinate axes, the second overhead with just the graph (and no coordinate axes). Start with the two transparencies positioned so that the graphs are perfectly aligned, and plot some of the points of the new, shifted graph. When you have enough points to anchor the new graph, slide the second transparency over so that it matches the points that you have plotted.

The next example shows that the formula for a shifted function may not show any obvious connection to the original function. For example, have the students graph $f(x) = x^2 - 3$ and $g(x) = x^2 - 6x + 1$. It should be apparent that the graph of g is obtained from the graph of f by shifting three units right and four units up. Hence, $g(x) = f(x-3) + 4$. Algebraically simplifying this expression yields $g(x) = (x-3)^2 - 3 + 4 = x^2 - 6x + 1$. This is a good example as it points out that a relationship between two functions can be difficult to see simply based on their formulas.

Sometimes it can also be difficult to visualize a horizontal shift between two graphs because distances become distorted. For instance, graph the functions $f(x) = 2^{-x} + 1$ and $g(x) = 2^{-(x+1)} + 1$ on the same set of axes. Use the window $0 \leq x \leq 5$ and $0 \leq y \leq 3$. Because the two curves appear to get closer together, many students fail to see that the horizontal distance between any two points with the same y-value is always one.

A constant theme in this text is to encourage students to correctly interpret the meaning of mathematical expressions. Problem 41 involves a cup of coffee that is cooling off to room temperature. It is a good problem for the students to do in groups. A common error comes in interpreting the function $H(t) + 15$. Most students indicate that the initial temperature of the coffee was 15 degrees warmer, but fail to notice that the temperature that the coffee approaches has also increased by 15 degrees.

It is worthwhile to explore a few extreme cases. For example have the students discuss the effects of a vertical and horizontal shift on a constant function. Also, the case of a vertical or horizontal shift applied to a linear function of the form $f(x) = x + b$ is interesting, since it is not possible to distinguish which transformation was applied by looking at the resulting graph.

Finally, as a thought-provoking question you can consider the function $f(x) = mx + b$ and ask what horizontal shift gives the same result as a vertical shift of one unit up.

Suggested Homework Assignment

Problems 1, 4, 8, 18, 28, 29, 40, 42 and some of your choice.

Problems Requiring Graphing Calculator or Computer

Problem 12–25, 30, 31, 32, 41, 43, 44.

Alternate In-Class Activity

Problem: 27. **Time:** 10 minutes.

5.2 REFLECTIONS AND SYMMETRY

Key Points

- Reflections across the x or y-axis
- Symmetry
- Algebraic and geometric descriptions of even and odd functions

Suggested Lesson Plan

Most of the difficulties in this section can be traced to students' trouble with function notation. Start with the following numerical example:

Table 5.17

x	-3	-2	-1	0	1	2	3	4
$f(x)$	2	4	6	8	10	12	14	16
$f(-x)$								
$-f(x)$								

Have the students fill in the last two rows. This type of exercise stresses the difference between inputs and outputs. For example, in the second row if the input is say -2, then the student writes $f(-(-2)) = f(2)$. This makes it look as though 2 is the input for the function. The problem is that $f(-x)$ represents the output for a new function whose input is x. To prevent this sort of confusion, define a new function g by the rule $g(x) = f(-x)$. It is then quite clear that $g(-2) = f(2) = 12$. Hence, an input for g of -2 yields an output of 12. Also note that the last cell in the $f(-x)$ row cannot be determined. While the $-f(x)$ values are more easily determined, you should still note that the expression $-f(x)$ represents a new function h by the rule $h(x) = -f(x)$. After the students have completed the table, be sure to emphasize the difference between acting on the input variable and then applying f, versus applying the function f first and then acting on the output variable.

Next, move to a function defined by a formula. The following example works well. Let $f(x) = \sqrt{x + 3}$, then define the functions $g(x) = f(-x)$ and $h(x) = -f(x)$ as above. Have the students find formulas for g and h. Graphing all three functions on the same set of axes shows the reflections over the axes. Point out the following connection between inputs and outputs and the corresponding points on the graph: $f(1) = 2$ and $g(-1) = 2$, so the point $(1, 2)$ is on the graph of f and the point $(-1, 2)$ is on the graph of g. In other words, opposite inputs must be used to give the same outputs. Hence the graph of g is obtained by reflecting the graph of f over the y-axis. Conversely, $f(1) = 2$ and $h(1) = -2$, so the same input yields opposite outputs. This shows that the graph of h is obtained from the graph of f by reflecting over the x-axis.

Introduce the idea of even and odd functions by sketching several functions, such as $f(x) = x^2 - 4$ and $f(x) = x^3 - 4x$, whose graphs are symmetric with respect to the y-axis and the origin. Point out that symmetry with respect to the origin can be seen by reflecting the graph over both axes. This is an excellent topic for tying together graphical information with their algebraic representations using functional language. The goal should be for the students to understand that if opposite x-values (inputs) give the same y-value (outputs), then the function must satisfy the relation $f(x) = f(-x)$. Furthermore, they should see that this condition implies the symmetry of the graph about the y-axis.

It is important that students know how to check if a function is even or odd algebraically. Example 4 gives a few such examples.

Reflections can be combined with horizontal and vertical shifts. The greatest source of error in these problems involves order of operations. A rule of thumb that can be suggested to students is to "Start with the x and work your way out." For example if the graph of f is given and g is defined by $g(x) = -f(x) + 3$, then the graph of g is obtained from the graph of f by first reflecting over the x-axis and then shifting up 3 units. Be ready for student difficulty with the $-f(x)$ notation. Students' difficulty also represents an opportunity to stress the meaning of function notation again. It may be helpful to remind students that $f(x)$ represents the value of the function for the input x, and is not merely a prelude to the real business of functions - their formulas. Remind students that graphically, $f(x)$ signifies the height of the graph of the function when the horizontal coordinate is x, so $-f(x)$ will be the negative of the height.

Example 5 in the text carefully discusses combining a vertical shift and a reflection applied to an exponential function. An example along similar lines is the following: Suppose a lake has a depth of 50 ft, but due to drought conditions the depth has been decreasing at a rate of 12% per month. Let $d(t)$ be the depth of the lake after t months. Have the students recall that $d(t) = 50(.88)^t$. Now let $f(t)$ be the distance from the original waterline down to the surface of the lake. Have the students interpret $f(0)$ and $f(t)$ as t approaches infinity. Have them find a formula for $f(t)$ in terms of $d(t)$. Sketch both graphs and discuss the transformation from one to the other.

Suggested Homework Assignment

Problems 2, 7, 13, 18, 21, 28, 29, 30, and some of your choice.

Alternate In-Class Activity

Problem: 31. **Time:** 20 minutes.

5.3 VERTICAL STRETCHES AND COMPRESSIONS

Key Points

- The effect of multiplying a function by a constant

Suggested Lesson Plan

As with previous sections, much of the students' difficulty here stems from not really knowing what notation such as $f(x)$ actually means. For many students, this may be simply what goes on the left hand side of the equals sign when you write the formula, and have no intrinsic meaning. Hence students' difficulty in getting to grips with the meaning of expressions such as $2 \cdot f(x)$.

Begin the lesson by sketching the graph of a function such as $f(x) = 5 - |x - 3|$. Observe that the following points are all on the graph: $\{(-3, -1), (-2, 0), (3, 5), (8, 0), (9, -1)\}$. Now introduce a new function: $g(x) = 2f(x)$. First have the students transform the given points by noting that for each input, the output is doubled. For example, Since $f(-3) = -1$, we see that $g(-3) = 2f(-3) = 2(-1) = -2$. Hence the point $(-3, -2)$ is on the graph of g. Similarly, the point $(3, 5)$ is transformed to the point $(3, 10)$. Pay particular attention to the points that have zero as the y-coordinate. Since these points are unchanged, we see that the graph of g is obtained from the graph of f by stretching away from the x-axis. Hence the 2 in $g(x) = 2f(x)$ is called a stretch factor. Note that it is important to work with examples that have x-intercepts. Examples that do not cross the x-axis appear to move away from the x-axis during the transformation, which may lead to student confusion between vertical stretches and vertical shifts. When the examples have points that stay put, much of this confusion can be avoided.

Next, ask the students to perform the same analysis on the function $h(x) = (-1/2)f(x)$. They should observe that the effect of the -1/2 is a combination of a stretch and a reflection. It is useful to write the function h as $h(x) = (1/2)(-f(x))$. This shows that transformations can be thought of as happening one at a time: first reflect the graph, then stretch vertically by a factor of $1/2$.

To complete this introduction, have the students write out formulas for g and h. All three functions can then be graphed on a calculator to confirm the above results. The absolute value function was given by ABS on early graphing calculators, but the notation abs(x) is now more common. You may wish to use this as opposed to $|x|$ when discussing function transformations. The reason is that abs$(x - k)$ looks more like $f(x - k)$ than does $|x - k|$.

Move to the case of stretch factors combined with shifts. Given the graph of some function f, compare the graph of $g(x) = 4f(x) - 3$ with the graph of $h(x) = 4(f(x) - 3)$. Observe that h is equivalent to $h(x) = 4f(x) - 12$. So the order in which transformations are applied is very important. Point out that the standard order of operations is in effect. In addition, when determining which transformations are being applied to a function, it is best to start *inside* the function and work toward the *outside* of the function.

It is important that students be able to recognize when one function is a transformation of another. Consider the following numerical example that gives the internal temperature of two different frozen dinners that are heating up in different microwave ovens. Both dinners start out at $0°$ Celsius.

Table 5.18

minutes t	0	2	4	6	8	10
dinner A $f(t)$	0	25	45	62.5	70	75
dinner B $g(t)$	0	20	36	50	56	60

Have the students work in groups to determine a formula for g in terms of f. Emphasize that they should not try to find an algebraic formula for f or g. Once they find the stretch factor of $4/5$, have the class compute several average rates of change of f and g. Observe that they are also related by the same stretch factor.

Finally, several good exercises involve even more abstract function notation. Problems 35 and 36 tie together the function notation to the graphical representation of functions.

Suggested Homework Assignment

Problems 6, 9, 10, 14, 15, 17, 26, 35, 36 and some of your choice.

Alternate In-Class Activity

Problems: Choose from 11–16 (graphing with formula). **Time:** varies.

5.4 HORIZONTAL STRETCHES AND COMPRESSIONS

Key Points

- Understanding the effect of multiplying the input variable of a function by a constant

Suggested Lesson Plan

Horizontally stretching/ compressing a graph is often a confusing idea for students, even though horizontal stretch/compression appears in many applications. For example, the exponential function $f(t) = e^t$ has been used to model continuous growth. When this was introduced it was not identified as a horizontal stretches, but with a rate of k, we write $g(t) = f(kt) = e^{kt}$. Furthermore, like horizontal shifts, horizontal stretches seem to run contrary to students' expectations. The common misconception is for students to think that $f(2x)$ will stretch the graph of $f(x)$ horizontally rather than compress it.

Start with a numerical example as follows: Let $h(x) = f(2x)$.

Table 5.19

x	-4	-3	-2	-1	0	1	2	3
$f(x)$	3	5	7	6	4	0	1	2
$h(x)$								

It is convenient to think of the graph of h as obtained from the graph of f by letting the points on the graph of f move to their new location on the graph of h. The difficulty here is that students always want to compare points that have the same inputs. In this case, ask them how the input has to change in order to get the same output. For instance, since $f(-4) = 3$, what input is needed for h to give an output of 3? We see that $h(-2) = f(-4) = 3$. Hence, $(-4, 3)$ is on the graph of f and $(-2, 3)$ is on the graph of h. It is important to note that there is insufficient data to completely fill in the table. You can also have the students try to find function values for $g(x) = f(1/2x)$ and $k(x) = f(-2x)$.

Move on to a graphical example such as the following. Consider the graph in Problem 21. Ask students to graph the transformation $y = f(2x)$ and to relabel points A and B as well as the horizontal asymptote. Abstract function problems such as this, with no numerical data tend to be much more difficult for students. Note that the text asks the students to sketch the graph of the transformed function and label the new locations of the points A and B. The x-coordinate of the point B is 2. If students substitute $x = 2$ into the function $y = f(2x)$, then they most likely will move point B to the location $(4, f(4))$. This is incorrect. They need to substitute $x = 1$ to obtain the same output as the original function, thus causing point B to move to the location $(1, 3)$. Next, discuss how to obtain a formula for a function in terms of another function. This can be done both numerically and graphically. As with vertical stretches, it is often difficult for students to see the difference between a horizontal shift and a horizontal stretch. Examples that pass through the origin are excellent here, because this gives a fixed point. Examples that don't include a fixed point get further away from the origin (or closer to the origin) as well as stretching. This can make it harder for students to see that all that is going on is a stretch. You might like to assign Problem 21 as an in–class exercise, or to work through the problem with the students. This example can be very helpful, as the appearance of the graph is very strongly suggestive of the nature of the transformations performed, while there is just enough numerical information present to determine the transformations, once the transformations have been identified. This can help to reinforce the importance of examining the data graphically as well as numerically in students' minds, and also illustrates that you don't need to start with an explicit formula for $f(x)$ in order to solve this problem.

Finally, wrap up the discussion by having the students summarize the effect of all the types of transformations discussed thus far in the text. You might have them complete the following table:

Table 5.20

Function	New Function	Graph of new function compared to graph of f
f	$g(x) = f(x + c), c > 0$	f is shifted c units to the left to obtain g
f	$h(x) = f(x - c), c > 0$	
f	$k(x) = cf(x), c > 1$	
f	$m(x) = cf(x), 0 < c < 1$	
f	$n(x) = f(cx), c > 1$	
f	$p(x) = f(cx), 0 < c < 1$	
f	$q(x) = -f(x)$	
f	$s(x) = f(-x)$	

Suggested Homework Assignment

Problems 4, 7, 10, 14, 18, 19 and some of your choice.

Problems Requiring Graphing Calculator or Computer

Problems 5–9, 22.

Alternate In-Class Activity

Problem: 16. **Time:** 15 minutes.

5.5   THE FAMILY OF QUADRATIC FUNCTIONS

Key Points

- The general formula for quadratic functions
- Completing the square

Suggested Lesson Plan

Students are generally familiar with quadratic functions, so it is possible to move through some of this material quickly. Start with the basic graph of $y = x^2$. Have the students determine the graphs of $y = x^2 + 1$, $y = (x - 3)^2$ and $y = (x - 3)^2 + 1$. Relate each shift to the new location of the vertex. Next, have the students graph some functions of the form $y = ax^2$. Be sure to include cases where $a < 0$. From here you can move to the general case of a quadratic function of the form $y = a(x - h)^2 + k$. Observe that the vertex is located at (h, k). The sign of a determines which way the parabola opens, whereas the magnitude of a determines whether the graph is narrower or wider than the graph of $y = x^2$.

Next, consider a function such as $y = -3(x + 4)^2 - 7$. Before graphing, the students should be able to state that the vertex is located at $(-4, -7)$, the graph opens downward and it is much narrower than the graph of $y = x^2$. Observe that this function has no x-intercepts or zeros as they are frequently called. In addition have the students determine the y-intercept.

Algebraically expand the expression for y to show the connection between this form of a quadratic function and the more familiar $y = ax^2 + bx + c$. We get $y = -3(x + 4)^2 - 7 = -3x^2 - 24x - 55$. You can now spend some time reviewing how to complete the square in order to reverse this process. There are several cases in which students routinely make errors. One case involves whenever $a < 0$, as in the example above. Note that in the text the a is only factored out of the first two terms. This is a good way to complete the square as it leads to the best derivation of the quadratic formula. However, students often do not add or subtract the correct amount to compensate for the term that they have added (see Example 2). Other confusing cases occur when $a = -1$ and when a is not a factor of b, as in $y = 6x^2 - 7x + 2$.

Now, ask the students to recall the number of zeros that a quadratic function can have. Hopefully, they will recall from Section 2.6 that a quadratic function can have two, one or no real zeros. This is evident when the function is in the form $y = a(x - h)^2 + k$. For example, if $a > 0$ and the vertex is above the x-axis, then there are no real zeros. If the function does have zeros, then they are algebraically solved for from the equation $a(x - h)^2 + k = 0$. This idea leads to the quadratic formula, where a function in the form $y = ax^2 + bx + c$ is converted to the form $y = a(x - h)^2 + k$. This algebraic process is very carefully outlined in the tools section at the end of the chapter. It provides an excellent practice of algebraic skills.

Conclude by doing a problem involving application to physics similar to the one from the Section 2.6 lesson plan. Consider a ball which is thrown upward from a bridge and is allowed to fall past the bridge all the way to the ground. Let $h(t) = -16t^2 + 56t + 150$ denote the height of the ball in feet above the ground t seconds after being released. Have the students work in groups to answer the following questions:

1. How high is the ball when it is released? How high is the bridge?

2. What is the maximum height attained by the ball? (Do this by completing the square and then check it with a graph.)

3. When does the ball hit the ground? (Do this by using the answer from question 2 and by using the quadratic formula.) There are two answers. Are they both valid?

4. When does the ball return to the height from which it was thrown?

Suggested Homework Assignment

Problems 2, 4, 10, 11, 16, 22, 31, 32, and some of your choice.

Problems Requiring Graphing Calculator or Computer

Problem 34. (Although not absolutely necessary, a graphing calculator aids in the solution of many problems in this section.)

Alternate In-Class Activity

Problem: 33. **Time:** 20 minutes.

Chapter 5 Review Problems Requiring Graphing Calculator or Computer

Problem 25, 41.

6.1 INTRODUCTION TO PERIODIC FUNCTIONS

Key Points

- Graphing a periodic function
- Amplitude, midline and period

Suggested Lesson Plan

This section provides an introduction to the graphs of trigonometric functions without formally defining them. As a slight variation on the ferris wheel example in the text, consider the following problem:

A ferris wheel of diameter 50 meters completes one revolution every 2 minutes. When you are at the lowest point on the wheel, you are still 5 meters off the ground. The goal of this exercise is for the students to sketch a graph of the height above the ground as a function of time for one complete revolution (starting from the lowest point).

Have the students work in pairs or groups to do this problem. Have them start by sketching a circle. Next, they should label points on the circle that correspond to each 15 seconds that pass. From this point it is best to make a table of values showing height above the ground as a function of time. Make sure that the students are careful to note that the rise in height during the first 15 seconds is less than the rise in height during the next 15 seconds. You can explain this by observing that if you tried to walk from the lowest position on the wheel up to the 3 o'clock position that the grade would not be very steep at first, but would get steeper as you went. In walking half the distance, you would not have gained half the height. (They cannot obtain the exact height at 15 seconds, but they should estimate it.) Now use the table of estimates to sketch the graph.

When all the students have completed their graphs, you can introduce the definitions of amplitude and midline. Note that amplitude is always positive. Finally, ask the students what the graph would look like if two revolutions were completed. This introduces the idea of period. Be sure to mention that a periodic graph repeats itself over any interval whose length is equal to the period. It does not matter where you choose to start.

It is a good exercise to rework the above example with the following modification: Have the students plot their height above the ground as a function of the distance traveled around the ferris wheel. This immediately brings in π and forces students to recall facts about circumference of a circle. This is a natural lead-in to the idea of radian measure in the next section.

Trigonometric models offer an excellent opportunity to reinforce the ideas of graphical interpretation. Give the class the graph of the following function $y = 20\cos((\pi/6)t)$. (Do not give them the formula, just the graph.) Explain that this function models the height of the tide above or below mean sea level as a function of the number of hours since 6:00 a.m. Have the students answer questions such as the following:

1. Is the tide rising or falling at 7:00 a.m.?

2. When does low tide occur?

3. What is the amplitude?

4. Give a complete description of the tide's behavior over a span of 24 hours. (You may wish to remark that tides do not actually have a period of twelve hours, but this is a simple model of tidal behavior.)

Caution: Some students are confused by how something going around (a ferris wheel) and something going up and down (a spring or the tide) can have the same graph. There is a tendency to relate the shape of the graph with the motion itself. Be sure to emphasize that what is being plotted is displacement over time, not the physical motion.

Suggested Homework Assignment

Problems 1, 3, 8, 9, 13, 18, 22, 23, 30 and some of your choice.

Problems Requiring Graphing Calculator or Computer

Problems 29.

Alternate In-Class Activity

Problem: 28. **Time:** 10 minutes.

6.2   THE SINE AND COSINE FUNCTIONS

Key Points

- The definitions of the cosine, sine and tangent functions in terms of the unit circle
- Relationship to right triangles

Suggested Lesson Plan

Begin by reminding the students that a function takes an input and assigns it a unique output. This is an important observation in this section, as students are not able to evaluate trigonometric functions according to simple rules. Furthermore, students who have encountered trigonometric functions before may think of them not as functions, but as buttons that you press on a scientific calculator. Those students who have encountered trigonometry before may have only considered right–angled triangles, so the idea of defining sine and cosine in terms of the unit circle may be completely foreign to them.

Have the students draw a unit circle. Now given any number, think of it as an angle θ. Note that the terminal side of θ intersects the circle in precisely one point $P = (x, y)$. We use this construction to define two functions: the cosine function that assigns θ to x and the sine function that assigns θ to y.

$$\cos \theta = x \qquad \sin \theta = y$$

Using x and y as output values can be confusing, especially using x, which to many students is intrinsically an input value. An alternative is to label the point P as $P = (a, b)$.

It is essential to keep emphasizing that cosine and sine are indeed functions. Start by computing some simple function values. You could have the students complete a table of values for both functions using θ-values such as $0, 90°, 180°, 270°, 360°$. Although it is tempting to start using radians from the start, students are usually more familiar with expressing angles in degrees. Remember that there are a lot of new perspectives on trigonometry embedded in this section, and the objective is to have students understand how the definitions of sine and cosine in terms of the unit circle are connected with the sine and cosine graphs. Adding a new (and to students very foreign) description of angles may distract from students' efforts to understand the definitions of sine and cosine.

Next, have the class estimate several function values without using a calculator. For example: Estimate $\cos(250°)$ and $\sin(250°)$. Also they could try estimating $\cos(500°)$ and $\sin(500°)$. As the students arrive at their answers, have them note why their answers have certain signs. Can they make any general claims about the signs of the output values based on the location of the terminal side of the input angle? They should also note that even though $500 = (2)(250)$, the output values for $\cos(500°)$ and $\sin(500°)$ are not twice the output values for $\cos(250°)$ and $\sin(250°)$. Finally, have the students compute these values on their calculators and compare them to their estimates. (Caution: calculators should be in DEGREE mode for this section. During and after the next section, it may be worthwhile to suggest to students that they always work with radians. Many students do not know how to change modes or even to determine the current status of their calculator.) This problem focuses on the underlying rule that defines the cosine and sine function. Contrast function values that have decimal inputs to those involving π. Discuss what type of input values have *nice* outputs. After working through the above problem, summarize by determining the domain and range for the cosine and sine function.

The graphs of cosine and sine are easily found from the table of values generated earlier. Note that some students may be very deeply confused, and it can be difficult to detect. Students are usually able to carry out the procedural aspects of using the data from the table to construct a graph, but the implications of what they are doing are not all that apparent. In particular, some students have trouble seeing how the graphs represent points on the unit circle. This can be especially tricky with the cosine graph, because what students think of as the y value on this graph is actually the x-coordinate of the point on the unit circle. Students are also sometimes confused by the fact that an angle, θ, is now being used as an x-coordinate on the graphs of sine and cosine. Students' difficulty here may stem from the fact that up until this point, they will have thought of angles as things you get when two lines intersect, rather than an alternative way to specify a position. This difficulty may provide you with a good opportunity to discuss not only the concept of what a function actually is (a relationship between two quantities, not a squiggle on a page framed by x and y axes) but what the graph of a function actually represents. Have the class confirm these graphs on their calculator. Many calculators have a default *Trig* window. After obtaining the graphs, have the students identify the locations of the points corresponding to the angles $\theta = 250°$ and $\theta = 500°$.

You could end this section by discussing how to define the trigonometric function of an angle given in a right triangle. The definitions of sine and cosine offered in this section may seem to be very abstract to many students, and right angled triangles may offer students another framework to try to get to grips with trigonometry. Furthermore, if you wish to illustrate any of the practical uses of trigonometry, right–angled triangles offer many possibilities. Since we have used the unit circle to define these functions, proceed as follows: Carefully draw an angle θ in quadrant I. Drop a vertical segment from the point $P = (x, y)$ to the x-axis. You now have a right triangle with adjacent side x, opposite side y and hypotenuse L. Note that we can define $\sin\theta = y/L = \text{opp/hyp}$, $\cos\theta = x/L = \text{adj/hyp}$. Later when we introduce $\tan\theta = y/x = \text{opp/adj}$, the students sometimes write "SOHCAHTOA" to remember this.

Suggested Homework Assignment

Problems 5, 6, 18, 26, 29, 30 (if not done in class), 33, and some of your choice.

Alternate In-Class Activity

Problem: 30. Time: 10 -15 minutes.

6.3 RADIANS

Key Points

- Angles on the unit circle
- Positive and negative angles
- Radian measure of angles
- Converting between degrees and radians
- Arc length

Suggested Lesson Plan

This section defines basic concepts and introduces language that is essential for working with the trigonometric functions. The first parts of this section may seem to be review for many students. However, using the radian measure in natural ways often presents difficulties for students.

Begin by reminding students of the precise details of the unit circle. Be sure to label the points of intersection with the axes. Define an angle in a circle as the angle measured from the positive side of the x-axis. Note that the line segment forming the other side of the angle intersects the circle in exactly one point that we call P. (The text does not use the term terminal side, though you can easily define and use it if you wish.) Point out the difference between positive and negative angles.

Discuss the idea of co-terminal angles through an example. Consider the angles $120°$, $-240°$ and $480°$. In each case, the terminal side intersects the unit circle in the same point in quadrant II. However, in thinking about these angles as displacements from the point $(1, 0)$, they are all different. Indeed, you should encourage the students to think of an angle as a dynamic process. The point P begins at $(1, 0)$ and moves around the circle to the point determined by the size and sign of the angle. Have the students find angles between $0°$ and $360°$ degrees that are co-terminal to $890°$, $1200°$, $-45°$ and $-234°$. This is not as simple as it appears. For example, in finding a co-terminal angle to $1200°$, many students will divide $1200°$ by $360°$ to get 3.333. At this point they often get stuck. Explain that this implies that $1200°$ can be written as $3 \times 360° + 120°$. Hence, $1200°$ is co-terminal with $120°$. For a slightly harder question, have them find an angle between $-1080°$ and $-720°$ that is co-terminal with $456°$.

Introduce measuring angles in radians as follows. Use the idea of displacement to imagine the point P moving from $(1, 0)$ in a counterclockwise direction. As it moves, the length of the arc traversed increases. At some point, P reaches a location where the arc length displaced is exactly equal to 1 unit. Observe that the arc length is equal to length of the radius as well. Define this angle to be 1 radian. Since the distance around the unit circle is 2π (approximately 6.28), it is possible to fit just over 6 radians into a circle. Note that there are exactly 2π radians in one revolution.

Take some time to let the students work with radians before dealing with conversion problems. For example, have the students label the angles that correspond to the intersection of the axes with the unit circle. Next, give them several angles in radians and have them sketch the approximate location of the terminal side. For instance, have them find the location of the following angles: $2, 3.5, 10, 7\pi/2, -\pi/2, \pi + 1$. Make the important connection that, in a unit circle, these angles are equal to the arc length displaced. The presence of π in radian measure causes a great deal of confusion. It is wise to use examples that both do and do not involve π. Always emphasize that π is just a number and that numbers like $\pi/2$ have specific values: $\pi/2 \approx 1.57$.

Briefly explain (or have the students determine) how to convert between radians and degrees. Often, students do not know whether to leave π in their answers. Have them complete the following table (the use of 2π in the degree row is intentional):

Table 6.21

degrees	30				-100	2π
radians		$9\pi/4$	-0.45	120		

Finally, introduce how to compute arc length in a circle of radius R. Start with the following example. How long is the arc length that corresponds to an angle of $30°$ in a circle of radius 4 meters? Note that $30°$ corresponds to a certain number of revolutions, namely $30/360$ or $1/12$ of a revolution. Since the circumference of a circle is given by $C = 2\pi R$, we see that the arc length in $1/12$ of a revolution is $(1/12)(2\pi)(4) \approx 2.094$ meters. From here it is easy to see that the arc length determined by an angle of θ degrees is given by $L = 2\pi R(\theta/360) = \pi R(\theta/180)$. Rewriting this as $L = \theta(\pi/180)R$ shows how to get the formula for arc length if the angle is in radians. Note that $\theta(\pi/180)$ is the number of radians corresponding to an angle of θ degrees. Hence if θ is an angle in radians, then it determines an arc length of $L = \theta R$ in a circle of radius R.

One of the objectives of this section is to help students become as comfortable working with radians as they are working with degrees. After working problems from this section, students should be comfortable working in degrees, radians and revolutions. They should understand that an angle in a circle of radius R determines an arc length which can be easily computed.

Suggested Homework Assignment

Problems 1–5, (choose some according to the needs of your students), 25, 30, 36, 39, 40 and some of your choice.

Alternate In-Class Activity

Problem: 44. **Time:** 10 minutes.

6.4 GRAPHS OF THE SINE AND COSINE

Key Points

- Graphing $y = A\sin(t)$ and $y = A\cos(t)$
- Graphing $y = \sin(t) + k$ and $y = \cos(t) + k$
- Amplitude, period, and midline

Suggested Lesson Plan

This section starts with the compilation of special values of the sine and cosine function. Begin by having the students graph the cosine and sine function. This will probably be review for most of the students, especially if you have had the students graph the functions from data that they generated in Section 6.1. Make sure that the students have their calculators in radian mode and that they know the intercepts of the sine and cosine graphs with the horizontal axis. Have students use the vocabulary: midline, period, and amplitude.

There are two aspects of working with functions based on sine and cosine. On one hand, students need to understand how algebraic modifications of the sine and cosine functions are reflected in the appearance of the graph of the function. On the other hand, students also need to be able to examine the graph of a function and produce a formula for that function. The next lesson will concentrate on the general shifts and stretches and on finding formulas for graphs using sine and cosine functions. This lesson will concentrate on helping students to understand how two algebraic modifications of the sine and cosine functions affect the amplitude and midlines of the graphs of these functions.

Start by considering functions of the form $y = A\cos(x)$ or $y = A\sin(x)$. Have the students graph a few examples such as $y = 2\sin(x)$, $y = -3\cos(x)$ and $y = 0.05\sin(x)$. Note that in the second example, the graph also reflects over the x-axis. Thus the parameter A simply changes the amplitude of the original function and may also cause a reflection over the horizontal axis. Relate this to the vertical stretching of functions that was discussed in Section 5.3.

Next, introduce vertical shifts. That is consider functions of the form $y = \cos(x) + k$ and $y = \sin(x) + k$. The most important reason to have vertical shifts is that it allows you to move the midline of the function, as we saw in the ferris wheel problems. Shifting the midline is necessary for most modeling applications. With the ferris wheel example we combine a vertical stretch and a vertical shift.

Because this is a short section you may want to give some time to solidifying the difference between $y = \cos(x) + k$ and $y = \cos(x + k)$. This last transformation is the horizontal shift. Students often find this more confusing than the other transformations discussed. This is probably because most examples that students are familiar with involve only a horizontal shift or a horizontal stretch. The confusion about $y = \cos(x + k)$ is compounded by the shift direction, which is left if k is positive.

Suggested Homework Assignment

Problems 2, 5, 8, 18, 19, 23, 27, 28 and some of your choice.

Problems Requiring Graphing Calculator or Computer

Problem 22.

Alternate In-Class Activity

Problem: 29. **Time:** 15 minutes.

6.5   SINUSOIDAL FUNCTIONS

Key Points

- Graphing $y = A\sin(B(t - h)) + k$ and $y = A\cos(B(t - h)) + k$
- Amplitude, period, frequency and horizontal shift
- Finding formulas for periodic functions using sine and cosine

Suggested Lesson Plan

As indicated in the previous lesson plan, the main point of this lesson is to help students understand how the algebraic changes in the sine and cosine functions are reflected in changes to the appearance of the sine and cosine graphs. Whereas the focus of the previous lesson was on starting with an algebraic change to the function and seeing how the graph of the function was affected, the focus of this lesson is on looking at a graph and finding a formula that will describe the graph. Thus this section may require extra time to complete.

Point out that many periodic phenomena that we wish to model have periods different from 2π. For example, the tide might have a period of 12 hours or a pendulum might have a period of 3 seconds. Thus, it is necessary to have graphs that have the shape of a cosine or sine function, but with different periods.

Have the students graph the function $y = \sin(2x)$ on the same axes with $y = \sin(x)$. They should observe that $y = \sin(2x)$ completes two periods for every one period completed by $y = \sin(x)$. Note that the original period was 2π and the new period is $2\pi/2$. Next, consider $y = \cos((1/4)x)$. Ask the students to predict what the period will be. Graphing shows the new period is much longer. The students should only see a quarter of a period compared to one complete period for $y = \cos(x)$. Changing the window to $-8\pi \le x \le 8\pi$ shows two complete periods of $y = \cos((1/4)x)$. Again, observe that the new period of 8π can be obtained from the formula $2\pi/(1/4)$. State the result that the period of $y = \cos(Bx)$ or $y = \sin(Bx)$ is given by $2\pi/B$. Relate these results to the material on horizontally stretching or contracting a function's graph.

Have the students graph a few functions involving both a new amplitude and a new period. Consider the function $y = -3\sin(\pi x)$. (Note, it is important to do examples where the period does not involve π.) Explain to the students that there are essentially four different graphs: cosine, sine, reflected cosine and reflected sine. The sine function starts at the midline, whereas the cosine function starts at the maximum or minimum value.

Take some time to look at a modeling problem. For example, suppose the tide rises 15 feet above and below mean sea-level. The tide patterns repeat every 12 hours. If the tide is at its lowest point at 10:00 am., then find a formula giving the height of the tide (relative to mean sea-level) as a function of the number of hours since 10:00 am.

To solve this problem, students should first realize that they need to use a reflected cosine graph. So the function will have the form $h(t) = -15\cos(Bt)$. To find B, note that the period is 12 hours. On the other hand, the period of the above function is determined from the formula $2\pi/B$. Equating these expressions gives $2\pi/B = 12$ or $B = \pi/6$. Hence the function which models the tide is $h(t) = -15\cos((\pi/6)t)$. Have the students determine an appropriate window to see one complete period of the tide and then graph the function.

Next, introduce horizontal shifts. Remind the students that if the graph of $y = f(x)$ is given then the graph of $y = f(x + c)$ is obtained by horizontally shifting the graph of $y = f(x)$ (shift right if $c < 0$ and left if $c > 0$). Consider the function $y = 3\sin(2x)$. Have the students graph this function, noting that it has amplitude 3 and period π. Now, consider the new function $y = 3\sin(2(x - \pi/4))$. Observe that x has been replaced by $x - \pi/4$. Hence, the graph of this function must be exactly the same as the graph of $y = 3\sin(2x)$, except shifted $\pi/4$ units to the right. Have the students graph both functions on the same set of axes to observe the relationship.

Continue by pointing out that $y = 3\sin(2(x - \pi/4))$ is equivalent to $y = 3\sin(2x - \pi/2)$. In this form, it looks like the shift is $\pi/2$, which is incorrect. Thus, given a function of the form $y = A\sin(Bx - C)$, it should be written as $y = A\sin(B(x - C/B))$. The same is true for the cosine function. The quantity C is called the phase shift and differs from C/B which is the horizontal shift.

Students often have difficulty factoring out certain quantities. Have the class determine the amplitude, period and horizontal shift for the following functions: $y = -2\cos(\pi x - \pi/2)$ and $y = 23\sin(x/4 + 2)$. The goal is for the students to see that the first function is simply a reflected cosine graph with amplitude 2, period 2, shifted $1/2$ units to the right.

You can summarize with a brief review of how the various transformations of the graphs of sine and cosine are encoded in the formula for the function. You could draw a graph of a transformed sine or cosine function, and write a transformed function $y = A\sin(B(t-h)) + k$ or $y = A\cos(B(t-h)) + k$. Have the students explain how you could use the graph that you have drawn to find the values of each of the parameters, A, B, h and k. By the end of this interactive lecture, students should have a schematic diagram indicating how they can examine a graph in determine all of the parameters that they will need to make a formula that describes the graph.

You might like to work through some of the examples given in this section, as these provide excellent illustrations of how to determine the formula that describes a periodic graph. Alternatively, you might like to have students work through some problems themselves, and help them when they get stuck. (Or to try a mixture where you work some problems and have students try some for themselves.) Problems 11 to 18 provide excellent problems for students to work on. Eight problems is probably too many, so select several that you think will be challenging for your students. You could encourage students to use their graphing calculators (if available) to graph the formulas that they produce and confirm that they have produced a formula that actually describes the graph that they were given.

Students often have difficulty deciding which function–sine or cosine–to use when they attempt to find formulas that describe graphs. Emphasize to the students that either is acceptable, and that the only area where this will cause a difference is in the horizontal shift. Students may have difficulty seeing this–showing them how sine and cosine are really just horizontal shifts of each other may be helpful here.

Students sometimes see working with functions defined by tables of data as a different kind of activity from working with functions defined by graphs or formulas. You might like to have students work on Problem 36 from the section's exercises. This problem requires some special attention from both you and the students, not only because the function is defined by data, but also because the maximum and minimum values of the function are not given in the table of data. An approach taken by many students in this problem is to assume that it is ok to use $2.952 - 2 = 0.951$ as the amplitude for the function. If students insist on doing this, ask them to use their calculators to check whether their formula gives the data in the table. When the values do not match up, you could ask students to graph the data in the table and conjecture on what is happening between $x = 0.2$ and $x = 0.3$. Students may have simply flattened out the graph between these two points so that it looks as though $y = 2.951$ is the maximum. Compare this to the sine and cosine graphs, and point out that these graphs rise to a maximum, rather that flattening out. Students may need assistance formulating a plan for finding the correct amplitude.

Once it seems that students have mastered the processes of finding formulas for periodic functions, have them work on some problems that have the students not only finding but using and interpreting the formulas that they find. Useful problems here include 35 and 42.

Suggested Homework Assignment

Problems 3, 6, 12, 17, 22, 25, 28, 34, 35, 41, or some of your choice.

Problems Requiring Graphing Calculator or Computer

Problems 35, 41, 42, 47.

Alternate In-Class Activity

Problem: 34, or do the following two: 28 and 29. **Time:** varies.

6.6 OTHER TRIGONOMETRIC FUNCTIONS

Key Points

- The definitions of the tangent function
- Trigonometric identities

Suggested Lesson Plan

Define the tangent function as $\tan\theta = \sin\theta/\cos\theta$. To understand what the tangent of an angle represents, draw an angle θ in the unit circle. Let $P = (x, y)$ be the intersection of the terminal side of θ with the unit circle. Note that $\tan\theta = y/x$. This is precisely the slope of the terminal side of θ, since it is a line segment between the origin and the point P.

Using this idea, have the students investigate the behavior of the tangent function. Ask them what happens as θ starts at 0, approaches $\pi/2$, and continues on to π. Observe that the tangent function is undefined when $\cos\theta = 0$, which is exactly where the terminal side of θ is vertical (and hence has no slope). Have the students try to express the domain of the tangent function. The idea is for them to realize that infinitely many input values (angles) must be excluded. The domain is $\theta \neq \pi/2 + k\pi$, where $k = 0, \pm 1, \pm 2 \cdots$. These types of expressions arise frequently and are often used incorrectly. Make sure that the students are clear on what k represents. The second difficulty is that this expression gives the values that must be excluded. You might have the students try to describe the domain in terms of intervals.

Many students will already know some of the trigonometric identities from previous classes that they have had, especially the identity, $\sin^2\theta + \cos^2\theta = 1$. However, few students seem to know where the identities come from, or what they might be useful for. You might like to use the right angle triangle from the graphical demonstration of the connection between $\tan\theta$ and the slope of the line that makes angle θ with the horizontal axis and the Theorem of Pythagoras to explain how to derive the fundamental identity $\sin^2\theta + \cos^2\theta = 1$. Emphasize that the main utility of trigonometric identities is that they sometimes allow us to simplify formulas that involve sine and cosine.

End this section by discussing how to define the trigonometric function of an angle given in a right triangle. Since we have used the unit circle to define these functions, proceed as follows: Carefully draw an angle θ in quadrant I. Drop a vertical segment from the point $P = (x, y)$ to the x-axis. You now have a right triangle with adjacent side x, opposite side y and hypotenuse L. Note that we can define $\sin\theta = y/L = \text{opp/hyp}$, $\cos\theta = x/L = \text{adj/hyp}$, and $\tan\theta = y/x = \text{opp/adj}$. Students sometimes write "SOHCAHTOA" to remember this.

Suggested Homework Assignment

Problems 1–16 (choose some according to the needs of your students), 18, 24, 31, 32, 36 and some of your choice.

Alternate In-Class Activity

Problem: 37. **Time:** 15 minutes.

6.7   INVERSE TRIGONOMETRIC FUNCTIONS

Key Points

- Solving trigonometric equations graphically and algebraically
- Introduction to the inverse trigonometric functions
- Reference angles

Suggested Lesson Plan

This is a difficult section for most students. The idea that an equation can have more than one solution is not inherently difficult for most students to grasp. More problems arise because there is not an easy, prescriptive method for finding all of the solutions of a given equation. In particular, students often struggle when they have to use the symmetry of the sine and cosine graphs to find the location of solutions.

Begin with an example of a simple trigonometric equation: $\cos \theta = 0.6$. Remind the class that there are two equivalent ways of solving an equation graphically. They could graph both $y = \cos \theta$ and $y = 0.6$ on the same axes and find the intersections. An alternative method is to graph $y = \cos \theta - 0.6$ and find the zeros (roots). Students should use the default trigonometry window on their calculators (in radian mode). Even though the calculator only shows finitely many intercepts, point out that the graph is periodic so that there are really infinitely many solutions.

Now, continuing with the same example, ask the students to find only the solutions that are in the interval $0 \leq \theta \leq 2\pi$. Have them note that the answers correspond to angles whose terminal sides are in quadrants I and IV. Sketch a unit circle and observe the symmetry in the relative positions of the two angles. Discuss the important idea that by finding the solution in quadrant I, the other solution can be been found by symmetry (refer to the unit circle). The students should understand that any solution to the equation $\cos \theta = 0.6$ must necessarily have its terminal side in quadrants I or IV.

Have the students try the following related problem: Solve $\sin \theta = 0.8$ for $0 \leq \theta < 2\pi$, given that one solution is $\theta \approx 0.93$ radians. Explain that there must also be a solution whose terminal side is in quadrant II. By studying a sketch of the unit circle, the students should see that the other solution must be $\pi - 0.93$ or 2.21. Have the students confirm that $\sin(2.21) \approx 0.8$ on a calculator.

At this point, you can introduce the inverse cosine and sine functions. Begin by sketching a graph of the cosine function. Note that this function does not have an inverse because its graph fails the horizontal line test. Observe that by restricting the domain to the interval $0 \leq \theta \leq \pi$, you can obtain a one-to-one function. This restricted cosine function does have an inverse, which we refer to as $\cos^{-1}$, or arccos, function. Explain carefully that by using any number between -1 and 1 as the input for the inverse cosine function, it will return an angle between 0 and π (quadrant I or II).

Return to the first example of solving $\cos \theta = 0.6$. Note that 0.6 is an output for the cosine function. Hence, computing $\arccos(0.6)$ gives an angle whose cosine is 0.6. Evaluating on a calculator gives 0.93 radians. Point out that the angle had to be in quadrant I, since the outputs of the cosine function are positive only in quadrants I and IV. Thus, this gives a method of solving trigonometric equations that does not rely on graphing.

Next, introduce the inverse sine function in a similar manner. Note that the output is always an angle in the interval $-\pi/2 \leq \theta \leq \pi/2$ (quadrants I or IV). Have the students use the inverse sine function to solve $\sin \theta = -7/8$ for $0 \leq \theta \leq 2\pi$. Computing $\arcsin(-7/8) = -1.07$ radians does not give an angle between 0 and 2π. By sketching a unit circle, the students should be able to see that they need to find angles in quadrants III and IV that have reference angles of 1.07. The correct solutions are $\pi + 1.07$ and $2\pi - 1.07$. It may also be helpful to sketch a graph of $y = \sin\theta$ and mark the locations of $\theta = -1.07$, $\pi + 1.07$ and $2\pi - 1.07$ on the θ-axis.

The next example combines the ideas of inverse trigonometric functions, graphing and algebra. Consider the case of riding a ferris wheel where your height above the ground, in feet after t minutes, is given by $h(t) = 50 - 42\cos(\pi/2t)$. Determine the times at which you are 64 feet above the ground during the first complete revolution of the wheel.

To solve this problem, the students should first note that one revolution takes $2\pi/(\pi/2)$ minutes. So the period is 4 minutes. Hence, they need to solve $50 - 42\cos((\pi/2)t) = 64$ for $0 \le t \le 4$. Have the students isolate the cosine term: $\cos((\pi/2)t) = -1/3$. Using the inverse cosine function gives one solution: $(\pi/2)t = \arccos(-1/3)$ or $t = (2/\pi)\arccos(-1/3) \approx 1.22$ minutes. By sketching a ferris wheel, it is clear that there is another time at which the height is 64 feet. Using the fact that the period is four minutes, we see that the other time occurs at $4 - 1.22 = 2.78$ minutes. Note that you start at the bottom of the ferris wheel and each quarter of a revolution takes one minute.

Finally, you can relate the inverse trigonometric functions to the right triangle definitions of the trigonometric functions. Consider a right triangle with an acute angle θ. Suppose the adjacent side is 4 meters and the hypotenuse is 13 meters. What is θ? Since $\cos\theta = 4/13$, we see that $\theta = \arccos(4/13) = 1.26$ radians.

Discuss the idea of reference angles by considering the example of finding $\cos(2\pi/3)$ and $\sin(2\pi/3)$. Have the students sketch $\theta = 2\pi/3$ in the unit circle. Note that the acute angle between the terminal side and the x-axis is $\pi/3$. Sketch $\pi/3$ on the same unit circle. Now observe using symmetry, that since the terminal side of $\pi/3$ intersects the unit circle at the point $(1/2, \sqrt{3}/2)$, then the terminal side of $2\pi/3$ must intersect the circle at the point $(-1/2, \sqrt{3}/2)$. Again, point out that the students should have been able to anticipate the signs of the answers simply based on the quadrant.

To see if the class really understands the idea of symmetry and reference angles, have them attempt the following problem: If θ is in quadrant II and $\cos\theta = -0.764$, then find $\cos(\theta + \pi)$ and $\cos(\pi - \theta)$. This type of problem is very difficult for most students. Try to get the class to sketch a unit circle showing the angles θ and $\theta + \pi$. Since they know the x-coordinate of one point of intersection, then, by symmetry, they should be able to find the x-coordinate for $\theta + \pi$.

Suggested Homework Assignment

Problems 1–29 (choose some according to the needs of your students), 34, 38, 42, 48, 52 (if not done in class), 53, 57 and some of your choice.

Problems Requiring Graphing Calculator or Computer

Problems 15, 27–29, 30–39, 45–48, 56, 57, 60.

Alternate In-Class Activity

Problem: 52. **Time:** 20 minutes.

Chapter 6 Review Problems Requiring Graphing Calculator or Computer

Problems 62, 63.

7.1 GENERAL TRIANGLES: LAWS OF SINES AND COSINES

Key Points

- Solving triangles
- The Law of Cosines and the Law of Sines
- Ambiguous Cases of the Laws of Sines and Cosines

Suggested Lesson Plan

Expect this section to be something of a break after the difficult and more abstract sections on inverse trigonometric functions involving the unit circle. The problems are very applied and the students have no difficulty understanding what is being asked.

Begin by reminding that to completely solve a triangle means to determine all three angles and the lengths of all three sides. Remind that the mnemonic SOHCAHTOA is a good way to solve right–angled triangles, but that these trigonometrical relationships do not apply if the triangle is not a right–angled triangle.

To motivate the new laws, you might like to indicate a problem that requires something beyond the familiar SOHCAHTOA. An example is Problem 39 from the problems at the end of this section. You might ask students to suggest ways of approaching this problem. For example, students might suggest connecting the stakes by a third side of the triangle, and then try to break this triangle up into a pair of right–angled triangles. The unfortunate thing here is that there is not enough information available to completely solve both of the right–angled triangles. You might like to point out to students that there is enough information to completely solve the triangle, but not by using right-triangles.

The Law of Cosines is proved in the text and may be covered if time permits. To give students an intuitive feel for the result, proceed as follows. Sketch a triangle with angles $A = 40$, $B = 60$ and $C = 80$ degrees. Note that it is close to being a right triangle. If angle C had been 90 degrees, then the Pythagorean theorem would have held for the sides: $a^2 + b^2 = c^2$. However, it should be evident in this case that $a^2 + b^2 > c^2$. Hence, some term that depends on the angle C must be subtracted from the left hand side to obtain equality. As shown in the proof, the correct term is $(2ab)\cos C$. Hence, the Law of Cosines gives $a^2 + b^2 - 2ab\cos C = c^2$. Since $C < 90$ degrees, $\cos C > 0$, so $a^2 + b^2 - 2ab\cos C$ really is smaller than $a^2 + b^2$.

You can similarly discuss the case in which the triangle is obtuse (say $A = 30$, $B = 40$ and $C = 110$ degrees). In this case, the term $2ab\cos C$ is negative, so $a^2 + b^2 - 2ab\cos C$ is actually larger than $a^2 + b^2$, as a sketch shows it should be. If you mentioned Problem 35 earlier, this could be a good opportunity to reprise this example by having students use the Law of Cosines to solve the problem.

Observe that the Law of Cosines is an equation that relates all three sides and one angle. Since there is no preferred angle in a non-right triangle, the Law of Cosines can be rewritten in the two equivalent forms: $b^2 + c^2 - 2bc\cos A = a^2$ and $a^2 + c^2 - 2ac\cos B = b^2$. Thus, it can be used if all three sides are known, or if two sides and one angle are known. You should encourage the students to memorize the form of the Law as opposed to the exact formula.

In the case in which only one side is known, the Law of Sines must be used. Again, the proof is in the text and may be given as time permits. The Law of Sines states that in any triangle, the ratio of the sine of an angle and the length of its opposite side is constant. Hence: $\sin A/a = \sin B/b = \sin C/c$.

There is an ambiguous case that should be addressed when discussing the Law of Sines. Consider a pair of triangles as in Example 4. In each triangle there is an acute angle of 40 degrees, an adjacent side of length 8 and an opposite of length 7. Note that one triangle is acute and the other is obtuse. Using the Law of Sines to find the angle opposite the side of length 8 yields the equation $\sin \theta = 0.735$. The students need to understand that there are two possible solutions to this equation. The acute angle solution is $\theta = \arcsin(0.735) = 47.3$ degrees. The other is obtained by computing $180 - 47.3 = 132.7$ degrees.

As an exercise, have the class solve the same triangle using the Law of Cosines. This leads to a quadratic equation which shows that there may be two solutions.

Suggested Homework Assignment

Problems 1–23 (choose a subset of these representative of the different cases that can arise), 24, 27, 31, 34 and some of your choice.

Alternate In-Class Activity

Problem: 39. **Time:** 15 minutes.

7.2 TRIGONOMETRIC IDENTITIES

Key Points

- The difference between an equation and an identity
- The Pythagorean and double angle identities

Suggested Lesson Plan

This section reprises some of the issues touched upon in Section 6.6 and delves into them much more deeply. Trigonometric identities arise frequently whenever trigonometric functions are used in applications. It is essential to be able to rewrite trigonometric expressions in different, more useful forms.

Begin this lesson by emphasizing the distinction between an equation and an identity. Consider the following equations:

1. $x^2 - 6x = 7$
2. $x^2 - 6x = 7 + (x - 7)(x + 1)$
3. $\cos(\pi - \theta) = \sin \theta$
4. $\cos(\theta + \pi) = -\cos \theta$

Note that equation (1) has solutions $x = 7$ and $x = -1$. However, substituting another x-value such as $x = 2$ yields $2^2 - 6(2) = 7$ or $-8 = 7$. Hence, only certain x-values satisfy equation (1).

Have the students substitute $x = 2$ into equation (2). The result is $-8 = -8$. Expanding the right hand side of equation (2) and simplifying shows that the equation is equivalent to $x^2 - 6x = x^2 - 6x$. This is an example of an identity. Clearly, the equation is satisfied for any x-value.

In equation (3), substituting $\theta = \pi/3$ yields $\cos(2\pi/3) = -\sin(\pi/3)$. This gives $-1/2 = \sqrt{3}/2$, which is false. Thus equation (3) cannot be an identity because there are values of θ that do not make the equation true.

Ask the students to substitute a few values of θ into equation (4). Since any value of θ seems to give a true statement, the equation warrants further investigation. Sketch a unit circle and draw a generic angle θ in quadrant I. Observe that the angle $\theta + \pi$ is in quadrant III. The cosine of an angle is the x-coordinate of the intersection of the terminal side with the circle. It should be clear that θ and $\theta + \pi$ have cosines of equal magnitude, but opposite in sign. Hence, $\cos(\theta + \pi) = -\cos\theta$ is an identity.

Discuss that an equation can be investigated graphically to determine if it may be an identity. In each equation, both sides may be viewed as a function. For example, in equation (3) above, we can define $f(\theta) = \cos(\pi - \theta)$ and $g(\theta) = \sin\theta$. Thus the equation can be expressed as $f(\theta) = g(\theta)$. If this equation were an identity, then the graphs of both functions would be identical. Graphing f and g on the same axes shows that it is not an identity. (Recall that the solutions to equation (3) correspond to the x-coordinates of the points of intersection of the two graphs.)

Have the students graph both sides of equation (4) on the same axes. Since the graphs appear to coincide, the equation may be an identity. Students should be cautioned against inferring an equation is an identity simply from the graphs. There are two problems. The first is that the graphs may appear identical, when in fact they are really just very close together. The second is that a calculator window does not show complete graphs of functions.

Introduce the Pythagorean identity by graphing $y = (\cos x)^2 + (\sin x)^2$. Note that the usual convention for writing powers of trigonometric functions (on paper) is $\cos^2\theta$ as opposed to either $\cos\theta^2$ or $(\cos\theta)^2$.

The Pythagorean identity is undoubtedly the most important relationship in trigonometry. Its usefulness lies in simplification and in being able to express the cosine of an angle in terms of its sine (or vice-versa). For example, if it known that $\sin\theta = \sqrt{5}/3$ and that θ is in quadrant II, then the Pythagorean identity can be used to find $\cos\theta$. Note that it is possible to find an exact value for the cosine. Also, knowing the quadrant is essential for obtaining the correct sign in the answer. Note that the answer had to be negative since we were looking for the cosine of an angle that was in quadrant II.

Introduce the negative angle identities by sketching an angle θ and its opposite $-\theta$ on the unit circle. Have the students express $\sin(-\theta)$ in terms of $\sin\theta$ and $\cos(-\theta)$ in terms of $\cos\theta$. These identities can also be seen by reflecting the graphs of $y = \cos\theta$ and $y = \sin\theta$ over the y-axis.

The double angle identities can now be stated. Have the students graph both sides of $\sin 2\theta = 2\sin\theta\cos\theta$. Despite this identity, many students still factor the 2 out of the expression $\sin 2\theta$. Observe that $\sin 2\theta$ and $2\sin\theta$ are very different expressions. When viewed as functions they have different amplitudes and periods.

A good example using a double angle identity is to have the students solve the equation $\sin 2\theta - \cos\theta = 0$. Applying the identity and factoring gives $(\cos\theta)(2\sin\theta - 1) = 0$. This leads to the equations $\cos\theta = 0$ and $\sin\theta = 1/2$, both of which can be solved exactly. Contrast this with a solution by graphical methods.

In general, the material in this section is difficult to motivate. The problems reflect this fact as there are few applied problems in the exercise set. However, the skills and ideas developed here arise in countless other problems and applications throughout calculus and physics.

Suggested Homework Assignment

Problems 3, 7, 9, 17, 22, 25, 26, 38, 41, 44 and some of your choice.

Problems Requiring Graphing Calculator or Computer

Problems 11, 24–40.

Alternate In-Class Activity

Problem: 43 or two identities like 14 and 15. **Time:** 30 minutes.

7.3   SUM AND DIFFERENCE FORMULAS FOR SINE AND COSINE

Key Points

- Sum and difference formulas for sine and cosine
- The Pythagorean and double angle identities

Suggested Lesson Plan

Trigonometric identities arise frequently whenever trigonometric functions are used in applications. It is essential to be able to rewrite trigonometric expressions in a different, more useful form. The angle addition formulas presented in this section are generalizations of the double and half angle formulas of earlier sections. Although students usually don't have any trouble accepting the angle addition formulas, they sometimes still make mistakes like writing $\sin(a + b) = \sin(a) + \sin(b)$.

A good example to show students why it might be useful for them to learn the angle addition identities is to have the students solve the equation $\sin 2\theta - \cos \theta = 0$. Applying the identity and factoring gives $(\cos \theta)(2 \sin \theta - 1) = 0$. This leads to the equations $\cos \theta = 0$ and $\sin \theta = 1/2$, both of which can be solved exactly. Contrast this with a solution by graphical methods of solving the equation.

It is up to you to decide how much of the derivations of the angle addition and subtraction formulas. An alternative to simply presenting the formulas that are justified in the text book is to have the students work on a problem like Problems 11 and 12. In such a problem, students test possible formulas for angle addition, and for the addition of sines and cosines.

There are some problems in the text that may be useful to help to increase students' familiarity with the identities presented. For example, consider Problems 18, 19 and 22. Students who have some familiarity with calculus might recognize the difference quotient from Problem 22, and it might be worth pointing out to students that when they come to study calculus, they will be working with expressions like this a great deal.

In general, the material in this section is difficult to motivate. The problems reflect this fact as there are few applied problems in the exercise set. However, the skills and ideas developed here can be important in other problems and applications throughout calculus and physics.

Suggested Homework Assignment

Problems 2, 6, 11, 13, 14, 19, 22, 24 and some of your choice.

Problems Requiring Graphing Calculator or Computer

Problems 11, 12.

Alternate In-Class Activity

Problem: 25 or 27. **Time:** 30 minutes.

7.4   TRIGONOMETRIC MODELS

Key Points

- Sums of trigonometric functions
- Damped oscillation
- Modeling with periodic functions

Suggested Lesson Plan

Although this is an interesting section which ties together several ideas from earlier in the text, it can be omitted if time is short. There are no references to it in subsequent material. It requires the students to integrate their ideas about trigonometry into their general knowledge about functions and graphs.

The point of this section is to expose students to some of the rich variety of functions that are possible by combining suitable elementary functions. Too often, many students come to view the different families of functions as separate subjects within the course. Sections such as this one are designed to dispel that notion by showing meaningful examples of using these functions in a new setting.

Divide the class into groups and have them work through the following example. Given $f(x) = 4\cos(2x)$ and $g(x) = 2\sin(3x)$, consider the function $h(x) = f(x) + g(x)$. Have the students determine the amplitude and period of both f and g. Graph f and g on the same set of axes. Before graphing h, have the class predict whether or not h will be periodic and what its amplitude will be. This is also a good time to recall how to obtain the graph of $f + g$ from the graphs of f and g.

Obtaining the graphs of complicated functions is easy using graphing calculators. You can encourage some experimentation by having the students graph several examples of $f + g$, where $f(x) = A\cos(Bx)$ and $g(x) = C\sin(Dx)$, where A, B, C and D integers that are reasonably close to zero.

Functions involving variable oscillation provide another collection of interesting problems. Consider the function $f(x) = x\cos x$. Encourage the students to think of f as a normal cosine function, but with a variable amplitude. Explain that as x takes on different values, the values of $\cos x$ oscillate between -1 and 1. However, the output of $\cos x$ is being multiplied by x; hence, the output for any particular input x must be between $-x$ and x. Illustrate this with a few specific values of x. For example $f(3) = -2.97$, $f(6) = 5.76$, $f(0.4) = 0.37$, etc. Note that whenever $\cos x = 1$ or -1, $x\cos x = x$ or $-x$. For instance, since $\cos(2\pi) = 1$, we see that $2\pi\cos(2\pi) = 2\pi$. Have the students graph $y = x$, $y = -x$ and $y = x\cos x$ on the same viewing window. They should observe that $y = x\cos x$ oscillates between the other two graphs as the preceding discussion indicates.

More generally, the graphs of $y = g(x)\cos x$ or $y = g(x)\sin x$ are periodic of varying amplitudes bounded between the graphs of $y = g(x)$ and $y = -g(x)$. Some interesting examples include taking g to be a decreasing linear function or a decreasing exponential function. The latter case leads to examples of damped oscillation and is useful for modeling physical phenomena such as the motion of a spring. Have the class investigate the behavior of a function such as $f(x) = 2^{(-0.1x)}\sin x$. Make sure they note that the amplitude of the oscillations never goes to zero, but simply keeps decreasing as the graph extends to the right. This is an important point because if students graph the function on their calculators, the exponential decrease of the amplitude makes the graph look non-oscillatory after a short amount of time.

You should contrast the preceding examples with functions of the form $y = g(x) + \sin x$ or $y = g(x) + \cos x$. Note that if $g(x)$ is a constant, then this is simply a vertical translation of the graph of $y = \sin x$. When $g(x)$ is non-constant, then the oscillations occur around a variable midline. Consider the case of the function $y = (3 + 0.5x) + \sin x$. Compare the graph of this function with the linear function $y = 3 + 0.5x$. The effect of the sine term is to cause the graph to oscillate around the line.

Finally, you might consider the case of oscillating functions that do not have a period (see also Problem 5). A typical example (that students are almost certain to encounter in a calculus course) is $y = \sin(1/x)$. This is a challenging example for most students in a pre–calculus course. Consider the similar function $y = \cos(1/x)$. First, have the students note the domain of this function. Next, consider the behavior as x tends to positive infinity. Since $1/x$ approaches zero, $\cos(1/x)$

approaches 1 (because $\cos 0 = 1$). Have the students graph the function for $1 \leq x \leq 10$ to see the behavior. Understanding the behavior as x approaches zero from the right is more difficult for most students. Ask the class to determine the x-values for which $\cos(1/x) = 1$ or -1. They need to see (though many do not) that $1/x = k\pi$, where k is an integer. Hence $x = 1/(k\pi)$. Now consider several values of k. Have the students get the decimal approximations: $1/\pi \approx 0.318$, $1/(2\pi) \approx 0.159$, $1/(3\pi) \approx 0.106$, $1/(4\pi) \approx 0.080$. They should observe that the values are getting closer to zero and closer together. Now have them graph the function of successively smaller window about zero to observe the infinitely oscillating behavior.

If you do not wish to consider oscillating, non–periodic functions, you might investigate some applications. The text includes the example of acoustic beats, which can be a good way to relate the seemingly abstract activity of adding trigonometric functions to a real phenomenon. Another application involving the superposition of a pair of oscillators is Problem 9, which you might ask students to work on when you have completed a discussion of Figure 7.39.

Suggested Homework Assignment

Problems 1, 3, 4, 5, 9 and some of your choice.

Problems Requiring Graphing Calculator or Computer

Problems 1, 2, 4, 8, 9, 10.

Alternate In-Class Activity

Problem: On one hand, shock absorbers have to oscillate (in order to absorb the shock of going over bumps), but on the other hand these oscillations have to dissipate (decrease in amplitude). Otherwise the vehicle would not stop bouncing around.

1. Brand X shock absorbers oscillate, completing 4 cycles in a minute. Write a formula for a function that shows this behavior.

2. Just after going over a bump, the amplitude of the oscillation is 2 cm. The amplitude decreases so that after 2 minutes, the amplitude is only $1/8$ cm. Assuming that the amplitude decreases exponentially, write a formula for a function that shows this behavior.

3. Combine your answers to parts (a) and (b) to find and graph a formula for a function that shows the dissipating oscillations.

7.5 POLAR COORDINATES

Key points

- Converting points between polar and Cartesian coordinates
- Equations in polar coordinates
- Polar graphs

Suggested Lesson Plan

Coordinates are used to specify location. Students are familiar with Cartesian coordinates which we denote by (x, y). However, there are other ways to express location. Polar coordinates express location by specifying the point's distance from the origin and by the angle made between the x-axis and the line joining the origin to the point. Polar coordinates are denoted by (r, θ). Note that θ is usually given in radians.

Have the students plot the location of several points given in polar coordinates. For example, they can plot the points $(2, \pi/6)$, $(5, \pi/2)$, $(4, \pi)$, $(1, 0)$, $(0, \theta)$.

Now discuss the idea of converting between coordinate systems. Plot the Cartesian point $(3, 4)$. Now make a right triangle that shows r and θ. By using simple right-triangle trigonometry, the students can discover that $r^2 = 3^2 + 4^2$ and $\theta = \arctan(4/3)$. Generalize these formulas to an arbitrary point (a, b).

Next, start with a point (r, θ) in polar coordinates and have the students derive the formulas $x = r\cos\theta$ and $y = r\sin\theta$. Have the students practice converting points between the two systems.

Students who are comfortable with trigonometry will probably see that the choice of θ is not unique. Indeed, adding an integer multiple of 2π to θ does not change the location of the point. Point out that the coordinates for a point do not have to be unique, they just have to specify a unique location.

Make sure the students understand that r and θ work together to specify location. Suppose they wish to find polar coordinates for the point $(-2, 3)$. Observe that this point is in quadrant II. Solving $r^2 = 2^2 + 3^2$ yields $r = \pm\sqrt{13}$. Now, $\theta = \arctan(-3/2) = -0.98$ radians. Thus θ is in quadrant IV. If this value of θ is used, then r must be negative. Hence one solution is $(-\sqrt{13}, -0.98)$. However, if r must be positive, then θ must be shifted by π radians: $\theta + \pi = 2.16$ radians. Hence, another polar representation for the point is $(\sqrt{13}, 2.16)$. In short, students should make sure their answer gives a point in the correct quadrant.

Now discuss the idea of graphs in polar coordinates. First recall that a graph in Cartesian coordinates is frequently given by an equation in x and y. For example, the equation $y = 3x - 2$ has a graph consisting of all points that satisfy it. These points can be generated by substituting x-values and computing y-values. Sometimes an equation is given implicitly as in $x^2 + y^2 = 1$. However, the graph is still the set of all points which satisfy the given equation.

The situation is similar for polar graphs. Consider the equation $r = 2 + \cos\theta$. By substituting in values for θ we can generate a table of values.

Table 7.22

θ	r
0	3
$\pi/3$	2.5
$\pi/2$	2
$2\pi/3$	1.5
π	1
$4\pi/3$	1.5
$3\pi/2$	2
$5\pi/3$	2.5
2π	3

Plotting the polar coordinates yields the graph.

Spend some time discussing the graphs of simple equations such as $r = 3$ and $\theta = \pi/6$. Contrast these graphs with the Cartesian graphs $x = 3$ and $y = 3$.

Have the students use the polar graphing mode on their calculators to graph some functions of the form $r = f(\theta)$.

Summarize this section by reviewing the conversion formulas between the two coordinate systems. Finally, discuss that graphs can be represented by equations in both coordinate systems. Some graphs have very simple formulas in one coordinate system, but not in the other.

Suggested Homework Assignment

Problems 5, 8, 12, 19, 24, 27, 32, 38, 42, 48, or some of your choice.

Problems Requiring Graphing Calculator or Computer

Problems 41–47.

Alternate In-Class Activity

Problems: Look at how parameters A, B and N effect the cardioid $r = 1 - A\sin(B\theta)$ with $0 \leq \theta \leq N\pi$ by using Problems 42, 43 and 44. **Time:** 20 minutes.

7.6   COMPLEX NUMBERS AND POLAR COORDINATES

Key Points

- Euler's formula
- Polar Coordinates
- Complex powers

Suggested Lesson Plan

This section is really a taste of things to come for students going beyond precalculus in their mathematical studies. You should present Euler's formula as an interesting fact about mathematics that is quite useful in more advanced contexts. The text provides some motivation in the idea that that Euler's formula allows us to extend the rules of exponents to include imaginary numbers.

Present the formula: $e^{i\theta} = \cos\theta + i\sin\theta$, where θ is in radians. Begin by observing that for any value of θ, both $\cos\theta$ and $\sin\theta$ are simply real numbers. Hence, the right-hand side of Euler's formula is a complex number. This implies the left-hand side must be a complex number. Have the class evaluate $e^{i\theta}$ for several simple values of θ. For example, you could have them complete the table below:

Table 7.23

θ	$e^{i\theta}$	$\cos\theta + i$	$\sin\theta$
0	$e^{(i0)}$	$\cos(0) + i$	$\sin(0) = 1$
$\pi/2$	$e^{(i\pi/2)}$	$\cos(\pi/2) + i$	$\sin(\pi/2) = i$
π			
$3\pi/2$			

Next, recall the connection between exponents and logarithms that allow you to write $a^x = e^{x\ln a}$. Thus, any formula involving e actually can be adapted to any exponent base. Consider evaluating 3^{2i}. Express this as $e^{2i\ln 3}$. Comparing this with Euler's formula, we see that $\theta = 2\ln 3$. Hence $e^{2i\ln 3} = \cos(2\ln 3) + i\sin(2\ln 3) \approx -0.59 + 0.81i$.

You can extend this to expressions like 4^{3+5i} by noting that it can be written as $(4^3)(4^{5i}) = 64e^{i5\ln 4}$.

Finally, you can demonstrate that Euler's formula provides an alternative method for deriving many trigonometric identities. For example, you might do the following calculation for your students:

$$e^{i(x+y)} = \cos(x+y) + i\sin(x+y) \quad \text{(Euler's formula)}$$

On the other hand,

$$e^{i(x+y)} = e^{ix}e^{iy} \quad \text{(Properties of exponents)}$$

Now by Euler's formula

$$e^{ix} = \cos x + i\sin x \quad \text{and} \quad e^{iy} = \cos y + i\sin y$$

Hence,

$$\begin{aligned} e^{ix}e^{iy} &= (\cos x + i\sin x)(\cos y + i\sin y) \\ &= \cos x\cos y - \sin x\sin y + i[\sin x\cos y + \cos x\sin y] \end{aligned}$$

Equating real and imaginary parts gives

$$\cos(x+y) = \cos x\cos y - \sin x\sin y \quad \text{and}$$
$$\sin(x+y) = \sin x\cos y + \cos x\sin y$$

Thus, the sum formulas for cosine and sine are consequences of the properties of exponents and Euler's formula. After doing this demonstration, better students may be able to derive the difference formulas.

Suggested Homework Assignment

Problems 1, 4, 5, 7, 8, 9, 18, 19, 20, 28 or some of your choice.

Alternate In-Class Activity

Problems: From the Check Your Understanding Section at the end of the chapter, do true and false: 47–52. **Time:** 15 minutes.

Chapter 7 Review Problems Requiring Graphing Calculator or Computer

Problems 35–37.

8.1   COMPOSITION OF FUNCTIONS

Key Points

- Finding the composition of two functions numerically, graphically and symbolically
- Interpreting the composition of two functions
- Decomposing a function

Suggested Lesson Plan

Begin by reminding the students that a function is simply a rule that takes an input and returns a single output. If you have two functions, then you can obtain a new function by the rule: start with an input, obtain an output from the first function; use that output as the input for the second function to obtain a final output.

Introduce the idea of composition through a numeric example used in symbolic representations. Let $f(x) = x^2 - 2x$ and $g(t) = 2t + 5$ (the use of different variables is intentional). Start with an input $x = 4$. Then $f(4) = 8$. Now use 8 as the input for g: $g(8) = 21$. Hence, the new function, called g composed with f, takes 4 as an input and returns 21 as an output. Emphasize that the function f is used first. Next, give the new function a name, say h. What is the rule for h? Based on the above discussion, the students should be able to see that $h(4) = g(8) = g(f(4))$. In general, the rule is $h(x) = g(f(x))$. Have the students determine several values for the function h. You can define another function by $k(t) = f(g(t))$. Observe that $k(4) = f(g(4)) = f(13) = 143$. So that the functions h and k are very different.

Rather than obtaining specific numeric outputs for specific inputs, it is possible to obtain general formulas for the functions h and k. Require the students to write out all the following steps when computing function composition formulas: $h(x) = g(f(x)) = g(x^2 - 2x) = 2(x^2 - 2x) + 5 = 2x^2 - 4x + 5$. Have the students verify that they still get $h(4) = 21$. Also, $k(t) = f(g(t)) = f(2t + 5) = (2t + 5)^2 - 2(2t + 5) = 4t^2 + 16t + 15$. Again, $k(4) = 143$. These types of problems are very good practice using function notation and algebraic skills.

You can also have the students find formulas for f and g composed with themselves.

Questions involving composition using data tables tend to be quite difficult. Have the students complete the following table. Note that some cells cannot be filled in. Have the students explain why some cells must be left blank.

Table 8.24

inputs	1	2	3	4	5
outputs for f	4	3	5	2	3
outputs for g	3	4	0	2	1
outputs for g composed with f					
outputs for f composed with g					
outputs for f composed with f					

Once the students are comfortable finding compositions numerically, it is straightforward to do a graphical example. Observe, that it may be necessary to approximate some function values from the graph.

It is important that students see the process of composition as very natural and common. There are many examples that deal with real-world situations. For example, suppose that oil is leaking out of a damaged tanker. The oil is forming a circular-shaped slick on the surface of the water. Suppose that the radius t hours after the leak began is given by $r = f(t) = 300t$ meters. Note that the area of circle is a function of its radius given by $A = g(r) = \pi r^2$. What does g composed with f represent? Find a formula for the area of the slick t hours after the leak began. Finally, ask for how many hours the oil has been leaking if the slick is estimated to have an area of 10,000,000 square meters. This motivates the use of the inverse function.

There are several other interesting applications and problems involving function compositions. An excellent problem is to have students complete the tables in Problem 31. One way to approach solving for the blank cell in the table for g is as follows: Since we want $g(1)$, we should write down an equation that involves $g(1)$. We know that $h(x) = g(f(x))$. Thus, to get $g(1)$, we need x so that $f(x) = 1$. We see that $x = 2$. Hence, $h(2) = g(f(2))$. This gives $g(1) = h(2) = -2$. This type of problem is difficult for many students as it involves a great deal of function language and abstract reasoning.

Suggested Homework Assignment

Problems 2, 6, 10, 16, 19, 20, 22, 25, 32, 39, 43, 44, 47, 56, 57.

Problems Requiring Graphing Calculator or Computer

Problem 36

Alternate In-Class Activity

Problems: 60. **Time:** 15 minutes.

8.2 INVERSE FUNCTIONS

Key Points

- Which functions have inverses that are also functions in their own right
- Notation, graphs, properties and finding formulas for inverse functions
- Using algebra to find the inverse of a function
- The relationship of the domain and range for a function and its inverse

Suggested Lesson Plan

This section may require extra time to complete, especially if you stress solving for inverses algebraically.

The inverse is a concept that students have already encountered in Section 2.4 and Section 4.1 when the logarithm function was introduced as the inverse of an exponential function. In this section, we are having a more general look at inverses.

To review the concept of an inverse, present two functions given by numerical tables where one has an inverse and the other does not. For the function that is not one-to-one, stress how trying to define an inverse would violate the definition of a function. Functions defined by tables in this way are often confusing for students who are accustomed to dealing with functions defined by formulas. Be very clear which column (or row) of the table represents the *independent* and which column (or row) of the table represents the *dependent* variable. Also, make sure that students know to try to use the abstract definition of a function to make sense of the situation.

Graphical examples are a source of confusion for students. Often students will have learned a procedure for graphing the inverse by using a reflection about the line $y = x$. The confusion arises because this procedure works even when we say that the given function does not have an inverse. Perhaps the best position to take is that we are normally only interested in the inverse when the inverse is a function in its own right. While it is mathematically possible to speak of an inverse existing for all functions, we shall only be interested in cases where the inverse is also a function.

With the preceding point appreciated by students, give two graphs of functions (no formulas) where one passes the horizontal line test and the other does not. Show how the notion of one-to-one is essential in being able to define an inverse that is a function in its own right. For the graph which does permit an inverse, mention that if the point (a, b) is on the graph of the function, then the point (b, a) will be on the graph of the inverse function. If you would like to give the students the procedure for sketching the graph of the inverse, this might be a good opportunity. Try to avoid listing the steps in the procedure, instead try to use the observation about (b, a) being a point on the graph of the function to motivate the procedure.

Now address the same issues algebraically with a function like $f(x) = \sqrt{x - 3}$. Consider the domain and range of this function (look at its graph). Observe that it is one-to-one. Now take a specific output value of the function, say 5. Stress that you want to use 5 as the input value for the inverse function, so to determine its output you must find the input value of f that gave 5. That is, solve the equation

$$\sqrt{x - 3} = 5,$$

giving $x = 28$. Hence, calling the inverse function g, we see that $g(5) = 28$. Note that $f(28) = 5$. It is a short jump now to doing this procedure for an arbitrary range value. So to find a general formula for g, solve

$$\sqrt{x - 3} = y$$

for x. This gives,

$$x = y^2 + 3,$$

so for an arbitrary input of y, the output is $y^2 + 3$, hence

$$g(y) = y^2 + 3.$$

Recall that the particular variable used is irrelevant in the definition of a function. Thus g is usually written as

$$g(x) = x^2 + 3.$$

Now discuss the domain and range of g. Students who are graphing g on their calculators may get the wrong graph unless they restrict the domain. This makes the point that the domain is an essential part of the definition of a function.

From here, it is easy to introduce the notation f^{-1} for the inverse function. The final step is to discuss how to construct the graph of f^{-1} from the graph of f. Caution: Since many students write $f^{-1} = 1/f$, it is important to stress that f^{-1} is the name of a function and it has no algebraic meaning.

There are several important examples and exercises in this section. Consider a function whose graph must be carefully traced to determine if it is a one-to-one function (for example, $f(x) = x^3 - 0.1x + 1$). Also, consider examples where the variable names are not x and y. An excellent problem is an invertible function for which it is difficult (or impossible) to find a formula for the inverse function. For example, consider $f(t) = t^5 + t + 1$. Have the students confirm that the function is invertible and ask them to find $f^{-1}(100)$. They need to understand that this involves solving the equation $t^5 + t + 1 = 100$. This type of exercise is a good graphing calculator problem that stresses conceptual understanding. Another example in a similar style is to ask students to find $f^{-1}(20)$ for a function that consists of the sum of an exponential and a power function, like $f(x) = 2^x + x^2$. Students may try to use logarithms to solve the equation $2^x + x^2 = 20$, but if they use the laws of logarithms correctly, there is not way to solve the equation except by tracing on a graphing calculator.

Additional Points

The lesson plan given for inverses presumes that students have reasonable facility with the algebra involved in manipulating formulas for functions. You must assess whether your students can cope with the lesson plan that focuses on the conceptual aspects of inverses. If this is not the case, you might like to consider removing some of the conceptual emphasis from the lesson, and spending more time on the general algebraic methods of finding the inverses. Decide what level of algebra is expected from the students. You may want them to be able to confirm that two functions are inverses of one another, or you may want them to algebraically find the inverse function for a given function. This last task is shown in the form of starting with $P = f(t)$ and finding $f^{-1}(P)$. However, some exercises require starting with $f(x)$ and finding $f^{-1}(x)$. Because now both functions are written with independent variable x, you may need to work some examples in class before assigning this type of problem.

It is important to stress the fundamental relationship between functions that are inverses of one another: The domain of f is the range of f^{-1} and the range of f is the domain of f^{-1}. This is a good point to review the three trigonometric inverse functions and to use the function-inverse notation. For each function have the students graph both the function and its inverse. Ask the students to give the reason that the graphs of the sine and cosine inverse functions have no graph outside of the interval $-1 \leq x \leq 1$.

A good exercise is to horizontally write the following four equations

$$9 = 3(5x + 2)^3 + 7, \qquad 9 = 3e^{5x+2} + 7, \qquad 9 = 3\sin(5x + 2) + 7, \qquad 9 = 3f(5x + 2) + 7$$

on the board, and solve for x. Ask for the steps in solving these equations:

1. Add -7 to both sides
2. Divide by 3
3. Use the inverse: $\sqrt[3]{\ }, \ln, \arcsin,$ and f^{-1}
4. Subtract 2 and divide by 5

Note that they are all algebraically the same.

Suggested Homework Assignment

Problems 6, 12, 16, 17, 20, 30, 32, 36, 40, 44, 46.

Problems Requiring Graphing Calculator or Computer

Problem 1–6. (Easier with a graphing calculator)

Alternate In-Class Activity

Problems: 41. **Time:** 10 minutes.

8.3 COMBINATIONS OF FUNCTIONS

Key Points

- Creating and interpreting new functions by arithmetically combining given functions

Suggested Lesson Plan

This section represents a generalization of several ideas (Trigonometric Models, for example) that students have already encountered in various, specialized settings.

It is straightforward to define the sum, difference, product and quotient of two functions. You can start by defining two functions numerically and having the students complete the table of values for the new functions. Consider the following:

Table 8.25

x	−1	0	3	6	8	9
$f(x)$	8	4	−1	0	4	6
$g(x)$	2	3	4	3	1	0

Be sure to give the new functions names such as letting $h(x) = f(x)/g(x)$. There are a few things to observe such as $h(9)$ is undefined. You can also ask questions such as what are the maximum values of f, g and the function k, where $k(x) = f(x) - g(x)$. These concepts are easy when given numerical data, but tend to be more difficult if only function graphs are given.

You should also point out the fact that the domain of a combination of functions may be different from the domains of the original functions. The same statement is true of the range. Consider an example such as $f(x) = \sqrt{(x-4)}$ and $g(x) = \sqrt{(5-x)}$. The domain of $h(x) = f(x) + g(x)$ consists only of the interval $4 \le x \le 5$. Also the range is the interval $1 \le y \le 1.414$ (approximately). Sketch two function graphs on the same set of axes, such as $f(x) = x^2 - 1$ and $g(x) = x + 2$. Ask the students to sketch the graphs of various combinations of the two functions.

This is good material to work on function interpretation and problem solving skills. Consider the following population problem: Suppose some foxes and some rabbits are introduced to a wilderness area. The population of foxes grows according to the rule: $F(t) = 80 + 10t$, where t is in months. The population of rabbits grows according to the rule: $R(t) = 15(1.2)^t$, where t is in months. Have the students work in groups to determine when the number of foxes minus the number of rabbits is greatest. They should find a window that clearly shows all three functions ($0 \le x \le 15$, $0 \le y \le 250$ works well). Next, ask them when the ratio of foxes to rabbits is greatest. They will have to think about an appropriate window, since the ratios are much smaller than the population values. You can use this problem to review several other concepts. The following questions are all useful: (1) When are the populations equal? (2) What type of growth does each population exhibit? (3) Why must the rabbit population eventually overtake the fox population?

Suggested Homework Assignment

Problems 6, 16, 18, 20, 26, 28, 30, 39, 41, and some of your choice.

Problems Requiring Graphing Calculator or Computer

Problem 23, 36, 41, 42.

Alternate In-Class Activity

Problems: 23. **Time:** 35 minutes.

9.1   POWER FUNCTIONS

Key Points

- Proportionality and power functions
- The general form of a power function
- The classification of power functions into six basic types

Suggested Lesson Plan

Power functions naturally come up in proportionality problems. Start with the example that the area, A, of a circle is proportional to the square of its radius, r. Have the students translate the statement into the equation $A = \pi r^2$.

Continue by defining a power function as one having the form $y = kx^p$, where k and p are constants. Go back to the circle example and point out that here $k = \pi$ and $p = 2$. Make sure the students understand the definition of a power function by having them determine if a given function is a power function, and if it is, to determine k and p.

Consider the following examples:

1. $y = \sqrt{3x}$ $(k = \sqrt{3},\, p = 1/2)$
2. $y = \pi/x$ $(k = \pi,\, p = -1)$
3. $y = x^3 - x^2$ (not a power function)
4. $y = -x^3/\sqrt{x}$ $(k = -1,\, p = 5/2)$

The remainder of this section is concerned with describing six basic types of power functions (those with $k = 1$ and $p = 2, 3, -2, -3, 1/2$ and $1/3$). These six power functions cover all the basic shapes that are likely to arise.

Have the students graph all six functions (they should do each one separately). In each case, they should note the end behavior, general shape, concavity, x-intercepts, vertical asymptotes and horizontal asymptotes. In each case, a clear graph is obtained by using a window which is smaller than the standard window ($-4 \le x \le 4$ and $-4 \le y \le 4$ works well).

Next, have the students graph several other power functions and note which of the six basic functions their graphs resemble. For example, they can sketch $y = 0.25x^{-5}$ or $y = 3x^{1/4}$, etc.

It is important that the students understand how to compare power functions of the same type, for instance $y = x^{1/2}$ and $y = x^{1/4}$. Note that if $x = 0.5$ is substituted for x, then $0.5^{1/2} = 0.707$ and $0.5^{1/4} = 0.84$; hence, the graph of $y = x^{1/4}$ is above the graph of $y = x^{1/2}$. However, substituting $x = 1.5$ shows that $1.5^{1/2} = 1.22$ and $1.5^{1/4} = 1.11$; hence, now the graphs have switched positions. Since both graphs pass through $(0, 0)$ and $(1, 1)$, we see that they must cross. Graphing the two functions on the window $0 \le x \le 2$ and $0 \le y \le 2$ shows this very clearly.

Have the students compare several other power functions. They should carefully note the behavior for $|x| < 1$ and $|x| > 1$. The situation can be summarized as follows: For $0 < p < q$, the graph of $y = x^p$ is above $y = x^q$ for $0 < x < 1$, and $y = x^p$ is below $y = x^q$ for $x > 1$.

If we modify the six basic power functions by letting $k = -1$, then we obtain six more basic graphs that are reflections over the x-axis. Thus, the students should be able to recognize twelve basic graphs. Given the graph of a power function, they should be able to identify if k is positive or negative and the type of exponent, p. Sketch several different graphs of power functions on the board and have the class determine this information.

Finally, do an example where a power functions models a situation where two quantities are proportional or inversely proportional to each other such as Problem 37 or 39.

Suggested Homework Assignment

Problems 14, 16, 20, 25, 34, 38, 43 or some of your choice.

Problems Requiring Graphing Calculator or Computer

Problems 25–27. (Easier with graphing calculator.)

Alternate In-Class Activity

Problem: 44. **Time:** 20 minutes

9.2 POLYNOMIAL FUNCTIONS

Key Points

- Standard terminology associated with polynomials
- The long-run behavior of polynomials
- Zeros of polynomials

Suggested Lesson Plan

The study of polynomials represents familiar ground for most students. This material is not too difficult and students typically enjoy it.

Spend a few minutes giving some examples of polynomials and discussing the standard notation and terminology associated with them. Be sure to emphasize that the degree is the highest power exponent appearing, not simply the exponent on the term which is written first. For example, $p(x) = 3x^4 - x + 2x^5 - x^3 + 100$ has degree 5 and leading term $2x^5$. Observe that though the coefficients can be any real numbers, the exponents must be non-negative integers. Hence $f(x) = \pi x^3 - \sqrt{2}x + e$ is a polynomial, whereas $g(x) = x^{1.5} + x^2$ is not.

The major point of this section is to understand the long-run behavior of polynomials. The main result is that when $|x|$ is sufficiently large the behavior of a polynomial is dominated by its leading term. This can be illustrated both numerically and graphically.

Begin with a numerical demonstration. Consider the polynomials $f(x) = x^4 + 5x^2 + 6x + 20$ and $g(x) = x^4$. First note that for small values of x, the output values are very different: $f(2) = 68$ and $g(2) = 16$. However, for larger x-values the difference is less striking $f(10) = 10{,}520$ compared to $g(10) = 10{,}000$. Though the two values differ by 520, the percent difference is quite small. Indeed, $f(10)$ is only 5.2% larger than $g(10)$. For larger x-values, the percentage difference is even smaller.

Now have the students demonstrate graphically the similarity of the long-run behavior of f and g. They should investigate several different window sizes until they find one in which both graphs are visible, but it is clear that the long-run behavior is essentially the same.

Finally, define the zeros (or roots) of a polynomial. Note that the zeros coincide with the x-intercepts of the graph. The next section explores zeros in some detail, however, knowledge of the long-run behavior of a polynomial can sometimes lead to the existence of zeros. For instance, consider the polynomial $p(x) = -10x^4 + 3x^3 - 9x + 12$. Since $p(0) = 12$, the y-intercept is above the x-axis. On the other hand, the long-run behavior of the polynomial shows that both ends go downward. Hence the graph of p must cross the x-axis at least twice.

There are many applications that involve modeling with polynomial functions. Consider finding the volume of a rectangular container in which the length is 2 meters greater than the width and the height is 2 meters greater than the length. The volume is given by $v(x) = x(x+2)(x+4)$, where x is the width. Expanding gives $V(x) = x^3 + 6x^2 + 8x$. You can also have the students find the polynomial representing the surface area of such a container.

Suggested Homework Assignment

Problems 5, 6, 8, 14, 18, 21, 22, 24, 25, 28 and some of your choice.

Problems Requiring Graphing Calculator or Computer

Problem 14, 16, 18–24, 26, 30.

Alternate In-Class Activity

Problem: 23. Alternately use 29 and/or 26 for an introduction to the idea of approximation functions with polynomials. **Time:** Depends on activity chosen.

9.3   THE SHORT-RUN BEHAVIOR OF POLYNOMIALS

Key Points

- Factored form of a polynomial
- Multiple zeros
- Reconstructing the formula for a polynomial from its graph

Suggested Lesson Plan

The focus of this section is to understand the behavior of a polynomial in the vicinity of its zeros. It is important to make the connection between the zeros and the factors of a polynomial.

Begin by considering the function $p(x) = (x+3)(x-5)$. The x-intercepts of such a function are easily found to be $x = -3$ and $x = 5$. On the other hand, expanding the expression gives $p(x) = x^2 - 2x - 15$, a 2nd degree polynomial. State that if c is a zero of a polynomial, then $x - c$ must be a factor.

Consider the polynomial $p(x) = (x+2)(x-1)(x-4)$. The zeros are -2, 1 and 4. Multiplying out the expression shows that p is a 3rd degree polynomial. Observe that the number of factors of a polynomial is equal to the degree (provided, of course, that the polynomial factors completely).

Now, consider the polynomial $f(x) = (x+3)(x-5)^2$. Have the students observe that there are only two roots: -3 and 5. However, there are three factors: $f(x) = (x+3)(x-5)(x-5)$. Whenever a root is associated to more than one factor, we say that we have a multiple zero or a repeated root. In this case, the root 5 is repeated twice. Have the students graph f on their calculators and observe the behavior at the roots. Note that the graph just touches the x-axis at 5. This still satisfies the definition of being an x-intercept even though the graph does not pass through the axis.

Next, have the students work together to graph the following polynomials. In each case, have them state the roots, the number of factors, the degree of the polynomial and how many times each root is repeated. They should observe the behavior of the graph at each root:

1. $f(x) = (x+3)^2(x-2)(x-4)^2$
2. $g(x) = (x+1)(x-2)^3$

3. $h(x) = x(x-3)^2$

4. $k(x) = x^2(x-3)$

5. $j(x) = x^3(x-2)^4$

6. $m(x) = (x+6)(x+3)(x-1)(x-2)$

Note that the functions h, j and k all have zero as a root. This often confuses students. Remind them that a root is any value of x which gives zero as an output value. It is also helpful to note that a factor of x can be written as $(x-0)$.

After doing this exercise, the students should be able to produce a possible factored form of a polynomial from its graph. Sketch several polynomials, showing different behaviors at the roots and have the students find possible formulas for them. They can check if their answers are reasonable by graphing on their calculators (if available).

In the above six examples, all the polynomials have a leading coefficient equal to 1. It may be necessary to find a different leading coefficient in order to satisfy additional conditions on the graph. For example, have the students find a 3rd degree polynomial satisfying the following conditions: It has a non-repeated root at -2 and a root which is repeated twice at 4. Its graph also passes through the point $(1, -2)$

The students should quickly arrive at the factored form $p(x) = (x+2)(x-4)^2$. However, computing $p(1)$ gives $p(1) = 27$. Hence this function's graph passes through the point $(1, 27)$. In order to fix this problem, note that multiplying a function by a non-zero constant does not change the location of the roots. Hence, the polynomial $p(x) = a(x+2)(x-4)^2$ still satisfies the conditions on the zeros. Now, the constant a can be determined so that the graph passes through the point $(1, -2)$. Indeed, $p(1) = a(27) = -2$. So $a = -2/27$. Thus the correct answer is $p(x) = (-2/27)(x+2)(x-4)^2$. Have the students graph to confirm that this is correct.

The set of graph-to-formula problems, starting with Problem 12, require students to find possible formulas to match the graph. Note that the answers are not unique since the number of times that a zero is repeated can only be determined up to whether it is even or odd. However, students should recognize if a root is not repeated since the graph passes straight through the x-axis at that point.

Finally, there is a subtle question that involves shifting the graph of a function in order to find a formula for it. Give the students the graph of $f(x) = x^3 - 6x^2 + 11x - 2$. By shifting the graph down 4 units it appears that the graph crosses the x-axis at 1, 2, and 3. Hence

$$f(x) - 4 = a(x-1)(x-2)(x-3).$$

Requiring the y-intercept to be -6 shows that $a = 1$. Hence $f(x) = (x-1)(x-2)(x-3) + 4$. Note that this is not the factored form of the polynomial; however it does give the correct formula.

Suggested Homework Assignment

Problems 3, 5, 10, 12, 20, 24, 28, 31, 40, 41, 43 or some of your choice.

Problems Requiring Graphing Calculator or Computer

Problem 11–14, 46, 47.

Alternate In-Class Assignment

Problem: 40. **Time:** 25 minutes.

9.4 RATIONAL FUNCTIONS

Key Points

- Graphs and formulas of rational functions
- Horizontal asymptotes: long-run behavior

Suggested Lesson Plan

The main emphasis of this section is on defining a rational function, and deciding what the graph of a rational function does as $x \to \pm\infty$. The topics of locating vertical asymptotes and finding possible formulas for rational functions given a graph are taken up in the next section.

Begin by defining a rational function as the ratio of two polynomials: $f(x) = p(x)/q(x)$. Give a few simple examples and have students graph them on their calculators to get a feel for the complexity of the graphs. For example have them graph

1. $f(x) = (x-3)/(x+2)$
2. $g(x) = 3x^2/[(x-1)(x-3)]$
3. $h(x) = (x^2+1)/(x-2)$

Up until now, we have ignored the (many) interesting, real applications of rational functions. At this point, you might like to have students work on Problem 19. This can be quite a difficult problem for students, especially deriving the formula for the concentration of copper. Some students find the denominator difficult to understand, because they do not realize that they need to include the total amount of copper in the total amount of alloy. Part (d) of this problem concerns the long–run behavior of a rational function (although it is not stated with the mathematical formalism $x \to \pm\infty$). A class-wide discussion of this part of the problem can serve as a natural introduction to the long–run behavior of rational functions.

To further investigate the long-run behavior of a rational function, note that the leading terms of the numerator and denominator dominate all the other terms. For example rewrite the function g as $g(x) = 3x^2/(x^2 - 4x + 3)$ and have the students investigate the output values for large input values of x. Observe that $g(x) \approx 3x^2/x^2 = 3$ when $|x|$ is large. Ask the students to graph g on successively larger viewing windows (in the x-direction) until the graph is indistinguishable from the line $y = 3$. The students should become comfortable with the term horizontal asymptote at this point. Use limit notation and have the students find

$$\lim_{x\to\infty} \frac{4x^3 + 5x - 2}{x^3 + 10x^2 + x + 15}$$

by considering the highest power terms. Then have the students write an equation for the horizontal asymptote and graph the function in a large window to check their work.

Suggested Homework Assignment

Problems 5, 6, 8, 11, 12, 15 (to review inverses), 20, 21, 24 and some of your choice.

Problems Requiring Graphing Calculator or Computer

Problem 16, 19, 20, 24.

Alternate In-Class Activity

Problem: 12. **Time:** 15 minutes.

9.5 THE SHORT RUN BEHAVIOR OF RATIONAL FUNCTIONS

Key Points

- Zeros of rational functions
- Locating vertical asymptotes of rational functions
- Local behavior of rational functions
- Using limits from the left and from the right to investigate local behavior
- Factored form
- Holes in graphs of rational functions

Suggested Lesson Plan

The roots of a rational function can be analyzed in the same manner as the roots of polynomials. Remind the students of the behavior of the a graph in the vicinity of a repeated root. Note that the roots of a rational function are found by setting the numerator equal to zero. Students frequently interchange the roles of the vertical asymptotes and the roots. Emphasize that a fraction will be equal to zero only if its numerator is zero. Use the three functions from yesterday.

1. $f(x) = (x - 3)/(x + 2)$
2. $g(x) = 3x^2/[(x - 1)(x - 3)]$
3. $h(x) = (x^2 + 1)/(x - 2)$

Consider the case of vertical asymptotes for these functions. Start with an easy example such as the function f above. Relate the existence of vertical asymptotes to the concept of the domain of a function. Indeed, the students should know that the domain consists of all real numbers except for $x = -2$. Thus, it is natural to ask what the behavior of the graph is for x-values near -2. Have the students make a table of values as shown below:

Table 9.26

x	-3	-2.1	-2.01	-2	-1.99	-1.9	-1
$f(x)$							

The table shows that as x approaches -2 from the left the function values get progressively more positive, but as x approaches -2 from values to the right of it, the function values become very negative. Remind students of the notation for limits from the left and from the right, so that they realize that the notation

$$\lim_{x \to 2^-} f(x) = +\infty \quad \text{and} \quad \lim_{x \to 2^+} f(x) = -\infty$$

makes these ideas precise. Graphing the function on a window such as $-3 \le x \le -1$ and $-20 \le y \le 20$ shows the characteristic behavior.

Return to the examples of g and h above and have the students determine the location of the vertical asymptotes. Note that the graph of g has two vertical asymptotes.

Caution: Many times, a graphing calculator will not show the correct graph near a vertical asymptote (often points on opposite sides of the asymptote are connected on the graph). This is a good example of where relying on technology without understanding the mathematics can lead you astray.

Holes in the graph of a rational function occur whenever the numerator and the denominator have a common factor of the same multiplicity. Often holes do not show up on a calculator screen. Consider the example $f(x) = (x^2 + x - 6)/(x^2 - 6x + 8)$. Factoring shows that both, numerator and denominator, have a common factor of $(x - 2)$. Hence, f is equivalent to the function $f(x) = (x + 3)/(x - 4)$, $x \neq 2$. Graphing this function on a decimal window should show the hole in the graph.

Finally, because rational functions can have asymptotes, they open up a wealth of interesting applied problems. A nice example is to consider a linear cost function such as $C(x) = 1000 + 5x$. This function gives the cost to produce say x liters of fuel. The 1000 represents the fixed costs (equipment, rent, etc.) and the 5 represents the variable cost per liter. Now introduce the function that gives the average cost to produce x liters: $A(x) = C(x)/x$. Investigation of this rational function shows that it has a horizontal asymptote of $y = 5$ and a vertical asymptote of $x = 0$. Have the students explain the significance of the two asymptotes. Many students seem confused by the idea that to make no fuel cost $1000, but the average cost to produce very small quantities of fuel approaches infinity.

Suggested Homework Assignment

Problems 2, 8, 10, 15, 17, 22, 36, 40, 42 or some of your choice.

Problems Requiring Graphing Calculator or Computer

Problem 18.

Alternate In-Class Activity

Problems: 17 and 19. **Time:** 15 minutes.

9.6 COMPARING POWER, EXPONENTIAL, AND LOG FUNCTIONS

Key Points

- Comparing the growth of power functions with exponential and log functions
- Finding formulas for power and exponential functions

Suggested Lesson Plan

The relative rate of growth of various types of functions is an important topic. One example comes from computer science, where the number of operations required for a program to solve a problem is often stated as a function of the size of the input data set. Hence, program A might complete the job in $3n^7$ steps, while program B might take 1.2^n steps. Which is better for large data sets of size n?

The first part of the text explains the effect of the parameter k on the behavior of the power function $f(x) = kx^p$ in the short and long terms. A major point here is that it is the power, p, that determines the long–term behavior of the power function, and that the larger the value of $p > 0$, the faster the power function grows. You might like to have students complete Problem 20, and then discuss the results. The discussion will probably parallel the discussion of Example 1.

You could continue with this theme by comparing positive growth exponential functions with power functions of the form $g(x) = kx^p$, p a positive integer. Have the students complete the following table comparing the values of $g(x) = 5x^4$ and $f(x) = (1.4)^x$.

Table 9.27

x	1	2	10	30	60	100
$g(x)$						
$f(x)$						

Small values of x show that the exponential function f has values far below the power function g values. However, by the time x reaches 60, the exponential function has the larger values. Computing $g(100)$ and $f(100)$ shows that f soon leaves g far behind.

Have the students work with their calculators to find viewing windows that clearly show the two graphs crossing. Also, have them find a large enough window so that the graph of the power function appears almost flat compared to the exponential function.

The same type of exercise can be done comparing a log function to a slow-growing power function. Consider the functions $g(t) = 2t^{1/3}$ and $f(t) = 3\ln(t)$. Indeed completing the same table as above shows that $f(t)$ starts out with larger values than $g(t)$, and seems to stay larger. However taking larger values of t, such as $t = 2000, 3000, \ldots$ shows that g eventually overtakes the function f.

As above, have the students find viewing windows that show the relative behavior of the two functions.

Thus, exponential functions grow faster than any power function and logarithmic functions grow slower than any power function. Make sure that the students understand that even though log functions grow very slowly, they do in fact keep growing (their range is all positive real numbers).

A similar analysis can be done comparing decaying power functions with decaying exponential functions. For example, you can have the students compare $g(x) = 3/x^2$ and $f(x) = (0.85)^x$.

Next, you can discuss finding formulas for various types of graph that pass through two given data points. Recall the three basic families of functions and the standard form of their equations: linear $f(x) = b + mx$, power $g(x) = kx^p$ and exponential $h(x) = ab^x$. Note that for each type of function there are two parameters that determine the exact shape of the graph. Hence, providing two data points uniquely determines the function.

Consider the example of finding a function of each type such that the graph passes through the points $(-1, 3/4)$ and $(2, 48)$ (this is Problem 13). Have the students graph all three of their functions on the same set of axes. Use a window with $-3 \leq x \leq 3$ and $-10 \leq y \leq 50$.

Suggested Homework Assignment

Problems 4, 7, 12, 14, 20 (if not done in class), 29, 30, 38 and some of your choice.

Alternate In-Class Assignment

Problems: 36. **Time:** 20 minutes.

9.7 FITTING EXPONENTIALS AND POLYNOMIALS TO DATA

Key Points

- Modeling data with exponential and power functions

Suggested Lesson Plan

In this section we will find exponential and power functions that best fit a particular set of data using regression with exponential and power functions on a graphing calculator. Remind students that we have seen models in Chapter 3 where quantities grow or decay exponentially. Many of the examples come from population models or applications in biology. Ask students why one would like to be able to find a function that models a given data set. Often we collect data to make predictions about future developments. As an example look at the data given in the table below, which gives the population in the Houston-Galveston-Brazoria metro area as a function of time.

Table 9.28

Year	1940	1950	1960	1970	1980	1990	2000
Population (thousands)	737	1070	1583	2183	3122	3733	4672

Have the students plot the population, P, as a function of time, t, in years since 1940. This can be done by hand, or by making a scatter plot on the graphing calculator. Plotting the data shows that P appears to be an exponential function of t. Hence, it is reasonable to fit a curve to the data that has the form $P = Ae^{kt}$. Since we do not know that any of our data points actually lie on the curve, we cannot solve for A and k by using the data points. Instead we will enter the data into a graphing calculator and use the exponential regression function to find the exponential function that best fits the data. Plotting this exponential function together with a scatter plot of the data shows how well the function fits the data.

Next, notice that the data can also be fit to a power function. In this case we wish to express P in the form $P = At^p$. As before we use the calculator to find the power function that best fits the data.

Graph the two functions together with the data and discuss which function provides a better model for the situation. As part of the discussion have the students use both models to predict the population in the Houston-Galveston-Brazoria metro area in 1975 and in 2010. Discuss why the numbers for 1975 are close together while the numbers for 2010 are farther apart.

It is important for students to realize that data may be well fit by more than one type of curve. Point out that fitting curves to data is often used for making predictions. Though an exponential function and a power function may both reasonably fit a set of data, they have dramatically different long term behavior. This points out the potential pitfalls in using a model to make predictions too far into the future.

Suggested Homework Assignment

Problems 4, 6, 16, 20, 25, 29, and some of your choice.

Problems Requiring Graphing Calculator or Computer

Problems 4–6, 13, 15–24, 26–30.

Alternate In-Class Assignment

Problem: 27. **Time:** 20 minutes.

Chapter 9 Review Problems Requiring Graphing Calculator or Computer

Problems 53.

10.1 VECTORS

Key Points

- The definition of displacement
- Physical quantities represented by vectors
- Addition and subtraction of vectors geometrically
- Scalar multiplication
- The magnitude of a vector

Suggested Lesson Plan

Start the lesson by emphasizing that displacement is not the same thing as distance. Indeed, if you walk 5 miles along a straight road, then this is certainly different than walking 3 miles along the road and then turning right and walking 2 more miles. Sketch a picture of this situation on the board. Note that in both cases you walk a distance of 5 miles, however your final locations are different. Have the students determine the distance between the initial location and the final location in both cases.

As long as changes in directions are given by 90 degree turns, then the Pythagorean theorem can be used to determine final separation distance. Consider the case of walking 3 miles East, 2 miles North and finally one mile East. By sketching the diagram of this motion, it is seen to be equivalent to walking 4 miles East and 2 miles North. Hence the total separation between the initial and final locations is $\sqrt{16 + 4} = 2\sqrt{5} \approx 4.47$. Note that this is considerable less than the 6 miles walked. Have the students describe a displacement of 6 miles which results in the final distance between starting and ending points being one mile.

In general, there is no reason that changes in direction have to be given by 90 degree angles. Consider the situation in which you drive North along a straight road for 5 miles. Suddenly the road veers sharply 30 degrees toward the East. You continue traveling in this new direction for another 3 miles. How far are you from where you started? By making the appropriate sketch (strongly encourage your students to sketch the situation), the problem is seen to be equivalent to finding the unknown side of a triangle. Using the Law of Cosines yields the correct answer.

Finally, address the situation of combining three or more displacements. For example, suppose you travel 3 miles West, then 4 miles Northwest. You then change directions by 15 degrees more toward the North and travel 2 more miles. Have your students sketch the situation. You may need to explain how compass directions are related to each other. Now, have the class first determine the distance of the path between the starting point and the point before the last change in direction. As in the example in the text, the students will first have to use the Law of Cosines and then the Law of Sines. In solving this problem, be sure that the students have their diagrams labeled with the correct angles.

Introduce the geometric representation of vectors as directed line segments. Emphasize the idea that a vector consists of both a magnitude and a direction. The idea that a vector does not have a fixed location is a very difficult concept for most students. Using a directed line segment to represent a displacement may help.

For example, consider the displacements West 3 miles and Northwest 5 miles. Each of these can be represented on a plane in which the direction North has been specified. There is no preferred placement of either vector on the plane until a starting point is specified. Stress this idea by drawing several parallel vectors that all represent the same displacement.

When adding displacements, it is assumed that one displacement begins where the other one ends. This explains the geometry behind adding vectors. Draw two non-parallel vectors of different length on the board and have students add them in both orders to see that vector addition is.

One way for students to get a feel for vector addition is to take several plastic drinking straws that have been cut to different lengths. Give each group of students three straws of different lengths. Have them select any two straws and determine their relative directions in order to add up to the other straw. The groups can experiment with the different possibilities. This exercise is also useful for exploring vector subtraction.

It is difficult for students to get a feel for what vector subtraction represents. However, examples involving both displacement and force serve well to motivate the idea. Consider the example of a vector $\vec{v}$ that represents North 3 miles. Suppose you wish the final displacement from your starting point to be the vector $\vec{w}$ that represents 7 miles Northwest. What displacement vector must be followed after traveling 3 miles North to achieve the result?

Call the unknown vector (displacement) $\vec{u}$. Then $\vec{u}$ must satisfy $\vec{v} + \vec{u} = \vec{w}$. By sketching the vectors $\vec{v}$ and $\vec{w}$ with their tails at the same point, it is clear that $\vec{u}$ must be drawn from the head of $\vec{v}$ to the head of $\vec{w}$. Note that $\vec{u} = \vec{w} - \vec{v}$. This geometric procedure defines vector subtraction.

Once the students have a feel for manipulating directed line segments to represent vector addition and subtraction, you can move on to problems involving analytic computation. Introduce the notation for the magnitude of a vector $\|\vec{v}\|$. Emphasize that the magnitude does not give any information about the direction: it is simply a non-negative real number that gives the length of the vector. Now, given two vectors, $\vec{u}$ and $\vec{v}$, you can consider the problem of finding the magnitude and direction of $\vec{w} = \vec{u} + \vec{v}$. Magnitude is an easily understood concept, however direction is often confusing. The reason is that directions must be given relative to some fixed frame of reference. Typically, the direction of $\vec{w}$ is given as an angle relative to the direction of $\vec{u}$ or $\vec{v}$.

Consider the following problem: A force $\vec{u}$ of 50 newtons acts on an object in a certain direction. Another force $\vec{v}$ of 20 newtons acts in a direction which deviates by 30 degrees from that of $\vec{u}$. What is the magnitude and direction of the resulting net force?

Have the students draw vectors representing $\vec{u}$ and $\vec{v}$. Note that they should be drawn with their tails at the same point and an angle of 30 degrees between them. We are looking for the vector $\vec{w} = \vec{u} + \vec{v}$. In order to sketch $\vec{w}$, the tail of $\vec{v}$ must be moved to the head of $\vec{u}$. Once this is done, the problem is reduced to finding an unknown side and an unknown angle in an obtuse triangle. By applying the Law of Cosines the magnitude of $\vec{w}$ can be easily found. Applying the Law of Sines yields the angle between $\vec{w}$ and $\vec{u}$. Thus the final answer should be given as the net force $\vec{w}$ has a magnitude of 68.1 newtons acting in a direction which deviates toward $\vec{v}$ by 8.4 degrees from the direction of $\vec{u}$.

Next introduce the idea of multiplying a scalar by a vector. If a force $\vec{u}$ is doubled, then the result is the new vector $\vec{u} + \vec{u}$. We can write this as $2\vec{u}$. Sketch both $\vec{u}$ and $2\vec{u}$ noting that the direction is the same. In general, multiplying a vector by a positive scalar k "scales" the length of the vector by a factor of k. Hence, the vector $1.65\vec{u}$ is 65% longer than $\vec{u}$.

Finally, discuss the idea of the vector $-\vec{u}$. By considering the subtraction $\vec{u} - 2\vec{u}$, it is clear the result has the same length as $\vec{u}$, but points in the opposite direction. Extend this to any negative scalar: For example, the vector $-4\vec{u}$ is obtained from $\vec{u}$ by thinking of it as $4(-\vec{u})$.

The language and notation associated with vectors is sufficiently abstract that students frequently confuse scalar quantities with vector quantities. Consider the problem of having the students identify whether each of the following expressions represents a vector, scalar or is undefined.

Let $\vec{u}$ and $\vec{v}$ be vectors and let k be any non-zero scalar.

1. $\vec{u} + (k^2)\vec{v}$
2. $\vec{u}^2 + \vec{v}$
3. $||2\vec{u} - 3\vec{v}||$
4. $\vec{u} + ||\vec{v}||$

Suggested Homework Assignment

Problems 5, 6, 7, 8, 9, 10, 12, 13, 19, or some of your choice.

Alternate In-Class Activity

Problems: Short group discussions on Problems 1–4 . **Time:** 5 minutes.

10.2   THE COMPONENTS OF A VECTOR

Key Points

- Components in the x and y directions
- Unit vectors
- Resolving a vector into components

Suggested Lesson Plan

This section deals with vectors in the coordinate plane. With this fixed reference frame, it is possible to choose preferred components. This allows for analytic computations with vectors.

Start by drawing an arbitrary vector on the board. Observe that there are many different pairs of vectors that sum to the given vector. Draw several such pairs. Now note that if the original vector is drawn in the xy-plane, then there is a preferred pair. Indeed, it is very convenient to express a vector as a sum of vectors that are parallel to the x and y axes.

Given any vector $\vec{v}$ in the xy-plane, it is straightforward to see that it can be written as $\vec{v} = \vec{v}_1 + \vec{v}_2$, where $\vec{v}_1$ is parallel to the x-axis and $\vec{v}_2$ is parallel to the y-axis. The vector $\vec{v}_1$ is called the x-component of $\vec{v}$ and $\vec{v}_2$ is called the y-component of $\vec{v}$. Now take a particular case such as drawing a vector from the point $(1, 2)$ to $(5, 4)$. Sketching the x and y-components shows that the x-component has length 4 and the y-component has length 2. That is $||\vec{v}_1|| = 4$ and $||\vec{v}_2|| = 2$. Make the important connection that if the lengths of the components are known, then the length of $\vec{v}$ can easily be found from the Pythagorean theorem: $||\vec{v}||^2 = ||\vec{v}_1||^2 + ||\vec{v}_2||^2$.

Next define a unit vector as any vector of magnitude one. Unit vectors are useful because multiplying a unit vector by a scalar k gives a vector of length $|k|$. There are two very important unit vectors that are given names. We define the vector $\vec{i}$ as the unit vector that points in the direction of the positive x-axis and the vector $\vec{j}$ as the unit vector that points in the direction of the positive y-axis. Thus, returning to the above example, we can write $\vec{v}_1$ as $4\vec{i}$ and $\vec{v}_2$ as $2\vec{j}$. Hence $\vec{v} = 4\vec{i} + 2\vec{j}$.

Many students have difficulty distinguishing the vector $\vec{v} = a\vec{i} + b\vec{j}$ from the point (a, b). Emphasize that $\vec{v}$ has no fixed location. Its tail can be located at any point. On the other hand, the point (a, b) has a fixed location.

The big advantage of working in components is that it allows for easy computation. Suppose $\vec{v} = 3\vec{i} + 5\vec{j}$ and $\vec{w} = 2\vec{i} + 4\vec{j}$. What are the components of the vector $\vec{v} + \vec{w}$? Have the students sketch $\vec{v}$ with its tail at the origin. They can then sketch $\vec{w}$ with its tail at the head of $\vec{v}$. Now have them sketch the sum $\vec{v} + \vec{w}$ and observe that the x-component has length 5 and the y-component has length 9. Hence $\vec{v} + \vec{w} = 5\vec{i} + 9\vec{j}$. Generalize this to the statement that to add to vectors, you simply have to add the corresponding components.

The same idea as above applies to scalar multiplication. If $\vec{v} = a\vec{i} + b\vec{j}$, then $k\vec{v} = ka\vec{i} + kb\vec{j}$. Many times students will perform these types of operations correctly without really understanding what is going on. Indeed, adding the components of vectors and multiplying them by scalars follow the standard rules of algebra. Try to make the students see the underlying geometric justification for these rules.

Often a vector in the plane is given in terms of its length and its direction relative to the positive x-axis. This is typically the case when analyzing forces. For example, suppose that a force $\vec{v}$ of 40 lb is applied to an object located at the origin. The direction of the force is 60 degrees from the positive x-axis. What are the components of $\vec{v}$? The solution to this type of problem is known as resolving a vector into components. The solution is found using elementary right-triangle trigonometry.

The length of the x-component is given by $\|\vec{v}_1\| = 40\cos(60) = 20$. Similarly, the length of the y-component is $\|\vec{v}_2\| = 40\sin(60) \approx 34.6$. Hence $\vec{v} = 20\vec{i} + 34.6\vec{j}$. Have the students interpret the physical meaning of the components. That is that applying a force of 20 lb in the x-direction and a force of 34.6 lb in the y-direction is equivalent to the original force.

Wrap-up the entire discussion of components by summarizing several key ideas:

1. There are many ways to write a vector as a sum of two other vectors. However, when the vector is in the xy coordinate plane, then there is a preferred way using $\vec{i}$ and $\vec{j}$.

2. Any vector in the plane can be expressed as $a\vec{i} + b\vec{j}$ (though a or b may equal zero).

3. If vectors are given in components, then adding vectors is done by adding corresponding components. Similarly, multiplying a vector by a scalar is accomplished by multiplying each component by that scalar.

4. The length of a vector can be found from the lengths of the components using the Pythagorean theorem.

5. Resolving a vector into components is accomplished by applying right-triangle trigonometry to the triangle formed by the vector and its components.

Encourage your students to answer questions involving components by sketching the relevant pictures and applying geometry, rather than memorizing formulas.

If there is time, you could indicate that all of the topics discussed here can be extended to three dimensional situations. (Students are intuitively familiar with three dimensions, although they usually have difficulty formalizing their ideas.)

Suggested Homework Assignment

Problems 2, 4, 6, 7, 10, 17, 21 and some of your choice.

Alternate In-Class Activity

Problems: 24. **Time:** 15 minutes.

10.3 APPLICATION OF VECTORS

Key Points

- Population vectors
- Price and consumption vectors
- Gravitational force vectors
- Position vectors

Suggested Lesson Plan

This section is designed to give students an introduction to some of the many uses of vectors. An important new idea is that vectors are useful for organizing certain types of information.

In this section, the notation (a, b) is introduced to represent the vector $a\vec{i} + b\vec{j}$. Though the ordered pair notation is potentially ambiguous, it has the advantage of easily extending to more than two components.

Examples from economics are appealing since they represent a class of problems that most students would not associate with the word vector. (If students have previously been exposed to vectors, it was most likely in their high school physics class.) The text discusses price and consumption for an inventory of cars. Here is another example that can be used in class.

A popular bagel shop sells several different kinds of bagels. The four most popular are onion, chocolate chip, sunflower and wheat in that order. The selling price for all bagels is $0.50 except for chocolate chip which are $0.55. This can be represented by the price vector $\vec{P} = (0.50, 0.55, 0.50, 0.50)$. Due to different ingredients each bagel costs a different amount to produce. The expenses per bagel can be displayed in the expense vector $\vec{E} = (0.32, 0.38, 0.29, 0.27)$. Let $\vec{I}$ be the inventory vector. If all the bagels are baked during the night, then at the start of the business day the shop has a certain number of each type of bagel. Denote this vector by $\vec{I} = (I_1, I_2, I_3, I_4)$. So for example, I_3 represents the number of sunflower bagels that can be sold that day. Let $\vec{C} = (C_1, C_2, C_3, C_4)$ represent the consumption vector. This vector gives the number of bagels of each type purchased each day. Have the class discuss the meaning of the following expressions or equations:

1. $\vec{I} - \vec{C}$

2. $\vec{C} - 0.8\vec{I} = 0$

3. $\vec{P} - \vec{E}$

As an introduction to the dot product (to be discussed in the next section), have the students write down expressions that would give the following values:

1. The revenue for the day from the sale of the four types of bagels.

2. The profit for the day from the sale of the four types of bagels.

3. The maximum profit possible for the day from the sale of the four types of bagels.

Another important application (particularly for students in science majors) is to problems involving gravitational force. The text discusses (Example 6) the gravitational force of a space craft due to both the earth and the moon. This is a difficult example and it is worth spending some time on. Make sure that the students are clear on what objects are vectors and which are scalars. Whenever a vector quantity is used, it is a good idea to briefly explain why a scalar would be inadequate to describe the situation.

As a final example, you can address the issue of position vectors. Any vector that has its tail at the origin is said to be a position vector. Since vectors have no preferred location, every vector can be thought of as a position vector. Make sure the students are clear on the following point: If a vector $a\vec{i} + b\vec{j}$ is drawn with its tail at the origin (as a position vector), then the head of the vector is located at the point (a, b). You might draw several position vectors such as $3\vec{i} + 2\vec{j}$, $-4\vec{j}$, $-5\vec{i} + \vec{j}$, etc.

Position vectors are really a way of thinking of points as vectors. Since there is a well-defined arithmetic associated with vectors (but not with points), it is often convenient to make this association. The example of computer graphics is discussed in the text. Since so many students are familiar with computer games, this topic should be easy to motivate.

Suppose the origin is located in the lower left corner of the computer screen. If an alien spaceship's initial location is the point $(6, 1)$ and the ship moves 7 units in a direction that makes an angle of 160 degrees with the positive direction of the x-axis, then is the ship's final position still visible on the computer screen?

The solution to this requires that the students convert the displacement vector into components. Indeed, $\vec{d} = 7\cos(160)\vec{i} + 7\sin(160)\vec{j} \approx -6.58\vec{i} + 2.39\vec{j}$. Now viewing the initial position as a displacement from the origin as $\vec{v}_{\text{start}} = 6\vec{i} + \vec{j}$, we see that the final position is given by $\vec{v}_{\text{final}} = \vec{v}_{\text{start}} + \vec{d} = -0.58\vec{i} + 3.39\vec{j}$. This is associated with the point $(-0.58, 3.39)$. This is not visible on the screen.

Suggested Homework Assignment

Problems 1, 8, 12, 13 (if not done in class), 14, 15, 18.

Alternate In-Class Activity

Problems: 18. **Time:** 20 minutes.

10.4   THE DOT PRODUCT

Key Points

- Computation of the dot product using components
- The geometric formula for the dot product
- Applications of the dot product to finding angles between vectors
- Work

Suggested Lesson Plan

The dot product is an important concept that can be difficult to motivate. It is difficult because it takes two vectors and returns a scalar whose value can be hard to interpret in a meaningful way. Start by presenting the formula for computing the dot product of two vectors from their components. Simply state that the formula is a useful tool for many applications involving vectors. Stress repeatedly that computing the dot product of two vectors gives a scalar. The scalar may be positive, negative or zero. Let the students get comfortable with the formula by computing several dot products.

An alternative way to motivate the definition of the dot product is to ask the question: Given two vectors, how can we determine the geometrical relationship between them? For example, when can we tell if the vectors are perpendicular? Begin with the two vectors and the Law of Cosines. The Law of Cosines can be manipulated to give that: $||\vec{u}|| \cdot ||\vec{v}|| \cos\theta = u_1 v_1 + u_2 v_2$. The vectors are perpendicular if $\theta = 0$, which is equivalent to $u_1 v_1 + u_2 v_2 = 0$.

Next, consider the case of computing the dot product of a price vector for several inventory items with the corresponding consumption vector. The result is the gross revenue. This is one example in which the dot product is a very natural operation. It also gives a sense that the dot product gives some sort of aggregate measure of something that depends symmetrically on both vectors. It is a difficult jump to the more geometric formula $\vec{v} \cdot \vec{w} = ||\vec{v}|| \, ||\vec{w}|| \cos \theta$. The text has a very nice derivation of this formula which more advanced students should be able to follow. This formula requires some explanation. First, make sure the students understand how θ is measured. Note that $0 \leq \theta \leq 180$ degrees. Discuss the two extreme cases of $\theta = 0$ and $\theta = 180°$.

Observe that since $||\vec{v}|| \neq 0$ and $||\vec{w}|| \neq 0$, the sign of the dot product is completely determined by the angle θ. If $\theta > 90°$, the dot product is negative. Hence the sign of the dot product tells us whether the two vectors point in the same general direction or in more opposite directions. The text uses the terms aligned and not aligned to describe this phenomenon. Have the students discuss the following situation: Given two vectors of fixed length, what values of θ make the dot product take on its maximum and minimum possible values. Also, for what value of θ is the dot product zero? What does this say about the two vectors geometrically?

An important use of the dot product formula is to find the angle between two vectors given in components. Indeed, if $\vec{v} = (3, 5)$ and $\vec{w} = (-2, 6)$, then $\vec{v} \cdot \vec{w} = 24$. On the other hand, $\vec{v} \cdot \vec{w} = ||\vec{v}|| \, ||\vec{w}|| \cos \theta = \sqrt{(34)} \sqrt{(40)} \cos \theta$. Hence $\cos \theta = 24/(\sqrt{(34)} \sqrt{(40)}) = 0.651$. Thus, $\theta = \arccos(0.651) = 49.4$ degrees (or 0.862 radians).

Have the students compute the dot product of a vector with itself to discover the formula $\vec{v} \cdot \vec{v} = ||\vec{v}||^2$. From here you can point out some simple consequences such as $\vec{i} \cdot \vec{i} = \vec{j} \cdot \vec{j} = 1$ and $\vec{i} \cdot \vec{j} = 0$.

One of the most common applications of the dot product is to physical problems involving work. The text develops and solves a series of problems involving pushing a refrigerator up a ramp. Here is another way to develop the concept.

Suppose you need to push your stalled car 100 feet down the road to the gas station. You apply a force to the car when you push it. Now force is a vector: it has a magnitude (how hard you are pushing) and a direction (the direction in which you are pushing). Since you are taller than the back of the car, it is quite likely that as you push, you are actually pushing slightly downward. Think of resolving your force vector into components: one parallel to the road and the other perpendicular to it. Only the component parallel to the road is making the car move. The other component is not contributing to the motion of the car. Physicists define work as the energy spent by a force times a displacement. If force is in pounds and displacement is in feet, then the units on work are foot-pounds (in the metric system the units are newton-meters).

Continuing with the example above, let θ denote the angle between the force vector (the direction you are pushing) and the road. The magnitude of the force parallel to the road is $||\vec{F}|| \cos \theta$. If we let $\vec{r}$ denote the displacement vector from where the car stalled to the gas station, then $||\vec{r}|| = 100$ feet. Hence the work done in pushing the car is $||\vec{r}|| \, ||\vec{F}|| \cos \theta$. This is just the dot product of $\vec{r}$ and $\vec{F}$.

Take a particular example. Say that $||\vec{F}|| = 130$ lbs and you are pushing downward at a 10 degree angle with the road. How much work is done in moving the car? Because you are not pushing parallel to the road, the amount of force causing the car to move is $130 \cos(10) = 128$ lbs. Hence the work is $128 \cdot 100 = 12{,}800$ ft-lbs.

Suggested Homework Assignment

Problems 1, 4, 8, 12, 13, 15, 23, or some of your choice.

Alternate In-Class Activity

Problems: 17. **Time:** 15 minutes.

10.5 MATRICES

Key Points

- Matrices
- Addition, subtraction, and scalar multiplication
- Multiplication of a matrix and a vector

Suggested Lesson Plan

Any array of numbers can be treated as a mathematical object we call a matrix. Given information from a table, we can form a matrix and manipulate it algebraically. For example, consider the information given in the table below. Suppose four roommates want to organize their expenses. The table shows how much money each of them spent on food, books, car expenses and entertainment in January.

Table 10.29

	Jane	Mary	Anna	Lily
food	$120	$100	$160	$143
books	$48	$73	$52	$44
car	$120	$0	$110	$160
entertainment	$55	$47	$80	$63

Turn the table into a matrix (B_J, budget for January) and introduce the students to the terminology of matrices: entries, columns, rows, $m \times n$ matrix.

$$B_J = \begin{pmatrix} 120 & 100 & 160 & 143 \\ 48 & 73 & 52 & 44 \\ 120 & 0 & 110 & 160 \\ 55 & 47 & 80 & 63 \end{pmatrix}$$

Suppose we have another matrix that gives the budget of the roommates for February.

$$B_F = \begin{pmatrix} 110 & 105 & 130 & 173 \\ 0 & 33 & 71 & 15 \\ 115 & 0 & 130 & 130 \\ 70 & 4 & 65 & 74 \end{pmatrix}$$

Have the students add the two matrices and ask them what information the new matrix gives you. We can also multiply B_J by a scalar, for example by 5, to predict how much money the roommates should budget for the spring semester (January through May). Since the students have already seen the algebra of vectors, working with matrices does not add much new information and should not be difficult for them.

Multiplication of a matrix by a vector is less intuitive. To introduce multiplication of a matrix by a vector, look at an example like the one about the population of two countries that is given in the book. A similar example is the following: Suppose two cities A and B have populations (in thousands) given by $a_0 = 500$ and $b_0 = 750$ in the year 2000. Every year 4% of the the population of city A moves to city B and 7% of the population of city B moves to city A. We can compute the population in both cities one year later by looking at the equations:

$$a_1 = 0.96a_0 + 0.07b_0$$

$$b_1 = 0.04a_0 + 0.93b_0.$$

If we let $\vec{P}_0 = (a_0, b_0)$, we can rewrite the two equations as

$$a_1 = (0.96, 0.07) \cdot \vec{P}_0$$

$$b_1 = (0.04, 0.93) \cdot \vec{P}_0.$$

Let $\vec{P}_1 = \begin{pmatrix} a_1 \\ b_1 \end{pmatrix}$, then we can introduce the matrix equation which gives the same information:

$$\vec{P}_1 = \begin{pmatrix} 0.96 & 0.07 \\ 0.04 & 0.93 \end{pmatrix} \vec{P}_0.$$

Have the students compute the populations for $\vec{P}_1$ and $\vec{P}_2$ to practice multiplication of a matrix by a vector.

Finally, generalize this idea to any size matrix.

Suggested Homework Assignment

Problems 2, 4, 7, 8, 9, 14 .

Alternate In-Class Activity

Problem: 8. **Time:** 15 minutes.

11.1 SEQUENCES

Key Points

- Definition of a sequence
- Arithmetic and geometric sequences

Suggested Lesson Plan

Start by illustrating the idea of a sequence with several well-chosen examples, like the ones in Example 1 from the text, for instance. Emphasize that a sequence is any ordered list of numbers (finite or infinite). Since many students incorrectly assume that there must be a definite pattern or formula to call something a sequence, it would be helpful to include some examples like part (d) of Example 1, where there is a rule involved but no obvious pattern to the numbers. Next, spend some time talking about the notation for sequences and the idea of the nth term of a sequence. Now would be a good time to do some examples of sequences which are generated from an explicit formula for the nth term.

As a lead-in to the idea of an arithmetic sequence, write the sequence 2, 6, 10, 14, 18, 22, ... on the board. Ask the students if they notice any pattern; try to get them to say that each pair of successive terms differs by 4. Point out that such a sequence in which there is a "common difference" between successive terms is called an arithmetic sequence. Now, use this specific sequence to help them guess a general formula for the nth term of the sequence. One idea to aid in this process is to write the following chart on the board and ask them to fill in the missing entries in the second column:

Table 11.30

n	1	2	3	4	5	$\cdots$	n
a_n	2	$2 + 1 \cdot 4$	$2 + 2 \cdot 4$			$\cdots$	

The last entry in the second column, $2 + (n - 1) \cdot 4$, gives the nth term of the sequence. Ask them what the significance of the number 2 and the number 4 in the general formula and ask them to calculate the 100th term in the sequence. You can then follow up by asking how the formula for the nth term would change if the sequence started with 3 instead of 4? if the sequence started with 3 and the common difference were 5 instead of 4? From here, it is relatively easy to deduce the general formula for the nth term of an arbitrary geometric sequence: $a_n = a_1 + (n - 1)d$, where d is the common difference between successive terms. Use caution when introducing the general notation, as students tend to have difficulty understanding the meaning of subscripts.

Next make the connection between linear functions and arithmetic sequences. Stress that a sequence is simply a function whose domain is the set of natural numbers. Now, given a typical linear function, say $f(x) = 6x + 8$, consider the values $f(1), f(2), f(3), \ldots$. Note that this gives an arithmetic sequence: $14, 20, 26, \ldots$. Ask the students how to obtain the graph of the sequence from the graph of the line. Point out the slope of the line is the common difference for the sequence. Describe the convention that the sequence is written using n as the independent variable and the subscript notation replaces the standard function notation. Thus $f(x) = 6x + 8$ becomes $a_n = 6n + 8$.

Explain that if a general formula for a sequence is known, then it is simply a matter of substituting the desired value of n to determine the nth term. On the other hand if the first term and the common difference are known, then the formula $a_n = a_1 + d \cdot (n - 1)$ should be used.

Now, lead into the idea of a geometric sequence by writing the sequence $3, 6, 12, 24, 48, \ldots$ on the board. Going through the same sort of process as you did with arithmetic sequences, you can introduce the idea of a common ratio and lead them to the general formula of $a_n = a_1 r^{n-1}$ for the nth term of a geometric sequence. Again, having them fill in the entries in the table below may be helpful.

Table 11.31

n	1	2	3	4	5	$\cdots$	n
a_n	3	$3 \cdot 2^1$	$3 \cdot 2^2$			$\cdots$	

To illustrate the connection between geometric series and exponential functions, you might consider going carefully through an example population growth like in Problem 28. Or, you might consider a similar example involving exponential decay. Doing an example involving exponential decay has the advantage that it corrects the common misconception among students that a geometric sequence has to be increasing. Whichever type of example you choose to do, you can ask the students to give a general formula for the nth term of the sequence and ask them to interpret its practical meaning.

Finally, if time permits, it would be helpful to conclude by giving your students a list of sequences and asking them to identify which are arithmetic, which are geometric, and which are neither, and then ask them to give the 100th term in each sequence. As an example, consider the sequences below:

- $\frac{1}{3}, \frac{1}{6}, \frac{1}{12}, \frac{1}{24}, \ldots$
- $2, 2, 2, 2, 2, \ldots$
- $1, -\frac{1}{2}, \frac{1}{3}, -\frac{1}{4}, \frac{1}{5}, \ldots$
- $a_1, a_2, a_3, a_4, \ldots,$ where $a_n = \frac{1}{n^2}$
- $-5, -2, 1, 4, 7, \ldots$
- $1 + 2p^2, 1, 1 - 2p^2, 1 - 4p^2, \ldots$

Suggested Homework Assignment

Problems 3, 4, 7, 9, 14, 18, 21, 27, 30, 31, and some of your choice.

Alternate In-Class Assignment

Problem: 26. **Time:** 20 minutes.

11.2 DEFINING FUNCTIONS USING SUMS: ARITHMETIC SERIES

Key Points

- Arithmetic series as models of growth
- Summation notation

Suggested Lesson Plan

This section deals with arithmetic sequences as a way of defining a new type of function. Begin by showing the students several sequences and have them decide which are arithmetic by examining the pattern. For example:

1. $3, 5, 7, 9, \ldots$
2. $1, 3, 6, 10, 15, \ldots$
3. $20, 40, 80, 160, \ldots$
4. $5, 2, -1, -4, \ldots$

Now move to the process of summing an arithmetic sequence. This problem is easily motivated by the example of wishing to count the total number of objects for a given situation. Consider a theater with 40 rows of seats. Suppose that the first row contains 18 seats and the number of seats increases by two per row. What is the total number of seats? Note that the number of seats in each row forms an arithmetic sequence: $18, 20, 22, \ldots$. We wish to compute the sum of all 40 terms. Note that the 40th row contains $a_{40} = 18 + 2 \cdot 39 = 96$ seats. Clearly the 39th row contains 94 seats and so forth. Hence, we wish to compute the sum $18 + 20 + 22 + \cdots + 94 + 96$.

As in the text, note that by pairing the terms appropriately we are simply adding up the same number many times. Introduce the S_n notation for a sum and write

$$
\begin{aligned}
S_{40} &= 18 + 20 + 22 + \cdots + 94 + 96 \\
&= (18 + 96) + (20 + 94) + (22 + 92) + \cdots \\
&= 114 + 114 + 114 + \cdots
\end{aligned}
$$

The only question is how many terms are being added up? Since the terms have been paired off, there are half as many pairs as terms. Hence there are 20 pairs. So the answer is $S_{40} = 20 \cdot 114 = 2280$ seats.

You may now (time permitting) develop the general formula for finding the sum as in the text. Next give a few examples of sequences and ask if they are arithmetic or not. For those that are arithmetic, have the students identify a_1 and d and then use the information to find a_{100} and S_{100}. Here are a few possibilities:

$$a_n = \frac{1}{n}$$
$$\frac{3}{4}, \frac{1}{4}, -\frac{1}{4}, \ldots$$
$$a_n = -3 - 3n$$
$$0.2, 0.02, 0.002, \ldots$$

Finish up the section by introducing sigma notation for sums. Students generally can expand a sum easily, but have a difficult time writing a given sum using sigma notation. Be sure to emphasize the difference between the sequence and its sum.

Suggested Homework Assignment

Problems 2, 3, 5, 8, 11, 14, 17, 18, 28, 32, 42 and some of your choice.

Alternate In-Class Activity

Problems: 23. **Time:** 20 minutes.

11.3   FINITE GEOMETRIC SERIES

Key Points

- Geometric series as models of growth

Suggested Lesson Plan

This section introduces geometric series through examples that combine linear and exponential growth. In addition to the examples in the text, the following problem can also be used.

A fast-food restaurant introduces a new sandwich. In the first month, the restaurant sells 50,000 sandwiches. The number of sandwiches sold each month increases by 20%. Assuming this trend continues for one year, how many sandwiches does the restaurant sell during the year?

Have students solve this problem by paralleling the development in the text. A table shows the pattern:

Table 11.32

Number of months	Number of sandwiches sold by the end of the nth month.
1	50,000
2	$50,000 + 50,000(1.2)$
3	$50,000 + 50,000(1.2) + 50,000(1.2)^2$

Let W_n denote the number of sandwiches sold by the end of the nth month. Obtain the formula $W_n = 50{,}000 + 50{,}000(1.2) + 50{,}000(1.2)^2 + \ldots + 50{,}000(1.2)^{n-1}$. Make sure the students understand why the final exponent is $n - 1$ and not n. Be sure to note that the sum contains n terms. It may be helpful to observe that the first term can be written as $50{,}000(1.2)^0$.

Have students compute W_n for several values of n. Note that for larger values of n, it becomes more and more complicated to compute the output value. In fact, for very large values of n, it either requires a computer or some other technique. This observation motivates the need for a formula to find the sum of a finite geometric series.

Lead the class through the algebraic steps as in Example 1. Go through this slowly, particularly the step where

$$1.2W_{12} + 50{,}000 = 50{,}000 + 50{,}000(1.2) + 50{,}000(1.2)^2 + \ldots + 50{,}000(1.2)^{11} + 50{,}000(1.2)^{12}$$

is rewritten as

$$1.2W_{12} + 50{,}000 = W_{12} + 50{,}000(1.2)^{12}$$

Make sure the students are clear on the algebraic steps used to arrive at the formula

$$W_{12} = (50{,}000(1.2)^{12} - 50{,}000)/(1.2 - 1) \approx 1{,}979{,}025 \text{ sandwiches.}$$

At this point you can ask the class how the answer would have been different if the initial number of sandwiches sold had been 40,000 and the increase had been 15% each month. The goal is to get the students to see that the structure of the problem is independent of the initial amount or the rate of growth.

From here you can introduce the definition of a geometric series as an expression of the form $a + ar + ar^2 + \ldots + ar^{n-1}$. Have the students identify a and r in the above example. If we denote the above expression by S_n, then the same algebraic derivation as in Example 1 yields $S_n = (ar^n - a)/(r - 1)$.

Return to the example of the fast-food restaurant. Now assume that the new sandwich is not a success. Even though 50,000 are sold the first month, the number of sandwiches sold in each subsequent month goes down by 20%. How many sandwiches are sold in one year?

Students frequently have difficulty recognizing how to match expressions to standard forms. Have the class examine several different sums to determine if they are geometric series. for those that are, also have them identify a and r. For example consider the following sums:

$$1 + 2 + 3 + \ldots + 10$$
$$3^2 + 3^3 + 3^4 + \ldots + 3^{18}$$
$$\frac{1}{2} + \frac{1}{4} + \frac{1}{8} + \ldots$$
$$2 - 4 + 8 - 16 - 32$$

Suggested Homework Assignment

Problems 1, 7, 11, 15, 16 (if not done in class) and some of your choice.

Alternate In-Class Activity

Problem: 16. **Time:** 20 minutes.

11.4   INFINITE GEOMETRIC SERIES

Key Points

- Infinite geometric series
- Present value
- Summation notation

Suggested Lesson Plan

This section extends the ideas of the previous section to infinite geometric series.

Begin by having the students recall the sandwich example from the previous section: 50,000 sandwiches are sold in the first month, but the sandwich is not a success and the number of sandwiches sold in each subsequent month goes down by 20%. If the trend continues forever, then the total number of sandwiches sold is given by the infinite sum: $50,000 + 50,000(0.8) + 50,000(0.8)^2 + \ldots$

This is a difficult concept for many students. Explain that you cannot really sum infinitely many terms. However, you can look at the sum for very large values of n, then investigate what happens as n gets even larger. Indeed,

$$W_{40} = (50,000(0.8)^{40} - 50,000)/(0.8 - 1) \approx 249,967 \text{ sandwiches.}$$

Now, note that $W_{41} = W_{40} + 50,000(0.8)^{40} \approx 249,967 + 7 = 249,974$ sandwiches. The last term represents the number of sandwiches sold in the last month (in this case only seven were sold).

Generalize the particular case of $n = 40$ to the formula $W_n = (50,000(0.8)^n - 50,000)/(0.8 - 1)$. From their knowledge of exponential functions, the students should recall that 0.8^n approaches zero as n gets larger. Hence the expression for W_n approaches $-50,000/(0.8 - 1)$ or $50,000/(1 - 0.8)$. Call this expression W. Students can also investigate the value of W_n by using the table feature on their graphing calculator. Note that in this example $W = 250,000$ sandwiches. In the first example from the previous section, where the number of sandwiches was increasing each month, the total number of sandwiches sold after n months clearly keeps increasing without bound. Thus, in order for an infinite geometric series to converge, we must have $|r| < 1$ (mathematically, there is no reason that r cannot be negative).

This makes a good point to summarize some facts about geometric series:

1. A geometric series is a sum of the form $S_n = a + ar + ar^2 + \ldots + ar^{(n-1)}$

2. Any finite geometric series can be summed using the formula $S_n = (ar^n - a)/(r - 1)$. If n is small, it may be more efficient to just add up the few terms directly.

3. An infinite geometric series is a sum of the form $a + ar + ar^2 + \ldots$

4. If $|r| > 1$, then $a + ar + ar^2 + \ldots$ gets larger and larger without bound as more terms are added. It does not converge.

5. If $|r| < 1$, then the magnitude of each subsequent term being added is decreasing exponentially. The result is that the partial sums converge to $S = a/(1 - r)$.

It is important to introduce sigma notation for expressing geometric series and other types of sums. The notation can be incorporated right from the beginning of the lesson or you can introduce it by re-writing many of the examples already discussed. Sigma notation looks complicated. You may need to encourage your students to write out the first few terms of a sum in order to see the pattern.

Finally, discuss the example of present value as an application of infinite geometric series. The example in the text that shows \$42 million is required in order to pay out \$2 million per year forever. It is interesting that this answer is arrived at via an analysis of an infinite geometric series. On the other hand, the solution can also be obtained by simple arithmetic using nothing more than percentages. This example brings a sense of concreteness to a fuzzy and abstract topic.

Suggested Homework Assignment

Problems 2, 3, 7, 11, 19 and some of your choice.

Alternate In-Class Activity

Problems: 10, 11. **Time:** 15 minutes.

12.1 PARAMETRIC EQUATIONS

Key Points

- Piecewise linear paths defined parametrically
- Circular paths defined parametrically
- Different motion along the same path
- Using two graphs to parametrically define a path

Suggested Lesson Plan

Introduce parametric equations through the following example: Consider the path that follows the straight line from the point $A = (1, 1)$ to $B = (3, 7)$. In order to give precise instructions to a robot (for example), then you must specify both the robot's x and y coordinate at each time during the trip from A to B.

Give the students the equations: $x = 1 + t$, $y = 1 + 3t$, where $0 \leq t \leq 2$. Have them complete the following table:

Table 12.33

t	x	y
0		
0.5		
1		
1.5		
2		

Upon completing the table, have the students plot the points (x, y). Point out that the parameter t is not visible in the graph, but rather that the value of t tells you the location along the path from A to B.

Now, since the resulting path is a straight line segment, it must have an equation of the form $y = b + mx$. Solve $x = 1 + t$ for t to get $t = x - 1$. Substitute into the other equation to obtain $y = 1 + 3t = 1 + 3(x - 1) = -2 + 3x$. Hence the line is $y = -2 + 3x$. Since only a portion of the line is shown, there is a restriction on the domain of $1 \leq x \leq 3$.

Next consider traveling from A to B along a different path. Suppose you first wish to travel vertically to the point $C = (1, 7)$ and then horizontally to B. Treat each segment separately. Observe that in traveling from A to C, the x-coordinate stays fixed. Every point along the path has the form $(1, y)$. So, to define parametric equations, we need only to make y vary from 1 to 7. Thus we define the equations $x = 1$, $y = 1 + t$, $0 \leq t \leq 6$. Have the students determine the equations for the path from C to B. One answer is $x = 1 + t$, $y = 7$, $0 \leq t \leq 2$.

It is a challenging problem to require the parameter for the path from C to B to start with $t = 6$. Point out that using the equations $x = 1 + t$, $y = 7$ does not work if t must begin at 6. Indeed, this causes the path to start at $(7, 7)$ rather than $(1, 7)$. Ask for suggestions from the class on how to fix this. The answer that you hope to get is $x = 1 + (t - 6)$, $y = 7$ or $x = -5 + t$, $y = 7$, $6 \leq t \leq 8$.

Now return to the first example: $x = 1 + t$, $y = 1 + 3t$, $0 \leq t \leq 2$. Modify this by replacing t by $2t$ and restricting the parameter to $0 \leq t \leq 1$. Thus we get $x = 1 + 2t$, $y = 1 + 6t$, $0 \leq t \leq 1$. Have the class investigate these two sets of parametric equations. Suggest that they think of t as representing time. It is an important idea that parametric equations provide more information than what path is followed; they describe how the path is followed.

Ask your students to modify the proceeding example so that the path is traversed four times as quickly as the original path. You can also discuss how to slow down the rate at which the path is traversed.

Next, consider the example of a circle defined parametrically. This example is discussed in the text, however it is so important to the topic of parametric equations that you should probably go over the essential parts of the example. Make sure that students work in radians. Emphasize the idea that in working with the equations $x = \cos t$ and $y = \sin t$, that x and y are both dependent variables that depend on t. We are plotting (x, y) and do not actually see the parameter in the graph of the path. Reinforce the idea (as in the text) that changing the parameter may change the rate at which the path is traversed without actually changing the path.

It is shown in the text that eliminating the parameter leads to the equation $x^2 + y^2 = 1$. Solving for y yields two different equations. Thus parametric equations often describe graphs which are not the graphs of functions.

Use the example of fox and rabbit populations to illustrate how relationships between variables can be analyzed graphically. In the example, both populations depend on time in a definite way. However, looking at the functional relationship between foxes and time or between rabbits and time (either numerically or graphically) does little to help you understand the relationship (mutual dependence) between the two populations.

Finally, discuss how to use the graphs of $x = f(t)$ and $y = g(t)$, $a \leq t \leq b$ to obtain the path defined by these equations. This is a difficult problem for students who do not have a solid grasp of graphical representations of functions.

Consider an example such as the one shown in Example 5. Have the students complete a table of values showing t, x and y. They can then plot the pairs (x, y) from their table. This intermediate step of making a table of values is quite useful when students are first doing these types of problems. The ultimate goal is to get students to view the problem as a dynamic process. For example, they should come to see that as t increases from 2 to 3, that x decreases from 1 to 0 and y remains fixed at 1. Hence, the result on the xy coordinate plane is that the path is a horizontal segment traversed from the point $(1, 1)$ to the point $(0, 1)$.

For a very challenging problem, have the students determine the parametric equations whose graph is one of their initials (Do not let them use "O", it is too easy. Something like "M" makes a good problem. This requires four different equations. Require all four segments to be traced as t varies from 0 to 1. In this way all four parametric equations can be entered on a graphing calculator and then drawn sequentially using the same window settings.

Suggested Homework Assignment

Problems 4, 5, 6, 14, 17, 22, 23, 27 (if not done in-class), 28 and some of your choice.

Problems Requiring Calculator or Computer

Problems 4–12, 21, 24–27, 32–35.

Alternate In-Class Activity

Problem: 27 or 35. **Time:** 25 minutes.

12.2 IMPLICITLY DEFINED CURVES AND CIRCLES

Key Points

- Parametric and implicit equations of circles

Suggested Lesson Plan

Begin by defining the term implicit. A graph or a curve is frequently defined by some equation relating two variables. Sometimes the curve is the graph of a function and the defining equation has the form $y = f(x)$. This is an example of an explicit relationship between y and x.

However, there are many simple and important curves that are not the graphs of functions, such as circles and other conics. As an example, consider the equation $x^2 + y^2 = 4$. In this equation, the roles of x and y are symmetric—there is no preferred choice of dependent or independent variable. Have the students try to solve for y in this equation. The result is that two formulas are needed to describe one curve. Have the students graph both formulas on a calculator to obtain the upper and lower halves of the circle.

In the previous section, parametric equations were introduced. Consider the equations $x = 2\cos t$ and $y = 2\sin t$, $0 \leq t \leq 2\pi$. In this context it is clear that neither x nor y have a preferred status. Have the students graph the curve using the parametric mode on their calculators. Again, they should get a circle of radius 4. Since both the parametric equation and the implicit equation give the same curve, there should be a way to translate between the two. Have students use the Pythagorean identity to get $x^2 + y^2 = (2\cos t)^2 + (2\sin t)^2 = 4(\cos^2 t + \sin^2 t) = 4(1) = 4$. It is common when eliminating the parameter to end up with an implicit equation in x and y.

Ask the students how they would obtain the parametric equations of a circle with a different radius. Most students will see that that the equations $x = a\cos t$ and $y = a\sin t$ give a circle of radius a. The implicit equation is $x^2 + y^2 = a^2$. When analyzing parametric equations, it is useful to look at the extreme values that x and y can take on. In this case, we see that both x and y ranges between $-a$ and a.

Have the class discuss how they would modify the parametric equations in order to move the center of the circle to say $(1, 3)$, and still have a radius of 2. Point out that the x range must now be $-1 \leq x \leq 3$ and the y range must be $1 \leq y \leq 5$. Observe that these inequalities can be rewritten as $-2 \leq x - 1 \leq 2$ and $-2 \leq y - 3 \leq 2$. Hence, we get $x - 1 = 2\cos t$ and $y - 3 = 2\sin t$. This gives $x = 1 + 2\cos t$ and $y = 3 + 2\sin t$. Generalize these equations to get the general parametric equations for a circle of radius a and center (h, k): $x = h + a\cos t$ and $y = k + a\sin t$.

The above development for the parametric equations of a circle should point the way toward obtaining the implicit equation. Use the above example, and have the students work backward from $x = 1 + 2\cos t$ and $y = 3 + 2\sin t$ to obtain $(x - 1)^2 + (y - 3)^2 = 2^2$. Generalize this to the equation $(x - h)^2 + (y - k)^2 = a^2$.

Suggested Homework Assignment

Problems 3, 6, 10, 13, 18 (if not done in-class), 19, 20 and some of your choice.

Alternate In-Class Activity

Problem: 18. **Time:** 20 minutes.

12.3   ELLIPSES

Key Points

- Parametric and implicit equations of ellipses

Suggested Lesson Plan

Having worked through the material on circles in the previous section, introduce the parametric equations of an ellipse. As an example consider the equations $x = 1 + 2\cos t$ and $y = 3 + 4\sin t$. Point out that the only difference between these equations and those above is that the y-range has been lengthened to $-1 \leq y \leq 7$. Hence, the curve will fit inside the non-square rectangle $-1 \leq x \leq 3$ and $-1 \leq y \leq 7$.

Have the students obtain the implicit equation for the above ellipse. If they use the same algebraic steps as for a circle they will run into trouble. This should motivate why the implicit form of an ellipse has constants in the denominator.

Any time standard forms of types of graphs are introduced, it is wise to make sure that students can recognize and manipulate the algebraic expressions involved. For example, given the equation $4(x + 3)^2 + ((y - 1)^2)/5 = 1$, have the students determine the values of a, b, h and k. In this case $a = 1/2$, $b = \sqrt{5}$, $h = -3$ and $k = 1$.

In general, implicit equations are very unintuitive for many students. This is a good opportunity to reinforce the idea that the set of ordered pairs that satisfy an equation in x and y give the graph of the equation. The implicit equations discussed here come from parametric equations which explains why the graph is a continuous curve. This is a difficult idea and students will need some time to get a feel for what the equations actually represent.

Suggested Homework Assignment

Problems 2, 6, 12, 14, 19, 23, and some of your choice.

Alternate In-Class Activity

Problem: 21. **Time:** 20 minutes.

12.4 HYPERBOLAS

Key Points

- Parametric and implicit equations of hyperbolas

Suggested Lesson Plan

Begin by having the students recall that the parametric equations $x = \cos t$ and $y = \sin t$ produce the unit circle $x^2 + y^2 = 1$ because of the trigonometric identity $\sin^2 t + \cos^2 t = 1$. Point out that we can obtain a new type of curve by making use of the trigonometric identity $\sec^2 t - \tan^2 t = 1$. Ask the students what implicit equation would result if we eliminated the parameter from the parametric equations $x = \sec t$ and $y = \tan t$; hopefully, they will notice that $x^2 - y^2 = 1$. Mention that this type of a curve is called a hyperbola.

Now, spend some time exploring the graphical properties of the hyperbola described by this equation. You might begin by asking the students if the curve has any x- or y-intercepts; by setting $y = 0$, it is easy to see that the x-intercepts are $(1, 0)$ and $(-1, 0)$, and by setting $x = 0$, we get an equation with no solution, meaning that there are no y-intercepts. Pick a few other values for x (the ones given in Table 12.1 in the text work nicely) and have the students figure out the associated y values and plot the resulting points; hopefully, they will notice that there are two different y values for each x value, which tells us something about the symmetry of the hyperbola. Once the students have completed this, take some time to examine the end behavior of the curve. One handy way to do this is to rearrange the terms in the equation $x^2 - y^2 = 1$ to obtain $(y^2/x^2) = 1 - (1/x^2)$. Ask the students what happens to the right hand side of this equation when we substitute x-values with very large magnitudes. They should be able to see that as x approaches $+\infty$ and $-\infty$, we obtain $y^2 \approx x^2$, or $y \approx \pm x$. Explain that this means that $y = x$ and $y = -x$ are asymptotes of our curve. Now, draw in the asymptotes and a "coordinate box" with corners at $(\pm 1, \pm 1)$ (like the one in Figure 12.27 from the text) to illustrate how the box corresponds to the vertices and asymptotes of the hyperbola. The students should note that the vertices of the hyperbola lie on the box, and that the asymptotes go though its corners. When you draw in the box, make sure that the students realize that this is not part of the graph of the hyperbola; it is simply a way to help us locate vertices and asymptotes.

Now, generalize to the parametric equations $x = a \sec t$ and $y = b \tan t$ and discuss the effects that the constants a and b have on the hyperbola. The implicit equation for the hyperbola becomes $(x^2/a^2) - (y^2/b^2) = 1$. To illustrate that a and b simply represent stretches or shrinks, you can simplify the equation to $(y^2/x^2) = (b^2/a^2) - (b^2/x^2)$, which suggests that the new asymptotes will be $y = (b/a)x$ and $y = -(b/a)x$. It is then clear that the coordinate box corresponding to this hyperbola is a rectangle (centered at the origin) with horizontal length $2a$ and vertical length $2b$. Now, draw in the coordinate box, the asymptotes, and sketch the hyperbola $(x^2/a^2) - (y^2/b^2) = 1$. Once you have reached this point, ask students how the hyperbola would have been different if we had started with $x = h + a \sec t$ and $y = k + b \tan t$. Viewing these equations in parametric form, it will be no surprise to most students that the hyperbola is simply shifted h units horizontally and k units vertically. From here, you can eliminate the parameter to obtain the most general implicit equation for a hyperbola: $(x - h)^2/a^2 - (y - k)^2/b^2 = 1$. Emphasize the meaning of each constant in the formula: (h, k) is the center of the hyperbola, a is the horizontal stretch or shrink factor, and

b is the vertical stretch or shrink factor. You might also mention that the ellipse $(x - h)^2/a^2 + (y - k)^2/b^2 = 1$ fits inside the coordinate box of the corresponding hyperbola, which illustrates the point that a hyperbola is like an ellipse that has been turned "inside out".

Next, ask the students what would happen if we switched the position of the negative sign in the general formula for the hyperbola; in other words, what would the hyperbola $(y - k)^2/b^2 - (x - h)^2/a^2 = 1$ look like? If students are puzzled by this, you might consider going back to the simplest case and let $h = k = 0$ and $a = b = 1$, so that the equation becomes $y^2 - x^2 = 1$. It is easy to see that the asymptotes are still $y = x$ and $y = -x$, but that the intercepts are now on the y axis at $(0, 1)$ and $(0, -1)$. Make a sketch of the hyperbola $y^2 - x^2 = 1$ and point out that the asymptotes and the box are identical to those of the hyperbola $x^2 - y^2 = 1$; only the location of the branches has changed. Another nice way to explain why the branches of the hyperbola $y^2 - x^2 = 1$ end up where they do is to point out that in going from $x^2 - y^2 = 1$ to $y^2 - x^2 = 1$, all that has happened is that the roles of x and y have been reversed, which is the same process that occurs when we calculate inverses. Therefore, we would expect the hyperbola $y^2 - x^2 = 1$ to be the reflection of the hyperbola $x^2 - y^2 = 1$ about the line $y = x$, a fact that can be easily observed when comparing the graphs of the two hyperbolas.

Finally, it would be helpful to have the students do some practice problems involving hyperbolas. Problems 1–4 give the graph of a hyperbola and ask for an equation, while problems 12–17 give the equations of several hyperbolas and ask for the basic features of the graph. If you ask students to work through problems like 12–17, it might be helpful to work through an example or two beforehand since these problems involve completing the square and other algebra skills that students often find difficult.

Suggested Homework Assignment

Problems 1, 5, 8, 9 (if not done in class), 15, and some of your choice.

Alternate In-Class Activity

Problems: 9 and 10. **Time:** 10 minutes.

12.5 HYPERBOLIC FUNCTIONS

Key Points

- Define cosh and sinh
- Identities and properties of cosh and sinh
- Parameterizing the hyperbola

Suggested Lesson Plan

The subject of the hyperbolic functions brings together many of the areas and ideas discussed in the text. The goal of this lesson is to make key connections to other topics previously studied.

Begin with the two definitions:

$$\cosh(x) = \frac{e^x + e^{-x}}{2} \text{ and } \sinh(x) = \frac{e^x - e^{-x}}{2}$$

The most obvious question should be why are these particular combinations of exponential functions important? You might indicate some of their significance by noting that the graph of the hyperbolic cosine describes the shape made by a chain or rope of uniform density when attached at both ends. For example, power lines strung between support towers give such a shape. You may also mention that the St. Louis Arch is the inversion of a such a shape (called a catenary).

On a more mathematical theme, point out that $e^x = \cosh(x) + \sinh(x)$. Now have the students verify that cosh is an even function, while sinh is an odd function. Thus, this gives a unique decomposition (into even and odd functions) of arguably the most important function in mathematics. This explains the occurrence of the denominator in the definitions. You might assign as an exercise the generalization of this idea to any function. Indeed, given a function f, then defining

$$g(x) = \frac{f(x) + f(-x)}{2} \quad \text{and} \quad h(x) = \frac{f(x) - f(-x)}{2}$$

gives $f(x) = g(x) + h(x)$, where g is even and h is odd.

Discuss the graphs of cosh and sinh, being sure to discuss the end-behavior in each case. This ties in very naturally with the earlier study of exponential functions, and students should have no trouble seeing that both cosh and sinh behave like $\frac{1}{2}e^x$ for large values of x.

The reason these functions are referred to as hyperbolic trigonometric functions can be explained by examining some of their properties. First note the important identity $\cosh^2 x - \sinh^2 x = 1$ and its similarity to the Pythagorean identity $\cos^2 x + \sin^2 x = 1$. It is a good exercise for students to establish the identity for themselves. However, the algebra involved causes confusion and it may be helpful to work an example of expanding an expression like $(e^x - e^{-x})^2$. The other relations to trigonometry require the material on complex numbers and Euler's Identity. Using the fact that $e^{ix} = \cos(x) + i\sin(x)$, it is an algebraic exercise to establish $\cosh(ix) = \cos(x)$ and $\sinh(ix) = i\sin(x)$ (though probably not worth doing in class unless you have extra time).

The connection to hyperbolas can be made through the use of parametric equations. It is reasonable to ask what graph is generated by the parametric equations $x = \cosh(t)$ and $y = \sinh(t)$ (since the corresponding equations with cosine and sine generate a circle). From the above identity, it is easy to see that eliminating the parameter t gives the implicit equation $x^2 - y^2 = 1$. From the previous section, this is seen to be a hyperbola. There is a subtle point to be mentioned here. The function cosh is always positive, meaning that x must always be positive in the implicit equation. On the other hand y takes on both negative and positive values. Hence, we only get the right branch of the hyperbola. As an interesting side point, mention that one branch of a hyperbola is the path followed by some celestial bodies as they whip around a massive object (such orbits are not periodic).

Suggested Homework Assignment

Problems 1, 2, 3, 21 (derive identity in answer), 24 and some of your choice.

Alternate In-Class Activity

Problem: 22. **Time:** 15 minutes.

12.6 GEOMETRIC PROPERTIES OF CONIC SECTIONS

Key Points

- Finding focal points

- Geometric definitions of conics
- Reflective properties of conics

Suggested Lesson Plan

Having worked through the material on parametric conic equations in the previous sections, we now focus on applications and the geometric definitions of conics.

Make a decision about the time allotted to this section. In depth, this section could require more than a class day. The chapter is organized by taking the conics in order: ellipse, hyperbola and parabola. If you are short for time, you may need to present all three geometric definitions. Then present the three reflective properties and a quick application. The students can later read the section in order by conic.

Whether presentation is grouped by conic or by property, focal points are an essential topic that must be addressed, and in the case of the parabola a directrix defined.

For each conic the focal point can be derived algebraically from the standard form of the equation

$$\frac{x^2}{a^2} + \frac{y^2}{b^2} = 1, \ \text{if } a > b, c = \sqrt{a^2 - b^2}$$

$$\frac{x^2}{a^2} + \frac{y^2}{b^2} = 1, \ \text{if } b > a, c = \sqrt{b^2 - a^2}$$

$$\frac{x^2}{a^2} - \frac{y^2}{b^2} = 1, \ c = \sqrt{a^2 + b^2}$$

$$\frac{y^2}{b^2} - \frac{x^2}{a^2} = 1, \ c = \sqrt{a^2 + b^2}$$

$$y = ax^2, \ c = \frac{1}{4a}, \ \text{directrix line, } y = -c$$

$$x = ay^2, \ c = \frac{1}{4a}, \ \text{directrix line, } x = -c$$

Make a decision about the amount of algebra you want the students to do. If the conics are centered at the origin and with symmetry about the vertical/horizontal axis, then the algebra is simple. If off-center then completing the square may be necessary.

There are several good websites that have interactive displays of conic graphs, use Google.com to search or try http://www.analyzemath.com/.

Showing the geometric property of each conic should be a highlight. Stress that these geometric definitions are equivalent to our original algebraic definitions and one can be derived from another.

1. An ellipse is the set of all points whose sum of distances from two focal points is constant. Illustrate by having two students each hold an end of a one meter string about half a meter apart against the chalkboard. Pull the string taut with a piece of chalk and trace an arc curve. Since the sum of the distances from the chalk to the two ends is constant, you are tracing an ellipse.

2. A hyperbola is the set of all points for which the difference of distances from two focal points is constant. This definition offers an explanation for why hyperbolas are essentially linear as they become more and more distant from the vertex. If the difference is say 2, then as the distances from the two focal points become 1000 and 1002, the point becomes close to equidistant from the focal points. This behavior is linear.

3. A parabola is the set of all points for which the distance from the focal point is equal to the distance from a line perpendicular to the line of symmetry. This property can be shown by having a set of strings of varying lengths pre-marked at the center. Hang the shortest string

from a point marked F on the chalkboard. Mark the center with a dot and draw a horizontal line going through the bottom end of the string. Have a student hold each successive string end to the focal point F and move the chalk to the middle of the string and position it so the bottom end of the string falls to touch the horizontal line. Mark each point as a point on the parabola.

The reflective properties are:

1. A beam in any direction from a focal point of an ellipse reflects to the other focal point. This is illustrated by a billiard ball at a focal point; when shot in any direction on any elliptical table it passes through the other focal point.

2. For a hyperbolic mirror, any beam aimed at the further focal point is reflected to the near focal point. Science stores have hyperbolic mirror toys that make objects appear in a place they are not.

3. A parabolic mirror reflects a beam from its focal point to be parallel to its line of symmetry. A flashlight or headlight is a good example. This property works both ways, so that satellite receivers are parabolic and the incoming signal reflects to the focal point for a strong signal collection point.

If you ask students where they see conic curves they may mention in a lamp shadow. This is a good example and can be explored in Problem 41 and the alternate activity. Another student might say in a suspension bridge. This is not a conic curve but a catenary and is presented in the next section.

Suggested Homework Assignment

A few of the Exercises and Problems 6, 20, 23, 26, 28, 30, 36, 39, and some of your choice.

Alternate In-Class Activity

Problem: 41 and follow up by positioning a lamp with a shade so it just touches a wall on which you place a large sheet of butcher paper. Mark the bottom point where the shade touches the paper and the horizontally projected height of the middle of the light bulb as well as the height of the top of the shade. Mark 10 or more points an the shadow curve above and ten or more points on the bottom shadow curve. Using the center of the bulb mark as the origin, measure and record the xy-coordinate values of the points on the shadows.

Use a graphing calculator or computer to graph the theoretical equations (from Problem 41) and your data points to see if the data points lie on the curve. **Time:** 20 minutes.

Chapter 12 Review Problems Requiring Graphing Calculator or Computer

Problems 27, 28, 29.

PART III

OUTLINE FORM LESSON PLANS

This section is an outline form of lesson plan. This kind of plan is often used by high school teachers as guide and checklist for each section. A set of suggested homework problems has been compiled by a group of experienced high school teachers.

1.1 FUNCTIONS AND FUNCTION NOTATION

Focus Points

Definition of a Function

- A function is a rule that assigns to each input a unique output. The inputs and outputs are also called variables.
- Each input yields one and only one output, but the same output can be associated with several inputs.

Numerical, Graphical, Symbolic, and Verbal Representations of Functions

- Stress the "Rule of Four" to represent functions in a variety of ways.
- Numerical representation: Discuss ways to organize sets of values in a tabular form. Present students with a table of values to determine whether one value is uniquely dependent on the other.
- Graphical representation: Discuss ways in which pictures or graphs can be used to represent functions. Present the students with a graph and discuss whether one variable is uniquely dependent upon the other.
- Verbal representation: Discuss ways in which a relationship between two sets of values may be expressed using the written language.
- Symbolic representation: Discuss ways to develop an algebraic expression of a function given a graphical, numerical, or verbal model. Present the students with an equation and discuss ways to analyze whether or not it is a function.

Function Notation

- Students should be able to recognize and translate the verbal phrase "Q equals f of t".
- In the function $Q = f(t)$, students should be able to identify t as the input and Q as the output.
- Q does not have to be related to t by a formula. The function may be given by a table, a graph, or a verbal description.

Relations versus Functions

- Emphasize the idea that two quantities can be related and yet not be functions of each other.
- Students must become familiar with the phrase: "A is a function of B" to distinguish between the input B and output A. It is equally as important that students be able to verbalize this correctly and know the precise meaning of what they say.
- When presented with a table of values for two variables, students must be able to determine if one variable is a function of the other, as in Example 5.
- A graphical representation of a relation must pass the vertical line test for it to be a function.

Suggested Problems

Exercises 1–4, 7, 9, 11, 13, 14
Problems 17, 19, 24, 33
Enrichment Problems 35, 36

1.2 RATE OF CHANGE

Focus Points

Rate of Change of a Function

- Discuss the rate of change of a function as the change in output for every unit change in the input. Discuss the four representations of functions, verbal, symbolic, numeric, and graphic, and how the rate of change may be obtained from each.

- Express the average rate of change for a function Q over an interval t as:

$$\frac{\text{Change in } Q}{\text{Change in } t}$$

Increasing and Decreasing Functions

- Describe a function $Q = f(t)$ as increasing on a given interval if the values of f increase as t increases on this interval. Similarly, f is decreasing on a given interval if the values of f decrease as t increases on this interval.

- $Q = f(t)$ may be called an increasing function if the average rate of change is positive over every interval, and is a decreasing function if the average rate of change is negative over every interval.

- Students should be able to recognize functions as increasing or decreasing on any interval given a verbal, symbolic, numeric, or graphic representation of a function.

Function Notation for the Average Rate of Change

- Students should represent the average rate of change symbolically in function notation as

$$\frac{\text{Change in } Q}{\text{Change in } t} = \frac{\Delta Q}{\Delta t} = \frac{f(b) - f(a)}{b - a}$$

- Have students calculate the average rate of change on a given interval using values from a graph, a table or a written problem. (See The Graphing Calculator Guide.)

Suggested Problems

Exercises 1, 3–6, 12
Problems 14, 15, 17, 18
Enrichment Problem 17

1.3 LINEAR FUNCTIONS

Focus Points

Definition of a Linear Function

- It is important to stress that a linear function will have a constant rate of change over every interval.
- Students will need to recognize a linear function by establishing a constant rate of change given a function in symbolic, verbal, graphic and numeric form.
- Stress the conceptualization that a linear function can be viewed graphically as a line, algebraically as an equation, and numerically as a table exhibiting a constant rate of change.

General Formula for Linear Functions

- Introduce the general form of a linear function $y = b + mx$. In doing so, you must emphasize the meaning of the parameters of slope as rate of change and vertical intercept in relation to the problem.
- Students need to master the ability to verbalize the meaning of slope as the change in "output per input" as pertaining to the problem.
- Equally as important, students must realize the value of the vertical intercept is the initial value where the input value is zero.
- Given information in verbal, graphical, and symbolic form, students must be able to write a linear equation in its general form.
- Note that a function's graph may look linear without actually being a line. (See The Graphing Calculator Guide.)

Suggested Problems

Exercises 2, 4, 7
Problems 11, 13, 14, 18, 23, 30
Enrichment Problems 29, 31

1.4   FORMULAS FOR LINEAR FUNCTIONS

Focus Points

Formulas For Linear Functions

- It is important that students be able to calculate slopes and y-intercepts for linear functions, but it is even more essential that they be able to interpret them. Students should also be able to give appropriate units for the slopes and y-intercepts.

- Students should understand the slope in two ways: (1) it tells the steepness of the line by telling you how much the line rises for each unit you move in the x-direction, and (2) it gives the average rate of change of the function over any interval on the x-axis.

- Students must be able to determine the equation of a linear function from a table of data, a graph, and a verbal description.

Finding Formulas From Tables, Graphs, and Verbal Descriptions

- Given either a table of values, a graph, or a verbal descriptions, students need to identify which are the independent and dependent variables. Once the slope and y-intercept are computed, the answer should be expressed in the form $y = b + mx$.

- In the formula $y = b + mx$, students must understand that b represents an initial value, while the slope m represents the constant rate at which that quantity is changing, either increasing or decreasing.

Alternate Forms for the Equation of a Line

- Students must be familiar with all three forms for the equation of a line: slope-intercept form, point slope form, and standard form.

- Make certain that students are able to convert from point slope or standard form into slope-intercept form, and be able to extract the slope and y-intercept information from each.

Suggested Problems

Exercises 2, 6, 7, 10, 15, 16, 18, 27, 28
Problems 35, 37, 38
Enrichment Problems 36, 43

1.5 GEOMETRIC PROPERTIES OF LINEAR FUNCTIONS

Focus Points

Interpreting the Parameters of a Linear Function

- Discuss the slope-intercept form for a linear function $y = b + mx$, where b is the y-intercept and m is the slope. Show how the parameters, b and m, can be used to compare various linear functions.
- Have students recognize the slope and y-intercept of a linear function given a graphic, symbolic, verbal, or numeric model.
- Students should be able to identify the slope and y-intercept from the standard and point-slope forms of linear equations as well.

The Effect of the Parameters on the Graph of a Linear Function

- Students should be able to recognize and interpret the y-intercept from the graph of a linear function, and how it changes as the b term changes in its equation.
- Students should be able to recognize and interpret the slope from the graph of a linear function and how it changes as the m term changes in its equation.
- Compare multiple linear functions graphically and discuss how changing the values of the parameters affects the graph of each function. Refer to Example 2.

Intersection of Two Lines

- Discuss what it means for two lines to intersect in practical terms and in the context of the problem. Discuss the practical significance of knowing this point.
- Have students calculate the intersection of two lines using an algebraic solution by solving the equations simultaneously. Be sure to consider cases in which there are more than two linear functions to compare, as in Example 3.
- Also have students find the point of intersection graphically using the capabilities of their calculators. (See The Graphing Calculator Guide.)

Equations of Horizontal and Vertical Lines

- Horizontal Line - Show that a horizontal line has a zero slope and follows the form of $y = k$, where k is some constant.
- Vertical Line - Show that a vertical line has no slope and follows the form of $x = k$ where k is some constant.

Slopes of Parallel and Perpendicular Lines

- Parallel Lines - Discuss the concept that parallel lines must have equal slopes. Illustrate this point from a graphic , symbolic, numeric, and verbal representation.
- Perpendicular Lines - Discuss the concept that perpendicular lines must have negative reciprocal slopes. Illustrate this point from a graphic , symbolic, numeric, and verbal representation.
- Have students compare vertical and horizontal lines as well, and justify why they are perpendicular to each other.

Suggested Problems

Exercises 2, 3, 5, 6, 9, 10
Problems 16, 17, 18, 25, 30
Enrichment Problems 34, 35

1.6   FITTING LINEAR FUNCTIONS TO DATA

Focus Points

The Basics

- Use the laboratory data on the viscosity of motor oil in this section to introduce the concepts of linear regression.
- Demonstrate how a scatter plot can be used to draw a line by eye. Use Transparency 1.6 in Part VI of this manual.
- Use the calculator to generate the regression equation from the scatter plot. (See The Graphing Calculator Guide.)
- Note that we make many assumptions when we obtain a regression line.

Interpolation and Extrapolation

- Interpolation is making predictions within the extreme data points.
- Extrapolation is making predictions beyond the extreme data points.
- Point out that interpolation generally tends to be more reliable than extrapolation. Note that data may be linear over relatively small time intervals, when in fact its long-term behavior can be far from linear.

Correlation

- Briefly explain the general concept of a "least-squares" line.
- Note that the correlation coefficient is a number between -1 and 1. It measures how well a particular regression line fits the data.
- Students should know if $r = 1$, the data lie exactly on a line of a positive slope. If $r = -1$, the data lie exactly on a line of a negative slope.
- Remind students that when they are given only two points, the regression equation will have a correlation coefficient of 1 or -1. However, this does not guarantee that the function is linear in the long run.
- Emphasize that a high correlation between two quantities does not imply causation. For example, there is a positive correlation between car sales and boat sales. However, one does not cause the other.
- Note that a correlation coefficient of 0 does not imply that there is no relationship between the two variables.

Suggested Problems

Exercises and Problems 1, 3, 6, 7, 8

2.1 INPUT AND OUTPUT

Focus Points

Finding Output Values

- Students should be able to calculate the value of a function's output using a particular input.
- Demonstrate methods of finding output values using input values in graphical, numerical, and symbolical representations.

Finding Input Values: Solving Equations

- Students should be able to calculate the value of a function's input when a particular output is known.
- Demonstrate how to find an input value using a formula, by setting the formula equal to the output value and solving the resulting equation.

Finding Output Values and Input Values from Tables and Graphs

- Given a table or numerical representation of a function, students should be able to identify and evaluate the input and output values.
- Given a graphical representation of a function, students should be able to identify and evaluate the input and output values.

Suggested Problems

Exercises 1, 3, 9, 11, 12, 18
Problems 25, 27, 29, 32, 33
Enrichment Problems 37, 39

2.2 DOMAIN AND RANGE

Focus Points

Definition of Domain and Range

- Students must be able to understand the meaning of domain and range in numerical, graphical, verbal and symbolic form.

- Verbally, define the domain as the set of input values which yield an output value and the range as the set of corresponding output values. Students need to start thinking in terms of inputs and outputs rather than the traditional "x" and "y". This is a good place to start emphasizing this if you have not done so already.

- In symbolic form $Q = f(t)$, the domain is the set of input values, t, while the range is the set of output values Q.

Realistic Domains and Ranges

- Point out that if the domain of a function is not specified, we usually assume that it is as large as possible, but there will be times in which the domain will have restrictions placed upon it to model a real life situation. The need for realistic restrictions are shown in Example 1 and Example 2.

- You may want to introduce your students to a model of a logistic function to discuss its domain and range as in Example 3. This is a good time to briefly mention the concept of end behavior with respect to the domain and range of the function in a realistic setting.

Finding the Domain and Range of a Function

- Initially, it may be helpful to have students look at the graphs of functions to find the domain and the range. The calculator is an invaluable tool for the students to "see" what is happening to each function in terms of the inputs and outputs and find the domain and range accordingly. This will also give students the chance to adjust the window of the calculator and understand its use. (See The Graphing Calculator Guide.)

- However, be sure that students understand that the calculator only gives them a general idea of domain and range. For example, have students graph

$$y = \frac{x^2 - 4}{x - 2}.$$

This illustrates to the students that they cannot rely on the calculator to determine the domain and range of the function.

- Once the domain and range have been found using the calculator, discuss why some functions have restrictions and why others may not have any. Discuss the effect these values would have on the equation of the function.

- When functions are defined by a formula, the domain and range can be found algebraically as well as graphically. Once students have grown comfortable with domain and range graphically, the algebra of the domain should come with some ease and have a great deal of meaning to the students.

- At this point, students will probably be reasonably comfortable with the procedures of finding domains algebraically by inspecting formulas. However, finding ranges is still probably more of an art than a science at this point. Finding ranges using algebra is usually quite difficult for the students until they realize that they are usually calculating the *forbidden* outputs.

Suggested Problems

Exercises 2, 3, 5, 9, 13
Problems 15, 16, 19, 20, 27, 29, 31
Enrichment Problems 34, 35

2.3 PIECEWISE DEFINED FUNCTIONS

Focus Points

What is a Piecewise Defined Function?

- A piecewise defined function employs different formulas on different parts of its domain.
- Illustrate a simple piecewise defined function to the students. Emphasize that this is one function with several different formulas in its rule. Discuss its domain and range.
- Give students several "real world" examples of piecewise defined functions, such as the cost of mailing a letter, and the charges on an electric bill. Have students come up with other examples.

Piecewise Defined Functions, Using the "Rule of Four"

- Students should be able to graph a piecewise defined function when given its algebraic representation. It may be helpful to have them generate a table of values prior to graphing.
- Have students graph several piecewise defined functions by hand and then by using a graphing utility. (See The Graphing Calculator Guide.)
- Be sure to have students graph continuous as well as discontinuous piecewise defined functions.
- Make sure that students understand that an open circle at a point shows that the point is not included in the graph and why this notation is necessary.
- There are a number of verbal representations of piecewise defined functions. The calling plan problem in Example 2 gives students the opportunity to write an equation from a familiar verbal description.
- Example 3 explains the Ironman Triathlon. It is an excellent example to cover with the class. Have students develop the pieces of the function without looking at the text. It can take twenty to thirty minutes to complete this class exercise. It is well worth the time spent.

The Absolute Value Function

- Remind students that the absolute value function gives the distance from a point on the number line to zero.
- Have students write a piecewise defined function for the absolute value function.
- This is a function that students should know and recognize.

Suggested Problems

Exercises 2, 5, 7, 10
Problems 12, 14, 16
Enrichment Problem 18

2.4 COMPOSITE AND INVERSE FUNCTIONS

Focus Points

Composition of Functions

- Students should become familiar with the symbolic notation for a composition of functions $h(t) = f(g(t))$.
- Students should be able to identify the inside function and the outside function for a composition functions.

Inverse Function Notation

- When the roles of the inputs and outputs have been changed as in $n = f(A)$ and $A = g(n)$, f and g are called inverses of one another.
- One of the most important facts that students must know when dealing with inverse functions is that if f and g are inverses, function f has inputs A and outputs n, while g has the inputs n and the outputs A. That is, the inputs for f have become the outputs for g and the outputs for f have become the inputs for g.
- Be sure students are comfortable with the notation for the inverse of the function f as f^{-1}, read "f–inverse".

Finding a Formula for the Inverse Function

- Students should be able to find the inverse of a function that is defined by a formula. In doing so, students use the fact of inputs and outputs "changing positions".
- Students should be alerted to the fact that the domain and range have "switched" as a result of the inputs and outputs changing.

Suggested Problems

Exercises 1, 2, 5–8, 14, 18, 22
Problems 28, 30, 36, 37, 40
Enrichment Problem 41

2.5   CONCAVITY

Focus Points

Concavity and Rates of Change

- Remind students that the average rate of change of a linear function is constant. Thus, its graph is a straight line.
- Explain that when the rate of change of a function increases, its graph bends upward. We say that such graphs are concave up.
- Discuss the two examples in the text that illustrate functions whose graphs are concave up.
- Have students calculate the average rate of change between various pairs of points on the graph. Note that the rate of change is increasing, causing the graph of the function to be concave up. (See The Graphing Calculator Guide.)
- Be sure that students understand that the value of a function can decrease, but if its rate of change is increasing, the function is concave up. This is often a very difficult concept for students to comprehend.
- Use Example 2 to illustrate a function that is concave down. Have students complete a table to illustrate that the rate of change is decreasing, causing the graph to be concave down.

Increasing and Decreasing Functions; Concavity

- Have students sketch graphs of functions that are:
    1. increasing and concave up
    2. increasing and concave down
    3. decreasing and concave up
    4. decreasing and concave down
- Use the graph of $y = x^2$ to demonstrate a function that is concave up everywhere. Note that the function decreases over an interval (decreases at an increasing rate), and then increases (increases at an increasing rate). Since the rate of change is continuously increasing, the function is concave up.
- Use the graph of $y = x^3$ to illustrate a function that continuously increases, but changes concavity. The function is first concave down (increases at a decreasing rate) , and then becomes concave up (increases at an increasing rate). Since the rate of change decreases, and then increases, the graph of the function is first concave down and then concave up.

Suggested Problems

Exercises 2, 3, 5, 11
Problems 14, 17, 18, 20
Enrichment Problems 21, 22

2.6 QUADRATIC FUNCTIONS

Focus Points

Finding the Zeros of a Quadratic Function

- The text uses the example of a baseball that has been hit straight into the air to introduce quadratic functions of the form $f(x) = ax^2 + bx + c$. This helps reinforce in students the idea that mathematics can be used to explain natural phenomena and provides motivation for further exploration. (See The Graphing Calculator Guide.)

- The concept of the zero can be used to determine when the ball strikes the ground by setting $f(x) = 0$. An easier quadratic equation should be given for the students to solve (such as Example 1).

- Students are generally familiar with quadratic functions, so it is possible to move through some of the material quickly.

- Students should be given several increasingly difficult quadratics to solve. Start with those that can be put into factored form: $q(x) = a(x - r)(x - s)$. Students should be able to identify r and s as the zeros of the quadratic.

- The quadratic formula

$$x = \frac{-b \pm \sqrt{b^2 - 4ac}}{2a}$$

can be used to find the zeros of a quadratic function if it is not factorable. Demonstrate that it can also be used to solve factorable quadratics.

- Discuss the possibility of a quadratic having no real zeros. Show how this results from the quadratic formula having a negative discriminant and discuss the consequences of this graphically.

Concavity and Quadratic Functions

- Students should see the difference between a linear function and a quadratic function in terms of their concavity. A linear function is neither concave up nor concave down. However, a quadratic function is either concave up or concave down everywhere.

- Relate the concavity of a curve to the rate of change. A curve that is concave up has increasing rates of change for successive x-intervals, while the opposite is true for curves that are concave down. Table 2.21 illustrates this well for a quadratic that is concave down.

Suggested Problems

Exercises 1, 2, 8, 9, 16
Problems 28, 31, 32, 33
Enrichment Problems 34, 35

3.1 INTRODUCTION TO THE FAMILY OF EXPONENTIAL FUNCTIONS

Focus Points

Constant Percent Rate

- Introduce the exponential function by comparing it to the linear function. Students can easily decipher between these two functions since a linear function has a constant rate of change, while an exponential function has a constant percent growth rate as shown in Example 1.

- Students should realize that exponential equations can represent increasing or decreasing functions. They should be able to recognize this in symbolical, numerical, verbal and graphical form. Students will find that an increasing exponential function will model a growth function such as the size of an increasing population, while a decreasing exponential function will model a decaying function such as the amount of a radioactive substance.

- It is important for students to make the connection that the graph of an exponential function is not a line, but a curve that will be concave up or down. Stress that for an increasing exponential function, we are taking a constant percent value of a bigger output each time but in a decreasing exponential function we are taking a constant percent value of a smaller output value each time.

Growth Factors and Percent Growth Rates

- Stemming from the fact that each input takes a percent of a bigger/smaller value comes the idea of an *annual growth factor*. Students must internalize the notion that the constant percent value is the growth rate, but the annual growth rate takes the initial value, whether salary, population etc., and adds the additional percent growth rate to it. For example:

$$\text{New Salary} = \underbrace{100\% \text{ of Old Salary} + \text{Percent Growth Rate}}_{\text{Annual Growth Rate Factor}}$$

- The same is true for decreasing functions, but it is vital for students to realize that they must subtract the percent growth factor to find the annual growth factor.

- Students should now foresee that the annual growth factor for an increasing exponential function will be greater than 1, while the growth factor for a decreasing exponential function will hold a value between 0 and 1, exclusive.

General Formula for the Family of Exponential Functions

- Once the students are comfortable with the notion of how exponential functions increase and decrease, they need to be able to work with and write equations for these functions in their general form. In general form:

$$f(t) = ab^t \text{ where } b > 0$$
$$\text{or}$$
$$f(t) = a(1 + r)^t \text{ where } 1 + r = b$$

- Students must be able to identify the parameters of this equation and use the information to have an idea of what the function would look like graphically as shown in Figures 3.4 and 3.5.

- Students now need to use this general form to algebraically solve for any of the parameters as applied in the examples.

- Please note that Example 8 is a wonderful example of the power and speed of exponential growth and worth spending time on. There is an extension of this concept in Section 3.3, Example 2.

Suggested Problems

Exercises 1–4, 12, 13, 15, 16
Problems 19, 26, 28, 29
Enrichment Problems 32, 33, 35, 38

3.2 COMPARING EXPONENTIAL AND LINEAR FUNCTIONS

Focus Points

Identifying Linear and Exponential Functions from a Table

- Students should be able to compare linear and exponential models when given a table of values, and determine which function is linear and which is exponential.

- Demonstrate from a table of values with y as a function of x, that for a constant change in x, if the *difference* of consecutive y values is constant, then the table represents a linear function. (See The Graphing Calculator Guide.)

- Demonstrate from a table of values with y as a function of x, that for a constant change in x, if the *ratio* of consecutive y values is constant, then the table represents an exponential function. (See The Graphing Calculator Guide.)

Finding a Formula for an Exponential Function

- Students should be able to determine a formula for an exponential function in the form of $g(x) = ab^x$ when given a table of values.

- Demonstrate that if only two points are given, it is possible to fit either a linear or an exponential function to model the data. Use Example 1 to illustrate modeling a linear and an exponential function to two data points.

Similarities and Differences Between Linear and Exponential Functions

- Using the form $y = b + mx$ for a linear function and $y = ab^x$ for an exponential function, it is possible to illustrate certain similarities between these formulas.

- Linear functions have a y-intercept, which represents its initial value, and a slope, which represents its constant rate of change. Similarly, exponential functions have an a term, which represents its initial value, and a b term, which represents its constant growth factor.

- It is important to point out that an exponential function will always outpace a linear function in the long run. Use Example 3, the predictions of Thomas Malthus, to illustrate this fact.

Suggested Problems

Exercises 3, 5, 8
Problems 12, 16, 19, 31, 32, 34, 37, 38
Enrichment Problem 41

3.3 GRAPHS OF EXPONENTIAL FUNCTIONS

Focus Points

The Effect of the Parameters

- In the formula, $Q = ab^t$, the value of a tells us where the graph crosses the Q-axis. Have your students graph several different functions, changing only the value of a. Let them discover the role of this parameter. Note that the effect of the initial value is to change both the Q-intercept and the rate at which the graph rises.

- Next, have students graph several different functions, fixing the a value, but changing the value of b. First, use values of $b > 1$. Then, use values of b, $0 < b < 1$. Discuss the similarities and differences in the graphs.

- It should be clear to students that whether the function is increasing or decreasing depends on whether $b > 1$ or $0 < b < 1$, respectively.

- Students should note that, for $b > 1$, larger values of b cause the graph to climb more rapidly. They should also see that, for $0 < b < 1$, smaller values of b cause the graph to fall more rapidly.

- Students should be made aware that, for all values of $b > 0$, the graph is always concave up.

Horizontal Asymptotes

- Students should note that the t-axis is the horizontal asymptote for the graph of $Q = ab^t$.

- Discuss the meaning of an asymptote with your students. This can be a very difficult concept for some of them to comprehend.

- Be sure that students are familiar with the notation "$Q \to 0$ as $t \to \infty$" and "$\lim_{x \to \infty} f(x) = k$."

Solving Exponential Equations Graphically

- Example 2 refers students back to the "Yonkers Problem". It provides an excellent example of solving a real-world exponential equation.

- At this point, students can only be expected to solve exponential equations graphically. Some of your students may remember how to solve exponential equations algebraically. It is always a welcome addition to the class when a student asks if they can use logarithms to solve equations. Encourage them to do so if you'd like!

Fitting Exponential Functions to Data

- This section provides a brief introduction to the concept of exponential regression. A more thorough presentation is given in Section 9.7, "Fitting Exponentials and Polynomials to Data".

- You may want to take this opportunity to provide students with additional examples of exponential regression.

Suggested Problems

Exercises 3, 5, 7, 11, 13
Problems 15, 19, 28, 20, 21, 40, 43
Enrichment Problems 42, 44

3.4 CONTINUOUS GROWTH AND THE NUMBER e

Focus Points

Exponential Functions with Base e Represent Continuous Growth

- Start by making students understand that e is approximately 2.718... and shouldn't under any circumstances be confused with a variable!
- Students must be able to convert from the form $y = ab^t$ to the continuous form $y = ae^{kt}$. They must realize that b and e^k represent the same quantity.
- In the form $y = ae^{kt}$, k represents the continuous growth rate. When $k > 0$, the function exhibits growth. When $k < 0$ the function is decaying.
- Students should be able to differentiate among exponential graphs with differing growth rates. A graphing calculator is a useful tool.

Suggested Problems

Exercises 3, 5, 7, 9
Problems 12, 13, 18, 21, 23
Enrichment Problems 25, 28

3.5 COMPOUND INTEREST

Focus Points

Compound Interest

- The formula that gives the balance B with a principal P, an APR of r (the percentage converted to a decimal), and compounded n times a year is given by:

$$B = P \cdot \left(1 + \frac{r}{n}\right)^{nt}$$

- APR or Annual Percentage Rate is sometimes referred to as the *nominal rate*.

- The difference between nominal and effective interest rates should be discussed. Demonstrate how increasing the number of times interest is compounded per year given the same nominal rate results in a higher effective rate. Students should be made aware that r is equivalent to the nominal rate while $\left(\frac{r}{n}\right)^n$ is equivalent to the effective rate.

Continuous Compounding and the Number e

- Give students some numerical examples to demonstrate that there is a limit to how large an effective rate one can get by increasing the number of times interest is compounded per year.

- The formula for the balance B given a principal P, and compounded continuously at an annual rate r is given by:

$$B = Pe^{rt}.$$

- Have students compare situations of discrete versus continuous compounding and ask them under what conditions the two accounts would yield the same balances.

Suggested Problems

Exercises 1, 8, 10
Problems 17, 18, 20, 26
Enrichment Problem 23

4.1 LOGARITHMS AND THEIR PROPERTIES

Focus Points

What is a Logarithm?

- Point out to the students that in solving all of our exponential equations up to this point, we could not solve for the value of the exponent using algebraic methods. It is this situation where we look to logarithms for help.

- Students must be alerted to the fact that their calculators are set in base 10, the common logarithm. If a base is not indicated on a logarithm in the form $y = \log_a x$, where a is the base, it is understood to be 10.

- By instructing students to interchange between exponential and logarithmic form, students will begin to realize that a logarithm is really just an exponent.

Logarithmic and Exponential Functions are Inverses

- Another way of connecting the logarithmic function to the exponential function for the students is to explain that they are inverses of each other. That is, the logarithmic function "undoes" the exponential.

- Comparing the graphs of the exponential and logarithmic functions enforces this idea to the students when they see the graphs are simply reflections of each other across the line $y = x$.

Properties of Logarithms and The Natural Logarithm

- Before students can tackle the algebra of a logarithm, they must know the properties of logarithms. Enforce the importance of using these properties correctly to warrant the correct answer. The properties are outlined on page 154 with justifications of the product, quotient and power rules at the end of this section. Also outlined on page 156 are some common misconceptions and calculator errors that students often make. Use Transparency 4.1 to highlight this. Transparency masters are in Part VI.

- Give the students an exponential equation with a value of e in it. Discuss if they think the use of a common logarithm is sufficient to solve this exponential. They of course will be able to successfully solve the equation, but when we introduce the "natural logarithm", ln, the calculations become easier.

- Stress to students that the "natural log of x", ln x, is simply the inverse of the exponential function with base e. Similarly, the "common log of x" is the inverse of the exponential function with base 10. Students should make the connection that the same properties for the logarithmic functions will hold true for the natural logarithm. These properties are highlighted for students on page 155.

Suggested Problems

Exercises 3, 8, Any 11–18
Problems 20, 26, 28, 31, Any 34–50
Enrichment Problems 33, 52

4.2 LOGARITHMS AND EXPONENTIAL MODELS

Focus Points

Doubling Time

- It is important for students to realize that the doubling time for an exponentially growing quantity depends only on the rate, and NOT on the initial quantity.
- Problems involving doubling time should be discussed involving both the general and continuous forms of the exponential function. Both Examples 4 and 5 should be done with the class.

Half-Life

- The discussion of doubling time leads naturally into the discussion of half-life. The similarities and differences between the two situations should be discussed (how one situation represents growth and the other, decay). Discuss how this is related to the parameters b and k.
- Both Examples 6 and 7 should be done with the class.

Converting Between $Q = ab^t$ and $Q = ae^{kt}$

- Students should recognize that b and e^k represent the same quantity. As a consequence, students should also know that $k =\ln b$.
- Students must be able to convert between general and continuous forms and vice versa. They must understand the difference between continuous and annual rates (especially in interest related problems).

Exponential Growth Problems That Cannot Be Solved By Logarithms

- Have students recognize that certain types of growth problems are unsolvable using logarithms, particularly those equations that contain a mix of exponential and non-exponential terms. Example 12 gives an illustration of this.
- These problems can be solved graphically with a calculator or computer.

Suggested Problems

Exercises 3, 4, 9, 23, 26
Problems 31, 35, 36, 41, 44
Enrichment Problems 59, 60, 61

4.3 THE LOGARITHMIC FUNCTION

Focus Points

The Graph of the Common Logarithm

- Students should know that the domain of the log function is the set of positive numbers and its range is the set of all real numbers.

- Have students look at the graph of the log function. Point out the x-intercept, the lack of a y-intercept and note how slowly the graph increases.

- Students should graph the functions $y = \log x$ and $y = 10^x$. Discuss the similarities between the two graphs, and the fact that the logarithmic graph is a reflection of the exponential graph across the line $y = x$.

Asymptotes

- Remind students that the x-axis is the horizontal asymptote for the graph of $y = ab^x$. Note that the y-axis is the vertical asymptote for the graph of $y = \log x$.

- Be sure that students are familiar with the notation "as $x \to 0^+$, $f(x) \to -\infty$" and "$\lim\limits_{x \to a} f(x) = \infty$."

- Point out the difference between the process of finding a vertical asymptote and a horizontal asymptote.

Graph of Natural Logarithm

- Discuss the similarities and differences in the graphs of $y = \log x$ and $y = \ln x$.

- Students should also note the similarities and differences in the graphs of $y = \ln x$ and $y = e^x$.

Real World Applications of Logarithms

- The concept of pH values will relate students' study of logarithms to information that they learned in their science class. This can help students to recognize that logarithms are not simply mathematical abstractions, but are highly relevant to quantities that students already know about.

- Explain the concept of an "order of magnitude" to your students. The Richter scale is a further example of this concept.

- The discussion on sound intensity and decibels will be of interest to your students. Explain to them that intense sound hurts your ears when too much energy is applied over the surface of your eardrum. The softest audible sound intensity is approximately 10^{-16} watts/cm^2, which we denote by I_0.

- Example 5 reminds students of the sound intensity of loud music. Perhaps it will help them to better understand their parents' complaints! An interesting project for students would be to do further research on the decibel rating of other familiar sounds.

Suggested Problems

Exercises 4, 5, 11, 16, 18
Problems 19, 20, 21, 22, 27, 31
Enrichment Problems 36, 37

4.4 LOGARITHMIC SCALES

The Solar System and Beyond

- Linear Scales: Using the data from Table 4.4, show the distance from the sun to the first five planets on a linear scale. Using the proper scale, the points will be reasonably spaced. However when the remaining planets are added into the data and graphed, it becomes increasingly more difficult to distinguish between the points in such a wide range of data values.

- Log Scales: Using a log scale instead of a linear scale enables us to plot a wide range of data values and still be able to distinguish between the different points. Using the data from Table 4.4, we are now able to plot all of the data points, including Proxima Centauri and the Andromeda Galaxy.

- Demonstrate the concept of plotting large values on a log scale by using the values from Example 1.

- Demonstrate the plotting of very small values in comparison to larger ones using the values from Table 4.5 and Example 2.

Log-Log Scales

- Use the values from Table 4.6 to plot on a log-log scale. Show the students that when exponential data is plotted on a log-log scale, the resulting graph appears linear.

Using Logs to Fit an Exponential Function to Data

- Demonstrate how a log scale can be used to linearize data. Once the data is linearized, it is possible to find a formula for the data in the form of $y = b + mx$. Use the example of compact disc sales to illustrate this process.

Suggested Problems

Exercises 1, 5, 7
Problems 11, 12, 13, 19
Enrichment Problems 20, 22

5.1 VERTICAL AND HORIZONTAL SHIFTS

Focus Points

Formulas for a Vertical or Horizontal Shifts and Their Graphs

- Once students graphically "see" the vertical/horizontal shifts in Example 1 and Example 2, the heating schedule for an office building, as well as other functions on their calculators, they must become familiar with the effect of these shifts on the formulas.

- Start with a function $f(x)$, with a vertical shift resulting in $g(x)$. Discuss what values were affected by the shift from looking at the graphs of $f(x)$ and $g(x)$. Students will easily point out that the output values change, while the input values remain the same.

- Students should recognize a vertical change as $g(x) = f(x) + k$, where $|k|$ is the number of units shifted vertically. If k is positive, the shift is up and if k is negative, the shift is down.

- Similarly, students will find that a horizontal change will affect the input values. This change will yield that $g(x) = f(x + k)$, where $|k|$ is the number of units shifted horizontally. If k is positive, the shift is left and if k is negative, the shift is right.

- A common student error is to assume that $f(x + 2)$ will shift the graph of $f(x)$ to the right two units. Stress that the shift is to the left when you add a positive amount to the input. For example, if $g(x) = f(x + 2)$, then $g(3) = f(5)$, $g(7) = f(9)$, and $g(-3) = f(-1)$. The values of $g(x)$ are the values of $f(x)$ but the graph of $g(x)$ is shifted to the left of $f(x)$ by two units.

Inside and Outside Changes

- When $g(x) = f(x + k)$ there is a change to the input value, so it is considered an inside change to f.

- When $g(x) = f(x) + k$ there is a change to the output value, so it is considered an outside change to f.

- Example 6 and Example 7 are good examples to help students understand the interpretation of these changes and verbally express the effect of the inside or outside change while not just focusing on the graphs of the functions. Problem 41 is another such example that should be done in class or as an assignment.

- Students must be able to work with input and output changes as translations in symbolical, verbal, graphical and numerical form.

Combining Horizontal and Vertical Shifts

- Students must be able to combine two different translations on one function. Example 8 refers back to the office heating problem and allows the students to graph and interpret the function $r(t) = f(t - 2) - 5$, which involves both horizontal and vertical shifts.

- At this point, have students take familiar functions such as $y = |x|$ and $y = x^2$, and sketch various translations of each, combining both horizontal and vertical shifts.

Suggested Problems

Exercises 1, 2, 3, 9, Any 12–19
Problems 26, 27, 28, 36, 41
Enrichment Problems 32, 43, 45

5.2 REFLECTIONS AND SYMMETRY

Focus Points

A Formula for a Reflection

- Discuss the effects on input and output values when a reflection across the x- and y-axes is performed. Students' prior knowledge of reflections will enable them to make the connection that a reflection across the x-axis changes the output values and a reflection across the y-axis changes the input values, as seen in Figures 5.10 and 5.11.

- Remind students that a reflection across both axes is a reflection about the origin as shown in Figure 5.12.

- As a result of the inside and outside change, the formula for a reflection across the x-axis will be $g(x) = -f(x)$ and a reflection across the y-axis will have the formula $g(x) = f(-x)$.

- Students must be able to work with reflections in symbolical, graphical, verbal and numerical form.

Symmetry About the y-Axis

- Point out the difference between reflections and symmetry to the students. Remind them that any function can be reflected, but not all functions have symmetry.

- Tell students that when a function is symmetric about the y-axis, as in $y = x^2$, it has even symmetry and is considered an even function.

- A function is called an even function if $f(-x) = f(x)$ for all values of x in the domain of f. Students must be able to recognize even functions symbolically, graphically and numerically. It is also important for students to check algebraically if a function is even, as in Example 2.

Symmetry About the Origin

- A reflection about the origin is equivalent to a reflection across both the x- and y-axes. When a function has symmetry about the origin, it is considered to be an odd function.

- A function is called an odd function if $f(-x) = -f(x)$ for all values of x in the domain of f. Students must be able to recognize odd functions symbolically, graphically and numerically. They must be able to check algebraically if a function is odd, as in Examples 3 and 4.

Combining Shifts and Reflections

- Reflections can be combined with horizontal and vertical shifts. It is important to stress the proper order of transformations when given a combination of transformations. A good rule of thumb is to tell the students to start from the "x on the inside and work your way out". For example if $g(x) = -f(x) + 3$, the graph of g is obtained by first reflecting across the x-axis and then shifting up 3 units.

- Be ready for students to have difficulty with the $-f(x)$ notation. Remind students that graphically, $f(x)$ signifies the height of the graph of the function when the horizontal coordinate is x, so $-f(x)$ will be the negation of the height.

Suggested Problems

Exercises 2, 7, 10, 11, 20-23
Problems 24, 29, 30, 32
Enrichment Problems 36, 41, 42

5.3 VERTICAL STRETCHES AND COMPRESSIONS

Focus Points

Vertical Stretch

- Similar to vertical translations, a vertical stretch or compression of a function is represented by an outside change to its formula. This is accomplished by multiplying the output by a coefficient.

- Demonstrate to the students that multiplying the output by a coefficient between 0 and 1 will compress the function vertically, while multiplying by a coefficient greater than 1 will stretch the function.

- Use the example of a stereo amplifier to illustrate the effects of vertical stretches or compressions on functions.

Negative Stretch Factor

- Discuss the effects of multiplying the output of a function by a negative coefficient. Show how this will result in a reflection of the function across the independent axis.

- Compare the function $y = f(x)$ to the transformation $y = -2f(x)$. Explain that this can be described as a combination of two transformations: a vertical stretch by a factor of 2, and a reflection across the x-axis.

Formula for Vertical Stretch or Compression

If f is a function and k is a constant, then the graph of $y = k \cdot f(x)$ is the graph of $y = f(x)$:
- Vertically stretched by a factor of k, if $k > 1$.
- Vertically compressed by a factor of k, if $0 < k < 1$.
- Vertically stretched or compressed by a factor of $|k|$ and reflected across the x-axis, if $k < 0$.

Stretch Factors and Average Rates of Change

- Demonstrate that stretching or compressing a function vertically does not change the intervals on which the function increases or decreases. However, the average rate of change of the function is altered by a vertical stretch or compression.

- The effects of vertically stretching or compressing should be represented graphically, symbolically, numerically, and verbally. Example 2 is a good illustration of this.

Combining Transformations

- Use a combination of horizontal and vertical shifts, along with vertical stretches and compressions to illustrate how each transformation affects a given function.

- Example 3 is a good illustration of a combination of horizontal and vertical translations, along with a vertical compression and a reflection of $y = f(x)$ across the x-axis. This will summarize all of the transformations covered so far.

Suggested Problems

Exercises 1, 4, 13, 14, 17
Problems 20, 21, 25, 26, 35
Enrichment Problems 37, 38

5.4 HORIZONTAL STRETCHES AND COMPRESSIONS

Focus Points

Horizontal Stretch: A Lighthouse Beacon

- While a vertical stretch is obtained by multiplication of a function's outputs by a constant "stretch factor", a horizontal stretch is obtained by multiplication of a function's input values by a constant factor.

- The text uses the example of a lighthouse beacon to demonstrate how horizontal stretches work by graphing the light intensity as a function of time. By changing the speed of the beacon's rotation (and the *times* at which the peaks occur), the students will see how the graph's shape is only affected in the horizontal dimension, while maintaining the same heights as before. This example should be discussed because it is a real world example that students are familiar with and it can be discussed quickly and easily.

Formula for Horizontal Stretch or Compression

- The general form for a horizontal stretch or compression is $y = f(kx)$, where k is a positive constant.

- The transformation is a stretch of factor $\dfrac{1}{k}$ when $0 < k < 1$.

- The transformation is a compression of factor $\dfrac{1}{k}$ when $k > 1$.

- If $k < 0$, the function is additionally reflected across the y-axis.

- Make sure that students can recognize how the transformation $y = f(kx)$ affects $y = f(x)$ in terms of its graph and its formula. Additionally, given a table of values for x and $f(x)$, students should be able to complete and analyze numerical entries corresponding to $f(kx)$.

Suggested Problems

Exercises 4, 5, 6, 10
Problems 12, 16, 19, 20
Enrichment Problems 24–27

5.5   THE FAMILY OF QUADRATIC FUNCTIONS

Focus Points

Exploration

- The section opens with the baseball example from Chapter 2. This provides an excellent introduction to the material that follows.
- Be sure to go over Example 1 with your students. Graph the two parabolas and have students see the transformations. Carefully review the four steps in the transformation, emphasizing the proper order, i.e., horizontal shift, vertical stretch, vertical reflection, and vertical shift.
- Perform several other transformations of the graph $y = x^2$ with your students. Be sure that they become comfortable with the concepts as they continue with the study of quadratics.
- Point out the axis of symmetry, and its relationship to the vertex.

Formulas for Quadratic Functions

- Students should become familiar with both the standard and vertex forms of the parabola.
- Point out that the parabola has vertex (h, k) and axis of symmetry $x = h$.
- Students should know that a parabola opens upward if $a > 0$ and downward if $a < 0$.
- Have your students convert from standard form to vertex form and vice versa.
- There are several cases where students routinely make errors in converting from standard form to vertex form. Provide students with examples where $a < 0, a \neq 1$ and a is not a factor of b.
- The Tools Section of this chapter provides students with detailed instructions on the method of completing the square, and numerous practice problems.

Finding a Formula from a Graph

- Students should be able to write the formula for a quadratic function when they are given the vertex and another point on the graph.
- Students should also be able to write the formula for a quadratic function when the two zeroes are given.
- Emphasize the importance of finding the value of a.

Applications of Quadratic Functions

- Example 5 revisits the baseball problem, using algebra. It is an excellent opportunity for students to sharpen their algebraic skills in the context of solving a "real world" problem.
- Example 6 provides students with a preview of an optimization problem that they may come across in their calculus class.

Suggested Problems

Exercises 1, 9, 14, 16
Problems 19, 27, 31, 32, 34
Enrichment Problems 33, 35

6.1 INTRODUCTION TO PERIODIC FUNCTIONS

Focus Points

Ferris Wheel Height as a Function of Time

- Use the concept of boarding a ferris wheel and riding it for one complete revolution to introduce the sinusoidal functions. Discuss your height as a function of time as you revolve around the ferris wheel to show the periodic nature of this motion.

- Demonstrate the concepts of period, amplitude, midline, frequency, and horizontal shift as it relates to the revolution of a point on a particular ferris wheel. Use the British Airways "London Eye" as an example with specific numerical values to find these components of its functional representation.

- Use Table 6.1 to show how the data repeats itself as it completes one revolution and begins another. Using the function $f(t)$ to describe the height as a function of time, point out that the output values will continue to repeat every 30 minutes, demonstrating the periodic nature of this motion.

Graphing the Ferris Wheel Function

- Plot the data from Table 6.1. Demonstrate that these data points should be connected by a smooth curve, and not with straight lines.

- Use Figure 6.5 to illustrate that by the time the wheel has rotated halfway between the 6 o'clock and 3 o'clock positions, it has already past the halfway point both horizontally and vertically. Therefore these points cannot be connected in a linear fashion.

Periodic Functions: Period, Midline, and Amplitude

- Show the students that a function f is periodic if its values repeat at regular intervals. The length of these intervals is called the period. This length can be obtained by determining the distance between two maximum (or minimum) values.

- Graphically, if any periodic function is shifted horizontally by its period, it will result in the same graph as the original.

- Symbolically, if the periodic function, $f(t)$, has a period of length c, then $f(t + c) = f(t)$, for all values of t in the domain of f.

- The midline of a periodic function is the horizontal line halfway between the function's minimum and maximum values. It can be easily found by taking the average of the minimum and maximum output values.

- The amplitude of a periodic function is the vertical distance between the function's maximum (or minimum) value and its midline.

Suggested Problems

Exercises 3, 6, 8, 10, 11
Problems 13, 18, 21, 22, 26
Enrichment Problems 27, 30

6.2 THE SINE AND COSINE FUNCTIONS

Focus Points

Using Angles to Describe Position on the Ferris Wheel

- Referring to the example of a ferris wheel, demonstrate that the position of any point on the wheel can be described using an angle of rotation. Each rotation of $360°$ or 2π radians represents one complete revolution.

- Assuming that the center of the ferris wheel model is at the origin, we begin to measure the angle of rotation from the 3 o'clock position as it turns counterclockwise.

- It is important to note that negative angles are measured similarly but in the clockwise direction. In addition, angles of rotation greater than $360°$ or 2π radians will result in wrapping around the circle more than once. Use a revolving door analogy to illustrate this concept.

The Unit Circle

- Define the unit circle as a circle with a radius one that is centered at the origin.

- Each point P on the circumference of this circle can located by its coordinates (x, y) or by its angle of rotation, θ, measured from the positive x-axis.

- Use Example 2 to illustrate how to locate various points on the unit circle based on its given angle of rotation.

Definition of Sine and Cosine

- Discuss the relationship between the rectangular coordinates for a particular point (x, y), and the trigonometric functions for sine and cosine.

- Suppose $P = (x, y)$ is the point on the unit circle specified by the angle θ. We can then define $\cos \theta$ as the x-coordinate and $\sin \theta$ as the y-coordinate for point P.

- Use Figure 6.18 to further illustrate this relationship between the coordinates of a given point and the cosine and sine values of its angle of rotation on the unit circle.

Coordinates of a Point on a Circle of Radius r

- Discuss what the effects might be if the radius of the unit circle is changed. Show the students that the coordinates can still be calculated using the cosine and sine values of its angle of rotation.

- Given the coordinates of any point $Q = (x, y)$ on a circle with a radius of r, and where θ is the angle of rotation, the x and y-coordinates are given by:
$$x = r \cos \theta$$
$$y = r \sin \theta$$

- Use Examples 5 and 6 to demonstrate how to calculate the values of various coordinates along circles of various sizes.

Suggested Problems

Exercises 1, 4, 5, 22
Problems 26, 30, 32, 35
Enrichment Problems 34, 35

6.3 RADIANS

Focus Points

Definition of a Radian

- Let students know that radian measure is just another way of measuring angles, where an angle of 1 radian is defined to be the angle at the center of a unit circle which spans an arc of length one.
- Students need to realize that since both radians and degrees can be used to measure an angle, they can be converted between one another.
- Stress that radians are the preferred measurement and used almost exclusively in calculus.

Relationship Between Radians and Degrees

- Explain the relationship between radians and degrees through the circumference of a unit circle.

$$C = 2\pi r \qquad \text{Known formula}$$
$$C = 2\pi \qquad \text{Let } r = 1$$
$$360° = 2\pi \qquad C \text{ has } 360°$$
$$57.296° \approx 1 \text{ Radian} \qquad \text{Divide by } 2\pi.$$

See Figure 6.31 for angles in radian measure marked on a circle.

- Once the notion of a radian is understood, students should be able to convert from radian measure to degrees and degrees to radians.

Arc Length

- Ask students how they would consider the arc length spanned in a circle if the radius were not one.
- As a result, students should come up with the idea of multiplying the radius, r, by the angle, θ. This warrants the formula, $S = r\theta$, where θ is expressed in radians. Example 5 is a good display of the use of this formula.

Suggested Problems

Exercises 4, 6, 14, 15
Problems 28, 29, 35, 37
Enrichment Problems 40, 43

6.4   GRAPHS OF THE SINE AND COSINE

Focus Points

Exact Values of the Sine and Cosine

- Use the unit circle to evaluate the sine and cosine of various quadrantal angles.
- Students should know that $\cos \theta$ is the x-coordinate of the point on the unit circle specified by the angle θ, while $\sin \theta$ is the y-coordinate.
- Students should know the exact values of the sine and cosine of $30° = \pi/6$, $45° = \pi/4$, and $60° = \pi/3$.

Graphs of the Sine and Cosine Functions

- Have the class prepare a table of values for various angles and the sine of these angles. Plot the points. Repeat the process for the cosines of the angles.
- Note that both the sine and cosine functions are periodic with a period of 2π (or $360°$) and an amplitude of 1.
- Elicit the various properties of the sine and cosine functions from your students. Be sure that they see the sine function is odd, while the cosine function is even. The domain of both functions is all reals, and the range is $-1 \leq f(x) \leq 1$.

Amplitude

- Students should recall that the amplitude is the distance between the midline and the highest or lowest point on the graph. Be sure to note that amplitude is always positive.
- Have students determine the amplitude of various sine and cosine functions from their formulas.
- Remind students that the constant A in the equation $y = A \sin t$ stretches or shrinks the graph vertically, and reflects it across the t-axis if A is negative.

Midline

- Students should recall that the graph of $y = f(t) + k$ is the graph of $y = f(t)$ shifted up vertically by k units.
- Have students generalize that the graphs of $y = \sin t + k$ and $y = \cos t + k$ have midlines $y = k$.
- Example 3 refers back to the ferris wheel problem. It provides a good opportunity to review the concepts covered so far.

Suggested Problems

Exercises 2, 5, 7, 15
Problems 18, 20, 22, 25
Enrichment Problems 28, 30

6.5 SINUSOIDAL FUNCTIONS

Focus Points

Introduction

- Point out to students that transformations of the sine and cosine functions are called sinusoidal functions.
- Introduce the formulas $y = A\sin(B(t - h)) + k$ and $y = A\cos(B(t - h)) + k$.
- Remind students that $|A|$ is the amplitude and, if $A < 0$, the graph is reflected across the t-axis.
- Also remind students that the midline is the horizontal line $y = k$.

Period

- Example 1 provides an excellent introduction to the concept of period. Have students graph $y = \sin(1/2t)$, and describe any similarities and differences to the graphs of the other two functions.
- Students should be able to conclude that the constant B determines the number of cycles the function completes on an interval of length 2π.
- Guide students to discover that the period, $P = 2\pi/|B|$.
- Be sure to take the time to carefully go through Examples 2, 3, and 4. Students need the opportunity to practice the concepts that have been covered so far.

Horizontal Shifts

- Students should see that the graphs of $y = \sin(B(t - h))$ and $y = \cos(B(t - h))$ are the graphs of $y = \sin(Bt)$ and $y = \cos(Bt)$ shifted horizontally h units.

Summary of Transformations

- The box on the bottom of page 272 provides an excellent summary of the roles of parameters A, B, h and k. Use Transparency 6.5 to highlight this. (Transparencies are in Part VI.)
- Be sure to allow time to carefully go through Example 6. There is quite a bit of material for students to comprehend.

Phase Shift

- Phase shift enables us to calculate the fraction of a full period that the curve has been shifted. It tells us the relative positions of two waves of the same period.
- Phase shift is significant because in many applications we want to know whether two waves will reinforce or cancel each other.

Using the Transformed Sine and Cosine Functions

- Example 8 is a good illustration of the "Rule of Four". Be sure to do this example with your students.
- Example 9 revisits the ferris wheel problem. It is an opportunity to tie up any loose ends. Have students rewrite the formula using the cosine function. (See Problem 32.)

Suggested Problems

Exercises 2, 5, 12, 17
Problems 19, 23, 27, 28, 36, 45
Enrichment Problem 40

6.6 OTHER TRIGONOMETRIC FUNCTIONS

Focus Points

The Tangent Function

- Define the tangent of an angle θ as $\tan\theta = \dfrac{\sin\theta}{\cos\theta}$. Explain graphically that the tangent ratio is the slope of the line passing through the origin and any point $P(x, y)$ on the circumference of the unit circle.

- It may be worthwhile as an exercise to have the students draw a ray from the origin through the circumference of the unit circle, and then see how the slope of this ray changes depending on the angle it makes with the positive x-axis. Have the students get a feel for how the values of the tangent change cyclically as the angle increases. Develop this into a sketch of the tangent function.

Relationships Between the Trigonometric Functions

- If θ is the angle measured counterclockwise from the positive x-axis, and $P(x, y)$ is the corresponding point on the unit circle, then $x = \cos\theta$ and $y = \sin\theta$. The Pythagorean Theorem then guarantees that $x^2 + y^2 = 1$, which gives the identity:

$$\cos^2\theta + \sin^2\theta = 1$$

- Have students try using this identity and the definition of tangent to evaluate the values of the trigonometric functions sine, cosine, and/or tangent, if they are given one of these three values and the quadrant in which the angle terminates. See Example 4 for a good example of the type of reasoning the students should be able to demonstrate.

The Reciprocals of the Trigonometric Functions: Secant, Cosecant, and Cotangent

- Define the following:

$$\sec\theta = \frac{1}{\cos\theta}$$

$$\csc\theta = \frac{1}{\sin\theta}$$

$$\cot\theta = \frac{\cos\theta}{\sin\theta}$$

Have the students try to explain the graphs of these three functions by analyzing the graphs of cosine, sine, and tangent.

- The identity $\cos^2\theta + \sin^2\theta = 1$ can be used to produce other trigonometric identities. Dividing through by either $\cos^2\theta$ or $\sin^2\theta$ gives $1 + \tan^2\theta = \sec^2\theta$ or $\cot^2\theta + 1 = \csc^2\theta$, respectively.

Suggested Problems

Exercises 1, 2, 5, 16
Problems 19, 21, 24, 31
Enrichment Problem 38

6.7 INVERSE TRIGONOMETRIC FUNCTIONS

Focus Points

Solving Trigonometric Equations Graphically

- The rabbit population problem (Section 6.5, Example 8 on page 274) is used again here to provide motivation for developing this section in more detail. With population problems, we are often interested in *when* certain populations occur, in addition to just *what* the populations happen to be. This problem is a bit hard initially, so have the students do Example 1. Have them estimate the answers mentally, and then use the calculator to get an answer graphically. The students should note that there are multiple answers.

- Graphical and numerical methods of solving these equations can be time consuming and unsatisfying. The lack of an algebraic method thus far will provide motivation to develop the inverse trigonometric functions—as was the case when logarithms were developed to deal with exponential equations.

Solving Trigonometric Equations Using the Inverse Cosine

- Reinforce the idea that the inverse of a function reverses the roles of the inputs and outputs. Thus the *inputs* for inverse cosine are cosine values (making the domain lie between -1 and 1, inclusive), and the *outputs* are angles (in radians). Due to the infinite outputs that exist for a given cosine value input, the inverse cosine *function* is defined to only have a range from 0 to π, inclusive.

- If $y = \cos t$, then the inverse function is denoted as either $t = \cos^{-1} y$, or $t = \arccos y$. Now, trigonometric equations (like $\cos t = 0.4$) may be solved algebraically (the solution being $t = \cos^{-1} 0.4$).

- Relate the graph of the cosine function to the graph of its inverse, and demonstrate that they are simply reflections of each other across the line $y = x$. Reiterate that restricting the range of the inverse cosine guarantees that we obtain a function. Explain to students that this is why the calculator only gives one unique answer.

- The inverse cosine function guarantees a unique angle answer for a given cosine input. However, the appropriateness of answers should be discussed with the students. Sometimes the unique answer generated by calculator or computer is not the complete or desired answer for a problem. The symmetry of the inverse cosine function can be used to ensure the desired answer is obtained.

The Inverse Sine and Inverse Tangent Functions

- As was done for inverse cosine function, we can develop inverse sine and inverse tangent functions. If we define $y = \sin t$, then $t = \sin^{-1} y$. The domain of the inverse sine function is $-1 \le y \le 1$. To ensure we have a function, the range is restricted to be only $-\dfrac{\pi}{2} \le t \le \dfrac{\pi}{2}$. Similarly, if we define $y = \tan t$, then $t = \tan^{-1} y$. The domain of the inverse tangent function is $-\infty < y < \infty$, and its range is restricted to be $-\dfrac{\pi}{2} < t < \dfrac{\pi}{2}$.

- Have the students work through Examples 3, 4, and 5. Make sure they are comfortable working with radian measure, as it can be difficult to get them away from degree measure!

Solving Equations Using Reference Angles

- Explain to students that the *reference angle* for any angle drawn to point P on the unit circle is simply the smaller angle made by the line connecting P and the origin, with the x-axis. The symmetry of the unit circle allows us to use these small reference angles to compute trigonometric values for *any* angle whatsoever. All students will need to know is what quadrant the angle in question will terminate. Once this is known, the entire problem can be done in terms of the reference angle.

- As a result, all reference angles are between 0 and $\dfrac{\pi}{2}$, inclusive.

- It is important that students be able to solve trigonometric equations for specific domains (and give all the multiple answers, if appropriate). At a minimum, Examples 8 and 9 should be discussed with the class.

Suggested Problems

Exercises 3, 4, 7, 10, 26
Problems 31, 37, 43, 47
Enrichment Problem 61

7.1 GENERAL TRIANGLES: LAW OF SINES AND COSINES

Focus Points

The Law of Cosines

- Just as the Pythagorean Theorem relates three sides of a right triangle, the Law of Cosines relates three sides of any triangle.
- Derive the Law of Cosines, $c^2 = a^2 + b^2 - 2ab\cos C$, for students by applying the Pythagorean Theorem as shown in Figure 7.1. Draw special attention to the fact that, if C is a right angle, the formula brings us right back to the Pythagorean Theorem.

The Law of Sines

- We can apply the Law of Sines to any triangle in which either two sides and one angle are known, or two angles and one side is known. This law is proven using Figure 7.4 in the text.
- For any triangle with sides a, b, and c, and opposite angles A, B, and C respectively,

$$\frac{\sin A}{a} = \frac{\sin B}{b} = \frac{\sin C}{c}.$$

- Explain to students the drawback to the Law of Sines, known as the ambiguous case. The drawback of course lies in the fact that when the Law of Sines is applied, we are left with only the sine of the angle. Since there can be two angles between 0 and 180 degrees with the given sine value, we must consider both cases as shown in Example 4.

Suggested Problems

Exercises Select from 1–19
Problems 26, 31, 34, 38, 39
Enrichment Problems 35, 36, 40

7.2 TRIGONOMETRIC IDENTITIES

Focus Points

Equations Versus Identities

- Be sure to emphasize the distinction between an equation and an identity. While an equation will have only *certain* x-values that satisfy it, an identity is satisfied for *any* x-value. In proving the identity, students will find that the left side of the equation will equal the right side for all values of x.

- Discuss the fact that an equation can be investigated graphically to determine if it may be an identity. In each equation, both sides may be viewed as functions. If the equation were an identity, then the graphs of both functions will be identical. Students should be cautioned against inferring that an equation is an identity simply from looking at the graphs. The graphs may appear identical, when if fact they are really just very close together.

The Tangent and Pythagorean Identities

- Make students aware that identities such as $\tan\theta = \dfrac{\sin\theta}{\cos\theta}$ and $\cos^2\theta + \sin^2\theta = 1$ are used frequently. It is essential to be able to rewrite trigonometric expressions in different forms as shown in Examples 2 and 3.

- The Pythagorean identity is undoubtedly the most important relationship in trigonometry. Its usefulness lies in simplification and in being able to express the cosine of an angle in terms of its sine or vice-versa.

Double Angle Formulas

- The double angle formulas for sine, cosine and tangent are equally as useful as the Pythagorean Identities in the process of proving an identity.

- The derivation for the double angle formulas:

$$\sin 2t = 2\sin t \cos t$$
$$\cos 2t = 1 - 2\sin^2 t$$

are given in the text, while the derivations of:

$$\cos 2t = 2\cos^2 t - 1$$
$$\cos 2t = \cos^2 t - \sin^2 t$$
$$\tan 2t = \frac{2\tan t}{1 - \tan^2 t}$$

are left as exercises in the Exercises and Problems Set.

- Stress to students the importance of practice and trial and error in proving these identities. Encourage students to take different paths in their work and explore different approaches to the same problem. In general, the material in this section may be difficult to motivate. However, the skills and ideas developed here arise in countless other problems and applications throughout calculus and physics.

Other Identities

- Other identities such as negative angle identities are at the end of the section. Note that the inside cover of the text contains a summary of all the identities covered in this section. Use Transparency 7.2 in Part VI of this manual.

Suggested Problems

Exercises 1, 4, 8, 10, 14, 18
Problems 21, 24, 35, 41
Enrichment Problems 42, 43

7.3   SUM AND DIFFERENCE OF SINE AND COSINE

Focus Points

Sums and Differences of Angles for Sine and Cosine

- The angle addition and subtraction formulas in this section are generalizations of the double and half angle formulas of earlier sections. These formulas can be used to find the exact value of $\cos 105°$, for example, by using $\cos(60° + 45°)$.

- Although students usually do not have any trouble accepting the angle addition and subtraction formulas, they sometimes make mistakes such as writing $\sin(a + b) = \sin a + \sin b$.

- The justifications for these formulas are done at the end of the section. It is up to you to decide how much of the derivations you would like to cover with your students.

Rewriting $\sin t + \cos t$

- The sum formula can be used to simplify sums of sines and cosines as shown in Figure 7.23.

- This concept can be extended to find that the sum of any two cosine and sine functions having the same periods can be written as a single sine function. Following the derivation in the text leads to: $a_1 \sin(Bt) + a_2 \cos(Bt) = A \sin(Bt + \phi)$.

- The depth and detail in which you would like your students to go with this material is at your discretion.

Suggested Problems

Exercises 5, 6, 8, 9, 12
Problems 17, 18, 19
Enrichment Problems 20, 22, 25

7.4 TRIGONOMETRIC MODELS

Focus Points

Sums of Trigonometric Functions

- Show how the sums of trigonometric functions can be used to model, predict, and explain real-life phenomena.
- Example 1 demonstrates how the sum of two sinusoidal functions with the same period may be combined to create one resulting sinusoidal function. Students should be able to obtain the equation for this trigonometric function algebraically. Figures 7.27 and 7.28 illustrate this real-life behavior graphically.
- Example 2 is a good problem to demonstrate what happens to the sum of two sinusoidal functions that do not have the same period. Figures 7.29 and 7.30 are good graphical illustrations of this behavior.

Damped Oscillation

- Use the model of the spring bobbing up and down from the ceiling to illustrate the behavior of damped oscillation. This motion will not continue infinitely, but will instead oscillate less each time and eventually come to rest. Ask the students to find a way to alter the sinusoidal function to model this behavior.
- It is helpful to show how the amplitude must be decreased with each cycle. First, try modeling this by decreasing the amplitude linearly with each cycle. Illustrate how this method is inadequate because the amplitude will increase again at a later point.
- Have the students try different methods of decreasing the amplitude. Demonstrate that an exponential decay of the amplitude combined with a sinusoidal function will best model this behavior.

Oscillation With a Rising Midline

- Show that an oscillation with a rising midline will have a constant amplitude. In this case, it will be the midline that will be increasing. Use Example 3 to demonstrate this behavior.
- Show the students that this can be achieved by increasing the midline linearly.

Acoustic Beats

- Discuss the example using acoustic beats to again illustrate the sum of sinusoidal functions.
- Use Figure 7.39 to illustrate graphically this behavior of combined intensities, and discuss how this can be applied to the tuning of a piano.
- Discuss the concepts of pitch and volume and how they are affected as the sinusoidal functions are combined.

Suggested Problems

Exercises 1, 2
Problems 3, 4, 5
Enrichment Problems 9, 10

7.5   POLAR COORDINATES

Focus Points

Relation Between Cartesian and Polar Coordinates

- Be sure that students know how to convert from polar coordinates to Cartesian coordinates and vice versa.
- Students should be warned that, in general, $\theta \neq \tan^{-1}(y/x)$. They must take into account the quadrant in which the angle terminates.
- Give students the opportunity to name several pairs of polar coordinates for a point on the Cartesian plane.

Graphing Equations in Polar Coordinates

- Begin with Example 3 which introduces the equation $r = 1$, and compares it to the equation $y = 1$. This example also enables students to see that some equations are simpler in polar coordinates while others are simpler in Cartesian coordinates.
- The Archimedean spiral in Example 4, the rose curve in Example 5, and the limaçon in Example 6 introduce students to some of the classical polar curves. (See The Graphing Calculator Guide.)

Suggested Problems

Exercises 5, 11, 16, 18
Problems 23, 27, 33, 39, 41, 44

7.6 COMPLEX NUMBERS AND POLAR COORDINATES

Focus Points

Extending the Definition of Functions

- Functions such as $y = \sqrt{x}$ were said to be undefined over a portion of the real numbers. Expressions such as $\sqrt{-8}$ were not thought about as having any significance. This section introduces the imaginary unit $i = \sqrt{-1}$ to deal with these previously disregarded quantities.

Using Complex Numbers to Solve Equations

- One of the most natural ways to introduce the imaginary unit is by solving quadratic equations. Often times a negative discriminant results from using the quadratic formula. Remind students again what this signifies graphically. Have the students rewrite the imaginary roots of the quadratic using the imaginary unit i in place of $\sqrt{-1}$.

- Define a *complex number* to be any number that can be written in the form $z = a + bi$. The *real part* of z is a, and the *imaginary part* of z is b, where a and b are real numbers and i is the imaginary unit.

- Inform students that imaginary numbers are not mathematically insignificant. They are used to help explain wave motion in electrical circuits and to deal with flows in fluid dynamics.

Algebra of Complex Numbers

- Define the *conjugate* of a complex number z as $\bar{z} = a - bi$. It may pay to remind students that complex solutions to equations always come in pairs, and also that z is a real number if and only if $z = \bar{z}$. Additionally, the product of a complex number and its conjugate is *always* a real number.

- Students must be able to do arithmetic with complex numbers and express the answers in $a + bi$ form. To this end, make sure that students realize that powers of i cycle in value with $i^1 = i$, $i^2 = -1$, $i^3 = -i$, $i^4 = 1$, etc. Examples 1, 2, and 3 should be done as practice.

The Complex Plane and Polar Coordinates

- Complex numbers can be represented in a plane by using the real part of z as the x-coordinate and the imaginary part of z as the y-coordinate. The xy-plane is then referred to as the *complex plane*, and the complex number can be thought of as $z = x + iy$.

- Use Figure 7.55 to explain how a complex number can be written in polar coordinates as:

$$z = x + iy = r \cos \theta + ir \sin \theta.$$

Have students convert from rectangular to polar coordinates and vice versa as needed.

Euler's Formula

- Euler's formula is interesting for students to see since it gives a link between the natural base e and the complex numbers. Students may not have the background to understand a proof, but for θ in radians we have:

$$e^{i\theta} = \cos \theta + i \sin \theta.$$

- Euler's formula can be used to give *Euler's identity* , which states that $e^{i\pi} + 1 = 0$ and relates the five fundamental constants in mathematics.

Polar Form of a Complex Number

- Show how Euler's formula can be used to rewrite a complex number in the *polar form* $z = re^{i\theta}$, where (r, θ) are the polar coordinates of z.

- The utility of this form is that it is much more convenient for finding powers and roots of complex numbers.

Euler's Formula and Trigonometric Identities

- Examples 10 and 11 can be done with the class to prove two well-known trigonometric identities that students have previously studied. Example 12 is an identity that expresses $\cos x$ in terms of the polar form of a complex number.

Suggested Problems

Exercises 5, 8, 11, 12
Problems 17, 23, 24, 26, 28
Enrichment Problems 30, 31

8.1 COMPOSITION OF FUNCTIONS

Focus Points

The Effect of a Drug on Heart Rates

- Use Tables 8.1 and 8.2 to describe functions for drug level over time, and heart rate versus drug level. Show that the heart rate over time can be described as the composition of these two functions. Use Table 8.3 to illustrate this.

- Students should become familiar with the symbolic notation for a composition of functions $h(t) = f(g(t))$.

Formulas for Composite Functions

- Students should be able to find a formula for a composition of functions algebraically, by substituting one formula as the input for the other.

- Use Example 2 to illustrate the procedure algebraically.

- Students should be able to find the composition of functions graphically as well. Use Example 4 to illustrate this.

Decomposition of Functions

- Sometimes it is helpful to work backwards to find the functions that went into a composition. This procedure is called a decomposition of functions.

- Examples 5 and 6 are excellent problems to illustrate the algebraic methods involved in decomposing a function. Example 5 relates this to an exponential function, and Example 6 uses a quadratic function.

Suggested Problems

Exercises 1, 7, 9, 16
Problems 21, 22, 24, 37, 53, 49, 51
Enrichment Problems 60, 61

8.2 INVERSE FUNCTIONS

Focus Points

Definition of Inverse Function

- Students should recall that the statement $f^{-1}(50) = 20$ means that $f(20) = 50$.
- In general, $f^{-1}(Q) = t$ if and only if $Q = f(t)$.
- Students should be familiar with the term "invertible".
- Remind students of some of the inverse functions that were covered in previous chapters, e.g., logarithmic and inverse cosine functions.
- Example 3 illustrates an analytical, numerical, verbal and graphical example of inverses.

Finding a Formula for an Inverse Function

- Students should now be ready to find formulas for inverse functions.
- Tables 8.15 and 8.16 give tabular representations of a function and its inverse. Calculations for finding the inverse of a linear function are also shown.
- Examples 4 and 5 provide additional examples of the algebra involved in finding a formula for an inverse.
- Students often have a difficult time with the algebra involved. Be sure to give them plenty of practice from the examples and problems at the end of the section.

Noninvertible Functions: Horizontal Line Test

- The text uses the function $y = x^2$ to provide a basic example of a function that does not have an inverse.
- Students should realize that the vertical line test is used to determine if a relation is a function and the horizontal line test is used in a similar manner to determine if a function is invertible.

Evaluating an Inverse Function Graphically

- Example 6 provides students with a function whose inverse cannot easily be found algebraically. Go through this example with the students. Be sure that they understand how to find $u^{-1}(4)$. Make up a couple of other examples to try with them.
- Example 7 ties together all of the concepts covered in this section so far. Go over it carefully with your students.

The Graph, Domain and Range of an Inverse Function

- Students should see that the graph of the inverse of a function can easily be found by reflecting the graph of the function across the line $y = x$. (See The Graphing Calculator Guide.)
- Emphasize to students that the outputs from the inverse function are inputs to the original function.
- Be sure that students understand that the domain and range of f^{-1} are obtained by interchanging the domain and range of f.

A Property of Inverse Functions

- Go through the numerical composition shown on page 367 for the population function. Provide students with a couple of additional examples. Then, generalize the result.

- Students should know that composing a function and its inverse returns the original value as the end result. This property will be useful to them in deciding whether two functions are inverses.
- Example 8 provides students with an algebraic and graphic example of a function and its inverse.

Restricting the Domain

- Restricting the domain of a function enables us to find the inverse of a function that would not pass the horizontal line test. The function $y = x^2$ is used again to illustrate this process.
- Students are reminded that the domains of the sine, cosine, and tangent functions in Section 6.7 were restricted in order to define their inverses.

Suggested Problems

Exercises 1, 10, 12, 22, 27
Problems 28, 31, 34, 41, 46, 49
Enrichment Problems 52–57

8.3   COMBINATIONS OF FUNCTIONS

Focus Points

The Difference of Two Functions Defined by Formulas: A Measure of Prosperity

- The predictions of Thomas Malthus provide a unifying theme for this section. The prosperity (or surplus, $S(t)$) of a country can be measured in many ways. One way is as the *difference* between the number of people that can be fed, $N(t)$, and the number of people actually living in the country, $P(t)$. We then have:

$$S(t) = N(t) - P(t).$$

This introduces the concept of an arithmetic *combination* of two different functions to create a unique new function. Explain that this is often done in mathematical modeling of real-life situations.

The Sum and Difference of Two Functions Defined by Graphs

- Continue with the Malthus problem and have the students graph $N(t)$ and $P(t)$ on the same set of axes. Use Figures 8.22 and 8.23 to help them understand the surplus function $S(t)$ as the vertical distance between the food supply and population curves.

Factoring a Function's Formula into a Product

- Another combination of functions that is useful to analyze is the product of several different component functions. Example 2 is a good way to show students how this works.
- In general, a product of functions

$$p(x) = f(x) \cdot g(x) \cdot h(x) \cdots$$

is equal to zero if and only if any of its components are equal to zero.

The Quotient of Functions Defined by Formulas and Graphs: Prosperity

- Return to the Malthus problem and define an alternate measure for the prosperity of a country: the per capita food supply, $R(t)$. Represent $R(t)$ as the *quotient* of the number of people that can be fed and the number of people living in the country. So we have:

$$R(t) = \frac{N(t)}{P(t)}.$$

- Use a graph of per capita food supply (Figure 8.25) to show how it obtains similar results to the aforementioned surplus model (Figure 8.23).

The Quotient of Functions Defined by Tables: Per Capita Crime Rate

- This section is a good example of how a table of data can be misleading to the untrained eye! Have the students work out the per capita crime rates for City A and City B year by year. They will see that City A, while having more overall crime, is actually safer percentage-wise. Make sure students realize that the larger amount of crime in City A is due to its much larger population than City B.

Suggested Problems

Exercises 6, 7, 8, 16, 21
Problems 23, 26, 28, 33, 41
Enrichment Problems 34, 35

9.1 POWER FUNCTIONS

Focus Points

Proportionality and Power Functions

- Use Examples 1 and 2 to introduce the concepts of direct and inverse proportionality and power functions.
- A quantity y is directly proportional to a power of x if $y = kx^n$, where k and n are constants, with $n > 0$.
- A quantity y is inversely proportional to a power of x if $y = \dfrac{k}{x^n}$, where k and n are constants, with $n > 0$.
- A power function is a function of the form $f(x) = kx^p$, where k and p are constants.

The Effect of the Power p

- It is helpful to show students the effect of the power p in the power function. Have students examine the differences when 0, 1, positive and negative integers, and positive and negative fractions are substituted in for p.
- Graphically demonstrate that $y = kx^0$ and $y = kx^1$ are both linear.
- Students should recognize that when a positive even integer is substituted for p in the power function, the result is a "u-shaped" curve and is symmetric about the y-axis. Similarly, when a positive odd integer is substituted, the result is a "chair-shaped" curve and is symmetric about the origin. Use Figures 9.4 and 9.5 to illustrate this effect.
- When negative integers are used for p in the power function, the graph resembles $y = 1/x$. If even integers are used, the graph is in quadrants I and II. If odd integers are used, the graph is in quadrants I and III. Use Figures 9.6 and 9.7 to illustrate this effect.
- Show students the effects of substituting fractional powers of p in the power function. If n is a positive even integer, the graph of $y = x^{1/n}$ resembles the graph of $y = x^{1/2}$. If n is a positive odd integer, the graph of $y = x^{1/n}$ resembles the graph of $y = x^{1/3}$. Figures 9.8 and 9.9 are good illustrations of this effect.

Finding the Formula for a Power Function

- As is the case for linear and exponential functions, the formula for a power function can be found from two points on its graph.
- Use Example 5 to demonstrate the steps involved in substituting values into a power function to find its equation.

Suggested Problems

Exercises 7, 8, 12, 16, 18, 20
Problems 25, 26, 32, 34, 35
Enrichment Problems 39, 41, 42

9.2   POLYNOMIAL FUNCTIONS

Focus Points

A General Formula for the Family of Polynomial Functions

- A polynomial function is a sum of power functions whose exponents are nonnegative integers. Example 1 is an excellent example to introduce a polynomial function for the first time. It draws on previous work done with exponential functions and takes it a step further.

- The general formula for a polynomial function can be written as

$$p(x) = a_n x^n + a_{n-1} x^{n-1} + \cdots + a_1 x + a_0,$$

where n is called the degree of the polynomial and a_n is the leading coefficient.

- Stress that students write polynomial functions in standard form, with its terms from highest to lowest powers written from left to right. Point out that the first term of the polynomial function is called the leading term. It is the most powerful and important term of the function.

- Discuss the graphs of polynomial functions as shown in Figure 9.14.

The Long-Run Behavior of Polynomial Functions

- Remind students how exponential functions grow faster and faster as the exponent becomes larger and larger. As a result of this, in a polynomial function, the absolute value of the leading term, provided x is large enough, will be larger than the absolute value of the other terms combined.

- Most importantly, if x is sufficiently large, the polynomial is dominated by the leading term. Demonstrate this to students both numerically and graphically, as in Example 2. Explain to them that this is what is meant by the long-run behavior of a polynomial function.

Zeros of Polynomials

- Explain to students that the zeros of a function are simply the x-intercepts, or the roots of the equation.

- Discuss various methods that can be used to find the roots of polynomial functions. The most familiar method of course is to factor or use the quadratic formula on quadratic functions. Show students that while factoring can sometimes help to find the zeros, numerical and graphical methods can also be used.

- The next section explores the zeros in more detail, but point out to students that the long-run behavior of the function can sometimes lead to determining the existence of zeros.

Suggested Problems

Exercises 1, 2, 6, 7, 9
Problems 11, 12, 14, 19, 21, 23
Enrichment Problems 26, 28, 30

9.3 THE SHORT-RUN BEHAVIOR OF POLYNOMIALS

Focus Points

Factored Form, Zeros and the Short-Run Behavior of a Polynomial

- As discussed in the previous section, the leading term determines the long-run behavior of a polynomial function, but polynomial functions with the same leading term may have very different short-run behaviors. Example 1 is a good illustration of polynomial functions of degree four and the differences in their short-run behavior. Use Transparency 9.3 in Part VI of this manual.

- The focus of this section is to understand the behavior of a polynomial in the vicinity of its zeros. It is important to make the connection between the zeros and the factors of a polynomial.

- Explain that some, but not all, polynomial functions can be factored as a product of other polynomials to determine the zeros and the short-run behavior of the function. Consider the function $p(x) = (x + 3)(x - 7)$. Students can determine that the zeros are -3 and 7 with ease. In multiplying the function out, we get a second degree polynomial function. Continue in this fashion using polynomials with three factors, four factors, etc. Discuss with students that the short-run behavior of the function tells us where the graph will cross the x-axis as well as where the function is positive and negative, while the long-run behavior will allow us to know the "shape" of the graph. This is illustrated in Figure 9.20.

- Once students have a good understanding of the short-run behavior, have them work in reverse. That is, tell them the zeros of the function and have them write the polynomial in its factored form.

Number of Factors, Zeros, and Bumps

- It is important for students to realize that the number of linear factors and in turn, zeros of a function will be less than or equal to the degree of the polynomial.

- Students should also note that when graphed, a polynomial function with two or more zeros will turn and change direction to create "bumps" between any two consecutive zeros. The graph of an nth degree polynomial has at most n zeros and turns at most $n - 1$ times.

- At this time it is important to discuss the graph of a polynomial function when there are multiple zeros as in the case of $f(x) = (x - 6)^3$. In this case, 6 is a zero three times. It is considered to have multiplicity 3.

- When a zero is repeated it will affect how the graph intercepts the x-axis. If the multiplicity is even, it will "bounce" off the x-axis. If the multiplicity is odd, it looks flattened out at the x-axis. Examples of these kinds of graphs are shown in Figures 9.22 and 9.23.

Finding the Formula for a Polynomial from its Graph

- Students must be able to find a possible formula for a polynomial function when given its graph. Note that the answers are not unique since the zeros can be repeated.

- Students must also take into account the "stretch factor" when writing these possible equations. While $y = (x + 2)(x - 8)$ has zeros of -2 and 8, so does $y = 4(x + 2)(x - 8)$, which will yield a graph that is vertically stretched.

Suggested Problems

Exercises 1–4, 9, 10
Problems 13, 15, 19, Any 22-35, 41, 46
Enrichment Problems 43, 48

9.4   RATIONAL EXPRESSIONS

Focus Points

What is a Rational Function?

- A rational function, r, can be written as the ratio of polynomial functions $p(x)$ and $q(x)$, as $r(x) = \dfrac{p(x)}{q(x)}$, where $q(x) \neq 0$.

- Look at the example about the average cost of producing a therapeutic drug. It is a good way of introducing the rational function for the first time to your students.

- Show students that the long-run behavior of rational functions is like that of the long-run behavior of power functions. Since the first term of a power function determines its value for a large enough x, the ratio of the first term of a rational function will determine its long-run behavior. Use limit notation to find the long run behavior.

- The long-run behavior of $r(x) = \dfrac{p(x)}{q(x)}$ is given by $y = \dfrac{\text{leading term of } p}{\text{leading term of } q}$.

- Graph various rational functions versus polynomial functions with the students. Discuss how the graphs of rational functions compare to that of polynomial functions.

What Causes Asymptotes?

- Students should recognize that the existence of asymptotes may be used to distinguish between rational functions and polynomial functions.

- Discuss that the horizontal asymptote will be determined by how fast the numerator and denominator are growing with respect to each other.

- Discuss with students when they think a rational function may have a vertical asymptote. Explain that a vertical asymptote will appear when the denominator becomes so small that it approaches zero. Caution students not to get into the habit of thinking that a vertical asymptote will always be present when there is a denominator. Consider the rational function: $r(x) = \dfrac{5}{x^2 + 7}$. The value of the denominator will never become less than 7.

Suggested Problems

Exercises 1–4, 7, 9, 12
Problems 13, 16, 20, 21
Enrichment Problems 23, 24

9.5 THE SHORT-RUN BEHAVIOR OF RATIONAL FUNCTIONS

Focus Points

The Zeros and Vertical Asymptotes of a Rational Function

- Guide students to realize that the zeros of a rational function are obtained by finding the zeros of the numerator, and the vertical asymptotes are obtained by finding the zeros of the denominator, provided that the numerator and denominator do not both have the same zero.
- Example 1 provides students with a good introduction to zeros and vertical asymptotes.
- Allow plenty of time to cover Example 2. There is a wealth of information in this one example.
- You may want to stop and do a couple of other examples of the concepts covered so far.
- Note that a graphing utility may not show the correct graph of a rational function near its vertical asymptote. This is a good time to review a notation like $\lim_{x \to 3^-} f(x) = \infty$. This is also a good example of where relying on technology without understanding the mathematics can lead you astray. (See The Graphing Calculator Guide.)

The Graph of a Rational Function

- The summary box on page 417 is an excellent review of the concepts covered.
- Be sure to point out to your students that the graph of a rational function can cross its horizontal asymptote. This is often a totally new concept to students. Note that while the vertical asymptote occurs where the function is undefined, the horizontal asymptote represents the limiting value of the function as $x \to \pm\infty$.

Finding a Formula for a Rational Function from its Graph

- Find a possible formula for the function in Example 3. Go through this very slowly, being sure that your students understand the concepts involved.
- Help students focus on the numerous pieces of information contained in a graph, such as the zeros, the vertical and horizontal asymptotes, and the behavior of the graph.
- Students should be led to discover how the components of the graph of a function correspond to the components of its equation. A graphing utility is worth its weight in gold to help with this discovery process. Trial and error are a necessary part of the process!
- Plan to go over several examples with your class.

When Numerator and Denominator Have the Same Zeros: Holes

- This subsection illustrates a function with a "hole" in it.
- Note that a graphing utility may not show the "hole". (See The Graphing Calculator Guide.)
- The material from this section provides a valuable background for studying the indeterminate form $\frac{0}{0}$ in calculus.

Suggested Problems

Exercises 2, 6, 9
Problems 12, 15, 17, 33, 35, 40

9.6 COMPARING POWER, EXPONENTIAL, AND LOG FUNCTIONS

Focus Points

Comparing Power Functions

- Remind students that for power functions $y = kx^p$ for large x, the larger the value of p, the faster the function climbs.
- Note that as $x \to \infty$, higher powers of x dominate lower powers. As $x \to 0$, smaller powers dominate.
- Example 1 demonstrates that, in the long run, the size of the power of a function has a greater effect on it than the size of its coefficients.

Comparing Exponential and Power Functions

- Give students some examples demonstrating that any positive increasing exponential function will eventually grow faster than any power function.
- Students should also discover that any positive decreasing exponential function will eventually approach the horizontal axis faster than any positive decreasing power function.

Comparing Log and Power Functions

- Guide students to discover that any positive increasing power function will eventually grow more rapidly than a logarithmic function.
- Students should see that, since exponential functions grow so rapidly, it would be expected that their inverses, the logarithmic functions, grow very slowly.

Suggested Problems

Exercises 1, 2, 7, 9, 10, 11
Problems 18, 22, 31, 35, 37
Enrichment Problems 38, 39

9.7 FITTING EXPONENTIALS AND POLYNOMIALS TO DATA

Focus Points

The Spread of AIDS

- Table 9.20 gives the total number of deaths in the US from AIDS from 1981 to 1996.

- First, fit an exponential function to the data. Then, fit a power function to the data. Finally, fit the data with a linear function.

- Discuss with students the fits of the three functions. Help them to understand that, although all three functions fit the data reasonably well, they give wildly different predictions for the future.

- Table 9.21 gives more recent data on AIDS deaths. Add this to the previous data. It should become apparent to students that none of the three types of functions that were used to model AIDS deaths exhibit this type of behavior.

- This example clearly illustrates that, while a certain type of function may fit a set of data over a short period of time, care must be taken when using a mathematical model to make predictions about the future.

Suggested Problems

Exercises 1, 4, 6, 7, 8
Problems 13, 17, 18, 21
Enrichment Problem 24, 26

10.1 VECTORS

Focus Points

Distance versus Displacement

- The concept of vector and scalar quantities should be introduced to your students in terms of displacement versus distance. Explain how in a *displacement*, the direction of movement matters, while direction is insignificant when discussing a *distance*.

Adding Displacements Using Triangles

- Explain that displacements can be represented as arrows on the Cartesian axes. The length of the arrow is called its *magnitude* and its orientation indicates the direction of motion.
- Show how the sum of two displacements can be represented geometrically by placing the arrows in a head to tail arrangement and creating a third arrow joining the tail of the first to the head of the second. The joining of these three will form a triangle that can be solved using the Law of Cosines or the Law of Sines.
- Demonstrate that reversing the order of displacement summation does not affect the resultant displacement. This is illustrated clearly in Figure 10.3.

Vectors

- Be sure to inform students of the plethora of applications that utilize vector quantities: velocities, forces, magnetic fields, economics, computer animation, and population studies to name a few. Students will appreciate the reassurance that mathematics is useful in real-life!

Vector Notation

- Clarify that $\vec{v}$ represents a vector quantity, while $||\vec{v}||$ represents its magnitude, a scalar quantity.
- Make the analogy that magnitude, $||\vec{v}||$, is to vectors as absolute value is to positive and negative numbers.

Addition of Vectors

- Define $\vec{w} = \vec{u} + \vec{v}$. The resultant vector $\vec{w}$ can be represented as the arrow drawn from the tail of $\vec{u}$ to the head of $\vec{v}$, when $\vec{u}$ and $\vec{v}$ are drawn head to tail with each other.
- Ensure that your students know the difference between the magnitude, $||\vec{w}||$, of a vector and the vector itself, $\vec{w}$. Show that $\vec{w}$ has a directional component as well. This directional component takes the form of an angle θ that $\vec{w}$ makes relative to its component vectors. Example 2 should be done in its entirety.

Subtraction of Vectors

- In a similar fashion to vector addition, the difference of two vectors, $\vec{w} = \vec{u} - \vec{v}$, can be represented geometrically as the arrow drawn from the head of $\vec{v}$ to the head of $\vec{u}$, when $\vec{u}$ and $\vec{v}$ are drawn tail to tail with each other.
- Do Example 3 with your students. This is a good time to point out to the students that the Law of Sines sometimes yields more than one mathematically correct answer when trying to compute the vector's direction (they may remember the Ambiguous Case from Chapter 8 and from previous mathematics courses). Care must be exercised when deciding which is appropriate.

Scalar Multiplication

- Use a simple example such as $\vec{u} + \vec{u} + \vec{u} = 3 \cdot \vec{u}$ to illustrate the effects of multiplication by a scalar constant. In this case the resultant is a single vector with the same directional component but triple the magnitude.

- In general, multiplication by a scalar constant, k, stretches the vector if $k > 0$. If $0 < k < 1$, the vector is reduced in size, and if $k = 1$ there is no effect on the size.

- Scalar multiplication by -1 has no effect on the magnitude of a vector, but it does reverse the direction so that the head points in exactly the opposite direction.

- The *zero vector* has no direction and a magnitude of zero.

- Tell students that vector subtraction can be thought of as vector addition if they notice that $\vec{u} - \vec{v} = \vec{u} + (-\vec{v})$.

Properties of Vector Addition and Scalar Multiplication

- Point out to students that vector addition and scalar multiplication share the same field properties as the real numbers. These include the commutativity and associativity of addition, the associativity and distributivity of scalar multiplication, and the additive and multiplicative identities. Use Transparency 10.1 in Part VI of this manual.

Suggested Problems

Exercises 2, 3, 6, 7, 9
Problems 12, 18, 19
Enrichment Problems 20–26

10.2   THE COMPONENTS OF A VECTOR

Focus Points

- This section begins the work of taking vectors and resolving them into their horizontal and vertical components. There are many reasons for wanting to do this. For instance, in projectile motion, gravity affects the vertical component of velocity, but not the horizontal component. Explain this to students to provide motivation for this section.

Unit Vectors

- Introduce the *unit vectors* $\vec{i}$ and $\vec{j}$. These are useful as they provide a mechanism for graphing vectors on the Cartesian axes, analogous to how x and y-coordinates enable us to plot points.

- The unit vectors are so named because they each have a magnitude of 1.

- To graph the vector $\vec{v} = 6\vec{i} - 4\vec{j}$, look at the $\vec{i}$ term to determine the horizontal component and the $\vec{j}$ term to determine the vertical component. So, from a given starting point, one would move 6 units right on the x-axis and 4 units down on the y-axis. Then draw an arrow from the starting point to this new point to graph the vector.

Resolving a Vector in the Plane into Components

- Use Figure 10.17 to help derive these formulas using simple right triangle trigonometry. If $\vec{v} = \vec{v}_1 + \vec{v}_2$, where $\vec{v}_1$ is the horizontal component and $\vec{v}_2$ is the vertical component, then: $\vec{v}_1 = (\|\vec{v}\|\cos\theta)\vec{i}$ and $\vec{v}_2 = (\|\vec{v}\|\sin\theta)\vec{j}$. Therefore we can rewrite $\vec{v} = (\|\vec{v}\|\cos\theta)\vec{i} + (\|\vec{v}\|\sin\theta)\vec{j}$.

- Example 4 provides a good classroom example for how to resolve a vector into its horizontal and vertical components.

- Example 5 illustrates the fact that by doing head-to-tail addition of seemingly different vectors taking very different directions can yield the same resultant vector. Students should understand after looking at this example that the resultant depends only on the starting and ending positions, and not on the path that was taken to get there!

Displacement Vectors

- Given two points P and Q, students should be able to resolve the vector $\overrightarrow{PQ}$ into horizontal and vertical components.

- Given $P(x_1, y_1)$ and $Q(x_2, y_2)$, then $\vec{v} = \overrightarrow{PQ}$ is given by:

$$\vec{v} = (x_2 - x_1)\vec{i} + (y_2 - y_1)\vec{j}.$$

Vectors in n Dimensions

- Make your students aware that in real-life, many problems deal with vectors in 3 dimensions. Vectors of the form $\vec{v} = 3\vec{i} - 6\vec{j} + 8\vec{k}$ may exist, where $\vec{k}$ represents a *vertical* component. These problems may be encountered by your students in a multivariable calculus class in the future.

- To generalize, vectors can also exist in n dimensions, where n is *any* positive integer. These concepts are covered in depth in advanced college level mathematics classes.

Suggested Problems

Exercises 2, 4, 6, 8, 9
Problems 14, 16, 18, 19, 21
Enrichment Problem 22, 23

10.3 APPLICATION OF VECTORS

Focus Points

Alternate Notation for the Components of a Vector

- Another way to write a vector such as $\vec{v} = 3\vec{i} - 4\vec{j}$ is in the form $\vec{v} = (3, -4)$. This form is advantageous due to its simplicity, but take care that it is not confused with a pair of *coordinates* by accident.

Population Vectors

- This section provides many real-world examples of the occurrence of vector quantities. You should feel free to delve as much or as little into this material as you choose.
- In Example 1 the populations of several states are expressed using the new notation. This is also an example of how vectors may have more than 2 components.

Economics

- Examples 4 and 6 are worth exploring in class. Example 4 deals with the vector quantities *inventory* and *consumption* in terms of a car dealership. Students are asked to interpret vector expressions involving these quantities. Example 6 examines forces exerted by gravity on a spaceship. This problem is good practice for students because it involves algebra as well as a solid understanding of the concepts learned in previous sections of the chapter.

Computer Graphics

- Some of your more computer savvy students will find this section interesting! Example 7 uses the positions of two computer graphics to help students understand the difference between a *position* vector and a *displacement* vector, the former being attached to the origin, while the latter need not be.

Suggested Problems

Exercises 1, 5, 8, 9
Problems 13, 15, 18
Enrichment Problem 19

10.4   THE DOT PRODUCT

Focus Points

The Dot Product

- Thus far, students have added and subtracted vectors, as well as multiplied vectors by scalar quantities. The dot product will enable students to now multiply one vector by another.
- To compute the product of $\vec{u}$ and $\vec{v}$, multiply each coordinate of $\vec{u}$ by the corresponding coordinate of $\vec{v}$. The result is called the dot product. It is important to note that the dot product yields a scalar quantity, and not another vector.
- Examples 1 and 2 are good illustrations of the process of multiplying vectors.

Properties of the Dot Product

Students should review the following properties involving the dot product.
- $\vec{u} \cdot \vec{v} = |\vec{u}| \cdot |\vec{v}| \cos\theta$
- $\vec{u} \cdot \vec{v} = \vec{v} \cdot \vec{u}$ (Commutative Law)
- $\vec{u} \cdot (\vec{v} + \vec{w}) = \vec{u} \cdot \vec{v} + \vec{u} \cdot \vec{w}$ (Distributive Law)
- $\vec{v} \cdot \vec{v} = \|\vec{v}\|^2$
- Example 3 is a good problem to illustrate the relationship of the angle between two vectors and the dot product. This can serve as a justification for the first property listed above.

What Does the Dot Product Mean?

- Use the illustration in this subsection to show the different effects when the angle between the vectors is $0°$, $90°$, and $180°$.
- Perfect alignment results in the largest possible value for $\vec{u} \cdot \vec{v}$, and occurs when the vectors $\vec{u}$ and $\vec{v}$ are parallel. In other words, the angle between them is $0°$.
- Perpendicularity results in $\vec{u} \cdot \vec{v} = 0$, and occurs when the angle between $\vec{u}$ and $\vec{v}$ is $90°$.
- Perfect alignment in opposite directions results in the most negative value for $\vec{u} \cdot \vec{v}$, and occurs when the angle between $\vec{u}$ and $\vec{v}$ is $180°$.
- A real life application of the dot product can be discussed using the Work formula, Work = $\vec{F} \cdot \vec{d}$. Use Figure 10.31 and its corresponding example to illustrate this.

Suggested Problems

Exercises 1, 6, 9, 10
Problems 12, 15, 17, 25
Enrichment Problems 23, 24, 26

10.5 MATRICES

Focus Points

Addition, Subtraction, and Scalar Multiplication

- Introduce students to the concept of expressing an array of numbers in matrix form. The matrix is usually written inside of parentheses, and represents the values in the rows and columns of a table. Each entry can be described in the following manner: we write p_{ij} for the entry in the ith row of the jth column.

- To multiply a matrix by a scalar quantity, just multiply each entry in the matrix by that quantity.

- To add or subtract two matrices, simply add or subtract the corresponding entries, providing that these matrices have the same number of rows and columns. Example 1 provides a good illustration of each of these procedures.

Properties of Scalar Multiplication and Matrix Addition

- Discuss the properties of commutativity of addition, associativity of addition, associativity of scalar multiplication, and distributivity of scalar multiplication.

Multiplication of a Matrix and a Vector

- Demonstrate the steps involved in the multiplication of 2-dimensional vectors and the resulting matrix that is formed. This will be a complicated procedure for the students at first and may need to be reinforced with several examples.

- In summary, we can say that given $\vec{P}_{new} = (x_{new}, y_{new})$ and $\vec{P}_{old} = (x_{old}, y_{old})$, then we can write $\vec{P}_{new} = A\vec{P}_{old}$ where A is the matrix $\begin{pmatrix} a & b \\ c & d \end{pmatrix}$.

- Use Example 2 to reinforce the steps involved in multiplying 2-dimensional vectors.

Matrix Multiplication of n-Dimensional Vectors

- Examples 3 and 4 are good practice for matrix multiplication in applied problems.

- Use Example 5 to introduce the polar coordinates into vector multiplication. Figure 10.32 illustrates this problem graphically.

Suggested Problems

Exercises 1, 4, 5
Problems 7, 9, 10, 11
Enrichment Problems 13, 14, 15

11.1   SEQUENCES

Focus Points

Notation for Sequences

- Define a sequence as any ordered list of numbers, where the individual numbers are the terms of the sequence. Explain that the list can be a finite or infinite list of terms.

- Since any particular sequence may have many terms, the sequence is denoted by $a_1, a_2, a_3,$ $a_4, \ldots, a_n, \ldots$ so that the first term is a_1, the second is a_2, and so on. We use a_n to denote the nth or general term of the sequence. Students tend to have difficulty understanding the meaning of subscripts. Be sure to stress that sequencing notation uses subscripts and not exponents. There is a difference!

- A sequence is considered alternating when the signs switch from positive to negative as shown in Example 2.

Arithmetic Sequences

- A sequence in which the difference between pairs of successive terms is a fixed quantity is called an arithmetic sequence. Examples 4 and 5 are good demonstrations of arithmetic sequences.

- Relay to students that it is often necessary to find just one specific term of the sequence rather than the whole sequence. For $n \geq 1$, the nth term of an arithmetic sequence is

$$a_n = a_1 + (n-1)d,$$

where a_1 is the first term, and d is the common difference between consecutive terms.

- Explain that if a general formula for a sequence is known, then it is simply a matter of substituting the desired value of n to determine the nth term. On the other hand, if the first term and the common difference are known, then the formula above should be used.

- It is important to point out that an arithmetic sequence resembles a linear function. However, for a sequence we consider only positive integer input values, while a linear function is extended to all values of n.

Geometric Sequences

- A sequence in which each term is a constant multiple of the preceding term is called a geometric sequence. In a geometric sequence, the ratio of successive terms is constant.

- As in arithmetic sequences, we may need to find a specific term of a geometric sequence. For $n \geq 1$, the nth term of a geometric sequence is $a_n = a_1 r^{n-1}$, where a_1 is the first term, and r is the ratio of consecutive terms.

- As an introduction, you should go over Example 7 with the students. At the conclusion, point out to the students that the geometric sequence resembles an exponential function. However, like the arithmetic sequence, the domain of a geometric sequence is restricted to positive integers.

Suggested Problems

Exercises 1–4, 5, 8–11, 14
Problems 19, 20, 23, 24, 26, 27
Enrichment Problems 39, 40

11.2 DEFINING FUNCTIONS USING SUMS: ARITHMETIC SERIES

Focus Points

Arithmetic Series

- The sum of the terms of a sequence is called a series. We write S_n for the sum of the first n terms of the sequence, called the nth partial sum.
- Define an arithmetic series by presenting an example of an arithmetic sequence as in Example 1. Explain to students that the sum of the terms of an arithmetic sequence is called an arithmetic series.

The Sum of an Arithmetic Series

- It can be an interesting exercise to see if the students can add the numbers from 1 to 100 as was asked of Carl Gauss. Allow students to think about how they may accomplish this without physically adding each of the terms.
- From this exercise, introduce the sum, S_n, of the first n terms of the arithmetic series with $a_n = a_1 + (n-1)d$ as $S_n = \frac{1}{2}n(a_1 + a_n) = \frac{1}{2}n(2a_1 + (n-1)d)$. Use this formula to demonstrate how Gauss achieved his sum so quickly.

Summation Notation

- Introduce the sigma notation, $\sum_{i=1}^{n} a_i$, and thoroughly explain what each part of the notation represents. Use Exercises 10–15 if the students need practice evaluating summations.
- Students will need some time and practice using the sigma notation to write the sum of terms as in Example 5. Have students write out the first several terms until they are comfortable with the pattern of the sequence. Once they find the pattern, the summation should fall into place.
- Example 6 is a good verbal problem to cover with students while Example 7 shows a graphical approach to series.

Suggested Problems

Exercises 1–4, 8, 10, 11, 17, 18, 23, 25
Problems 31, 32, 38, 41, 42
Enrichment Problem 43

11.3   FINITE GEOMETRIC SERIES

Focus Points

Bank Balance

- Students should understand the difference between an arithmetic series and a geometric series. A geometric series is obtained by *multiplying* a constant by the preceding term.

- Use the bank balance example as well as Example 1 to illustrate the behavior of a geometric series as it relates to the balance after each year.

- It might be helpful to compare a geometric series to the compound interest problems previously covered. Students should note that the exponential model only accounts for a single deposit, while the geometric series model accounts for a new deposit each year.

Geometric Series

- Define a finite geometric series as the sum of a finite number of terms of a geometric sequence, in which each term is a constant multiple of the preceding term.

- A finite geometric series is a sum of the form

$$S_n = a + ar + ar^2 + ... + ar^{n-1} = \sum_{i=0}^{n-1} ar^i.$$

- In addition, the sum of a finite geometric series of n terms can be given by

$$S_n = a + ar + ar^2 + ... + ar^{n-1} = \frac{a(1 - r^n)}{1 - r},$$

for $r \neq 1$. This formula is called a *closed form* of the sum.

Drug Levels in the Body

- Geometric series arise naturally in many different contexts. Use Example 3 to illustrate how the level of a drug in the body can best be modeled by a geometric series with decreasing terms. Show how each successive term models each injection.

Suggested Problems

Exercises 1, 3, 5, 9, 12
Problems 16, 17, 21
Enrichment Problem 22

11.4 INFINITE GEOMETRIC SERIES

Focus Points

Long Term Drug Level in the Body

- Have students revisit the drug level example from section 11.3. Discuss the effects of this drug level if the patient receives injections over a prolonged period of time. Using the formula for the sum of a geometric series, calculate the amount of the drug left in the body after various numbers of injections.

- Using this example, students should recognize that the drug level approaches 40 mg as the number of injections is increased. This level is called its *equilibrium* point.

- In general, this behavior can be related to an infinite geometric series, where the number of injections, n, approaches infinity.

The Sum of an Infinite Geometric Series

- Consider the geometric series $S_n = a + ar + ar^2 + ... + ar^{n-1}$. In general, if $|r| < 1$, then $r^n \to 0$ as $n \to \infty$, so

$$S_n = \frac{a(1 - r^n)}{1 - r} \to \frac{a(1 - 0)}{1 - r} = \frac{a}{1 - r}, \text{ as } n \to \infty.$$

- In this case, we say that the series *converges* to a certain value. Therefore, for $|r| < 1$, the sum of an infinite geometric series is given by

$$S = a + ar + ar^2 + ... + ar^n + ... = \sum_{i=0}^{\infty} ar^i = \frac{a}{1 - r}.$$

- However, for $|r| > 1$, then the infinite geometric series will not converge to a finite sum, but will grow larger and larger as $n \to \infty$. In this case we can say that the infinite geometric series *diverges* .

Present Value of a Series of Payments

- Discuss the definition of *present value, P,* of a future payment, *B,* as the amount which would have to be deposited, at some interest rate, r, in a bank account today to have exactly $\$B$ in the account at the relevant time in the future.

- If r is the yearly interest (compounded annually) and if n is the number of years, then $B = P(1 + r)^n$, or equivalently, $P = \frac{B}{(1 + r)^n}$.

- Use Example 2 to calculate the present value needed to cover Alex Rodriguez's signing bonus.

- Example 3 will give students practice in finding total present value using the summation notation.

Suggested Problems

Exercises 1, 4, 6, 8, 9
Problems 13, 16, 22, 23

12.1   PARAMETRIC EQUATIONS

Focus Points

The Mars Pathfinder

- The information about the Sojourner given in this section is fascinating. It provides a great introduction to parametric equations.
- It is clear that, in order to represent the robot's path, we need two functions, one for the robot's x-coordinate and one for its y-coordinate.
- Be sure to take the time to go through Examples 1 and 2. Plot the points one by one so that students can see how to generate the path.
- Discuss the concept of eliminating the parameter. This process is not intuitive to many students.

Different Motions Along the Same Path

- Example 3 describes the motion of a robot whose path is the same as that of the robot in Example 2. However, the robot is moving at half its original rate.
- Example 4 gives two other sets of parametric equations that will produce the same graph as that produced in Examples 2 and 3. However, each of these equations is produced by traveling along a very different path.
- At this point your students should realize the importance of indicating direction when sketching the graphs of parametric equations.

Other Parametric Curves

- This section introduces students to some interesting parametric equations.
- The Archimedean Spiral is re-introduced using parametric equations. This helps students reinforce the concepts developed in the section on polar equations.
- Students will also receive an introduction to Lissajous figures. Use a graphing utility to demonstrate other interesting curves to your students. (See The Graphing Calculator Guide.)
- The foxes and rabbits are re-visited for the last time. Now, we can see how the two populations are related. When students graph these equations they truly understand the meaning of the "circle of life".

Using Graphs to Parameterize a Curve

- Example 5 provides students with the opportunity to describe the motion of a particle by looking at graphs of its x and y components.
- It will probably be necessary to do more than one example. There are many of these to choose from in the exercises.

Suggested Problems

Exercises 6, 10, 14
Problems 21, 23, 29, 30
Enrichment Problems 24, 32

12.2 IMPLICITLY DEFINED CURVES AND CIRCLES

Focus Points

Introduction

- Students are reminded of the parametric equations for the unit circle that were introduced in the previous section.
- By eliminating the parameter, students can discover the implicit form of the equation of a circle.

Conic Sections

- Conic sections are so-called because they can be constructed by slicing, or sectioning, a cone.
- There are many models available to assist you in demonstrating this to your students.

Circles

- Example 2 presents students with parametric equations of a circle.
- Generalize the equations to produce the information found in the summary box.
- Eliminate the parameter to obtain the implicit equation for a circle.
- Example 4 provides students with the opportunity to complete the square and determine the center and radius of a circle.

Suggested Problems

Exercises 1, 3, 5, 12
Problems 13, 16, 19, 20, 24
Enrichment Problem 23

12.3   ELLIPSES

Focus Points

Introduction

- Explain to students that we are now going to consider the graph of an ellipse, which can be thought of as a "squashed" circle.
- The parametric equations for an ellipse are given in the summary box on page 529.
- Explain to your students that in the special case where $a = b$, these equations produce a circle of radius $r = a$. Thus, a circle is a special kind of ellipse.
- Go over Example 1 with your students, explaining the meaning of the values of a and b.
- Look at the equations in Example 2. Help your students to see what happens when the various components of the equation are changed.

Eliminating the Parameter t in the Equations for an Ellipse

- Go through the process of eliminating the parameters to produce the implicit equation for an ellipse.
- Provide students with some practice in graphing ellipses from their implicit equations.

Suggested Problems

Exercises 2, 6, 9
Problems 12, 16, 17, 18
Enrichment Problems 22

12.4 HYPERBOLAS

Introduction

- Investigate the curve given by the parametric equations $x = \sec t$ and $y = \tan t$. Use the identity $\sec^2 t - \tan^2 t = 1$ to eliminate the parameter, t, and get $x^2 - y^2 = 1$.

- Point out that, for $x \to \infty$, this curve resembles the graphs of $y = \pm x$.

- It is natural for students to inquire at this point as to what happens as $x \to 0$. Demonstrate that the curve cannot exist for $|x| < 1$, because that means y^2 would have to be negative, which is impossible.

A General Formula for Hyperbolas

- Define the parametric equations for the hyperbola: $x = h + a \sec t$ and $y = k + b \tan t$, with $0 \leq t \leq 2\pi$. Compare and contrast these to the equations for the ellipse given in the previous section.

- Use the aforementioned parametric equations along with the identity $\sec^2 t - \tan^2 t = 1$ to get the implicit equation for a hyperbola:

$$\frac{(x-h)^2}{a^2} - \frac{(y-k)^2}{b^2} = 1.$$

- Discuss the *unit hyperbola* centered at the origin that results when h and k are equal to zero and a and b are equal to one. Specifically, discuss how the asymptotes are the lines containing the opposite vertices of the rectangle centered at $(0,0)$ with width $2a$ and height $2b$. Discuss how changing the values for h and k move the "center" of the graph and changing a and b horizontally and vertically stretch the graph, respectively.

- While this hyperbola opens up left and right, the implicit equation

$$\frac{(y-k)^2}{b^2} - \frac{(x-h)^2}{a^2} = 1$$

opens up and down. Other than that, it shares all of the same features of our original hyperbola.

Suggested Problems

Exercises 1, 2, 5, 6
Problems 9, 11, 15
Enrichment Problem 18

12.5   GEOMETRIC PROPERTIES OF CONIC SECTIONS

Focus Points

A Geometric Definition of a Circle

- Remind students that circles have been defined parametrically (by the equations $x = h + r\cos t$ and $y = k + r\sin t$ when $0 \leq t \leq 2\pi$) and implicitly by the equation $(x-h)^2 + (y-k)^2 = r^2$. Point out that both of these are algebraic definitions.

- Geometrically, a circle is the locus of points in a plane at a fixed distance from a fixed point.

- Demonstrate this definition by calling two students up to the board. Mark a point on the board. Have one student hold one end of the string on the marked point. Wrap the other end of the string around a piece of chalk (or a marker) and have the other student trace the path that is formed as the marker is moved all around the board.

- You may want to investigate one of the interactive software programs that enable students to discover the geometric definitions of the conics.

- Discuss how a parameterization and an implicit equation can both give the same result as a geometric definition of a circle.

A Geometric Definition of an Ellipse

- Geometrically, an ellipse is the set of points in the plane for which the sum of the distances to two given points is constant. Point out that this definition is not altogether different from the geometric definition of a circle.

- Demonstrate this definition of an ellipse. Mark two points on the board. Take a piece of string and have two students hold the endpoints of the string on the marked points. Fit the chalk (or marker) inside the loop of the string. Have a third student come up and trace the path that is formed as the marker is moved all around the board.

- Point out that each of the fixed points is called a focus or focal point, and that the foci lie on the major axis and are equidistant from the minor axis. Also note that the constant sum of distances is the length of the major axis.

- Example 1, which discusses Pluto's distance from the sun, provides students with the opportunity to calculate the lengths of the axes and determine the focal points of an ellipse.

- Example 2 provides students with the opportunity to see the relation between the geometric and implicit definitions of an ellipse.

- Have students research a "whispering gallery". As discussed in the text, Statuary Hall in the United States Capitol is an example of a whispering gallery. For more information, you may want to visit http://en.wikipedia.org/wiki/Whispering_gallery

A Geometric Definition of a Hyperbola

- Remind students that an ellipse is the set of points in the plane for which the sum of the distances to two given points is constant. In contrast, a hyperbola is the set of points in the plane for which the difference of the distances to two given points is constant.

- Compare the various properties of a hyperbola to those of an ellipse.

- The reflective property of hyperbolas is demonstrated in Example 5, which discusses a hyperbolic mirror.

A Geometric Definition of a Parabola

- A parabola is the set of points in a plane for which the distance from a fixed point, called the focus, is equal to the distance from a fixed line, called the directrix.

- Provide students with graph paper and ask them to draw a set of axes and a line parallel to the x-axis. Have them mark a point on their paper that is not on the line, and plot points whose distance from the point and the line are equal.

- Example 7 connects the concept of focus and directrix to the equation of a parabola.

- You may want to introduce students to Archimedes' legendary use of parabolic mirrors, and also their use for headlamp reflectors in cars. See Example 8.

Suggested Problems

Exercises 2, 4, 6, 12, 16
Problems 21, 24, 32, 33, 38, 40
Enrichment Problems 42, 43, 44

12.6   HYPERBOLIC FUNCTIONS

Focus Points

Properties of Hyperbolic Functions

- Preface this unit by informing students of the frequent use of hyperbolic functions in engineering. For instance, the hyperbolic cosine function has a shape called a catenary. This shape is encountered when designing suspension bridges.

- Define the *hyperbolic cosine* and the *hyperbolic sine* functions as follows:

$$\cosh x = \frac{e^x + e^{-x}}{2}$$

$$\sinh x = \frac{e^x - e^{-x}}{2}.$$

- Show on a graph, as in Figures 12.53 and 12.54, how $y = \cosh x$ is the sum of the functions $y = \frac{1}{2}e^x$ and $y = \frac{1}{2}e^{-x}$, and $y = \sinh x$ is the sum of the functions $y = \frac{1}{2}e^x$ and $y = -\frac{1}{2}e^{-x}$.

- Verify that the hyperbolic cosine and hyperbolic sine share some of the properties of their trigonometric counterparts, namely that $y = \cosh x$ is an even function and $\cosh 0 = 1$, while $y = \sinh x$ is an odd function and $\sinh 0 = 0$.

- Discuss with your students the end behavior of the hyperbolic functions, and the fact that $y = \cosh x$ is always larger than $y = \sinh x$ for *all* values of x.

Identities Involving $\cosh x$ and $\sinh x$

- This section is a good opportunity to present your students with examples of the many similarities the hyperbolic functions share with their trigonometric counterparts. For instance, use the formulas for cosh and sinh to prove the identity $\cosh^2 x - \sinh^2 x = 1$. This should remind your students of the Pythagorean identity first seen in Chapter 6.

- Define the *hyperbolic tangent* as $\tanh x = \dfrac{\sinh x}{\cosh x}$.

- Use the aforementioned identity $\cosh^2 x - \sinh^2 x = 1$ to parameterize the implicit formula for the unit hyperbola $x^2 - y^2 = 1$. This gives the explicit parametric equations $x = \cosh t$ and $y = \sinh t$.

- Use the parameterization of the hyperbola to write explicit equations for each branch of the hyperbola as seen in Figure 12.56.

Suggested Problems

Exercises 1, 4, 6, 9
Problems 15, 16, 17, 24, 25

PART IV

DIRECTED LESSON PLANS

This section contains samples of directed
plans. This type of plan is often used for
courses that have multiple sections and u
exams. These lesson plans are designed f
80-minute class period. The time periods
shown on the left of each section. The pla
must be carefully constructed and need
monitoring since they often are taught by
graduate students (TAs) or less experienc
instructors. For an example of this kind o
program visit the University of Michigan
Department of Mathematics web site:
http://www.math.lsa.umich.edu/courses/1

1.1 LESSON 1

Starting Class

Announce: Students expected to have text and calculator; Website for course
Reading Assignment: Read Section 1.1 and 1.2
Homework Assignment: Section 1.1: 19, 27, 29, 32, 33; include any of Exercises 1–15 as appropriate for your class

0-20 Orientation and Course Information

- Self introduction - write your name and section number on the board
- Distribution of syllabus, course policies, and student data sheets
- Discussion of goals and expectations for the semester, including
  - Reading the text
  - Rule of Four
  - Cooperative Learning
  - Written and Verbal explanations
- Policies
  - Graphing calculators
  - Class quizzes
  - Uniform Exams
  - Course Attendance
- Stress that the course will require a solid effort of at least 8 hours per week outside of class.
- Indicate that a major component of the class is based on team homework, and that you will talk more about team homework in the next class period.
- Collect the student data sheets.

Ask if there are any questions. It is a good idea to indicate that there will be a quiz over course information possibly on the third class day.

20-35 Group Problem

Get the students involved in a group problem early in this class. Arrange the students at the minimum number of tables necessary, with either three of four students at each table. Start with a brief discussion of the concept of function. Emphasize from the outset that a function is nothing but a rule that uniquely assigns to one number some other number: this rule is not necessarily a "math formula." Students often believe functions and formulas are one and the same, so lead off with examples that deemphasize formulas in favor of tables, graphs, and verbal descriptions. To start the ball rolling, you can have them work out Exercise 7, Section 1.1, in their groups. Since they will not have worked in groups for you before, you should describe the process to them: They should introduce themselves to each other, then read the exercise, talk about it until they agree on the answers, and be prepared to report on their results. Tell them before they start that someone will be asked to explain their group's reasoning. When they finish, call on different groups to explain parts (a), (b), and (c).

35-50   Bug Graphing Problem

Ask them to work on Problem 28, Section 1.1. Have them read the exercise, then focus their attention back to the board and help them picture the situation by suggesting that they draw a diagram of the lightbulb and the bug's path. After most groups are finished, have a volunteer put the graph on the board. Make sure that students understand what is being represented on the vertical axis.

50-60   Discussion

Tie in the class discussion with a short lecture on the definition of a function and the various representations of a function, stressing the idea of the Rule of Four. You might start with a table or a verbal description, go to a graph, and only last bring up the symbolic representation. Graphically, discuss the vertical line test and why it "works."

60-80   More Group Work

Use the remainder of the class to have students work problems in groups. Suggested problems: Problem 10 stresses the use of a table and understanding function notation (two of the harder things for these students); Exercises 13–16 give you a chance to make sure everyone understands the axes and their labels. Ask students to volunteer to draw and label the axes for these problems on the blackboard.

Be certain to allow time before the end of class to come to closure and recap on any of the problems you have worked on in class!! Remind class of the reading and homework assignment. Re-stress that it is critical to read the book before they come to class, because you will not re-teach everything in the reading.

1.2   LESSON 2

Starting Class

Announce: Course website, Quiz on course information (or text reading) next class
Reading Assignment: Read Section 1.3
Homework Assignment: Section 1.2: Exercises 1, 3–7, 10, 11 or 12 (or as appropriate for your class); 16, 18, 20, 23
Team Homework: (due first class day of the second week) 1.1#36, 1.2#17, 1.2#24, 1.R#38 (R=Review section at end of chapter)

0-15   Team Organization

If there are students coming for the first time, give them the handouts from last class and tell them to see you after class to hand in the data sheet and ask questions. Announce the team membership (set via data sheets) and assign each team to a table. Give them a few moments to introduce themselves. Pass out and discuss the Team Homework Guidelines. (See handout following this lesson.) The first team assignment is due at the beginning of class on the last class day of the second week.

15-25   Team Homework Check

In groups, have the students look at their homework from 1.1 and compare answers. See if there are any problems that a group would like to see worked on the board. If there are questions, ask for volunteers to work the problem(s) or do them yourself, if there are no volunteers. Try to limit time to this activity. Encourage students to ask questions but also get them to come to your office or to the Math Lab if there are too many questions, especially if most of the class seems to understand.

25-45   Rate Discussion

The idea of rate of change (in particular average rate of change, since this is not yet calculus) will be addressed throughout the text. Then distribute Worksheet 1.2B. (See Worksheets in Part VI of this manual.) Ask them to match the stories with the graphs. (This should not be too hard, but encourage them to justify each choice using English). Then ask them to compute the average rates of change for each interval shown in the tables and match up the tables with the graphs. [This assumes, of course, that they have read the section beforehand a good thing to assume. If they can't get started, discuss how to compute average rate of change over an interval from a table, or ask for a volunteer to demonstrate at the board. Surely someone is prepared!] Divide the project so that different groups compute the rate of change for different tables. [In most classes this will mean that some groups will get the same tabular data. If a group finishes faster than the others, assign them another table to compute.]

45-50   Rate of Change and Increasing/Decreasing

Spend some time showing how the rates of change validate the earlier matching of verbal and graphical choices. Discuss the fact that all of these functions are decreasing functions, but they decrease in different ways. Point out how the data from the rates of change demonstrates the different types of change (i.e., faster and faster, constant, slower and slower, etc.).

50-55   Increasing/Decreasing

Discuss the terms *increasing* and *decreasing*. In the section, these terms are described graphically. It is fine to point out that if a function is increasing on an interval then the average rate of change is positive (and vice-versa), but don't fall into the trap of stating that if the average rate of change is positive (negative) the function is increasing (decreasing). In Example 4, second part, you might even want to pose the latter idea as a question, get a discussion going, and conclude by pointing out the second part of Example 4 in order to stress the importance of reading the text. It is fine to discuss (especially if it comes up) the idea of concavity, although the terms concave up and concave down don't come up in the text until Chapter 2. Most importantly, take an example like $y = x^2$, in Example 4, to make sure students understand that the function is decreasing for $x < 0$. Stress the fact that the terminology (by agreement) refers to the behavior of the function as x moves from left to right. Students have sometimes seen arrows on both ends of a graph of things like $y = x^2$ and tend to confuse long-term behavior with increasing/decreasing behavior. Discourage arrows on graphs.

55-60   Board Work on Graphs

Finally, associate the average rate of change with the slope of the line that joins two points on the graph of a function. Graphically illustrate this idea using function notation to determine the average rate of change. Problem 16 is a good in-class choice.

60-80   Group Work Check on Understanding

As time allows have teams do the True-False questions in Check Your Understanding, 1–17, starting on page 53. As a closing activity have the groups set a day and time for their first team homework meeting.

Suggestions for Team Homework

Meet at least twice during the week. Before the first meeting, try to get as far as you can individually on each of the problems in the set. The major amount of the work should be accomplished at the first meeting. Each person on the team should come to the first meeting with some idea of how to start each problem–or at least an idea of some questions to ask others in the group.

Before the second meeting, the Scribe should write a rough draft of the homework that will actually be submitted. During this meeting, the team should help to refine the draft so that the finished product will be polished and an acceptable representation for the group.

When the homework is due, **one** set of the solutions (typed or written very neatly) should be submitted *at the beginning of the class period*. The solutions should be written by the Scribe, and accompanied by a cover sheet written by the Reporter. Both the solutions and the cover sheet should be neat, legible, and with attention to correct English. No late or partial solution sets will be accepted.

Reporter's cover sheet should include:
- Dates and times of your meetings
- Each member's participation (you may give names or not, as you choose)
- Comments on how the group worked together
- Relevent comments you may want to include regarding the course or the assignment in general

Scribes report should include:
- Be written as if it is an explanation to another *student* (i.e., don't assume the reader will fill in between the lines)
- Include a paraphrase of the problem
- Clearly define functions and variables, using units where appropriate
- Keep in mind the *Rule of Four* (i.e., use diagrams or graphs or tables whenever possible)
- Be typed (or neatly written) using complete sentences, even when formulas or symbols are involved
- State the conclusion clearly and include any appropriate interpretations or justifications

Team homework will be judged on:
- An introductory paraphrasing of the problem
- Grasp of the main ideas
- Clear explanations of your thinking
- Use of the *Rule of Four* wherever possible (especially graphs even when not asked for)
- Appropriate, correct, and accurate mathematics
- A final summary of your findings
- Careful and honest Reporter's pages

1.3   LESSON 3

Getting Started

Announce: Content quiz on 1.1 and 1.2
Reading Assignment: Read Section 1.4
Homework Assignment: Section 1.3: 13, 14, 16, 18, 23, 26; include any of Exercises 1–10 as appropriate for your class

0-10   Quiz

Give a short quiz on today's reading assignment (Section 1.3) or on the course information. This need not be long or difficult, just enough to determine if they have actually read the section before class or to check that they understand the course goals and requirements. Announce the date and sections to be covered for the next in-class quiz.

10-20   Homework Check

This is a good time to get students to mix into new groups for in-class work, In their new groups, have the students look at their homework from Section 1.2 and compare answers. See if there are any problems that they would like to see worked on the board. If there are questions, ask for volunteers to work the problem(s). If explanations are required, be sure that anyone presenting the problem gives a complete explanation. Alert students that they will be required to explain/justify/interpret answers on team homework and exams.

20-30   Linear Family of Functions

Section 1.3 introduces the first family of functions. Students are familiar with the general formula for linear functions ($y = b + mx$) but often have not explored this family from its presentation by tables and verbal descriptions, or thought a lot about the interpretations of m and b within the context of a problem. The challenge for us is to present the material as fresh and to keep students from thinking that this material is just a rehash of what they have had before. Tie together linear functions and the rate of change, i.e., the rate of change is constant. Have students find a formula for a linear function given by data. Exercises 1–6 are examples of table pattern recognition. Ask students to work the problem in their groups and to justify their answers for each table. Ask them to come up with a formula to represent any linear function(s) that could generate the data shown. Note that while tables give discreet data (i.e., we do not know what is going on between the data points), we will often be asked to come up with formulas for mathematical models which might generate the data in a given table or which might model a graph shown in a figure. The formulas do not give unique solutions, nor should it be indicated that they do. In general, we are being asked to recognize patterns from tables or graphs that might lead to a particular family as a reasonable model, based on the information given.

30-40   Linear Model

Next, move to a simple linear modeling problem such as Problem 11. Emphasize that linear functions often arise naturally in the form

$$\text{Dependent variable} = \text{Initial value} + (\text{rate of change})(\text{independent variable})$$

For this reason we generally write $y = b + mx$ rather than $y = mx + b$, although either form is correct. Ask students to interpret m and b in the context of the problem. Note that in the context of the problem does not mean "change in y over change in x" for slope nor "y-intercept" for b. Encourage students to use words such as "The slope, m, indicates that the population is increasing at the constant rate of 58 people per year and b gives the initial population in year $t = 0$." Note: If you use Problem 11, or another example with time in years, make certain the students understand that the input, t, is the number of years after a certain date rather than the year itself. Problem 11 has $t = 0$ representing the year 2006. Make sure students understand the difference between $P(0)$ and $P(2006)$.

40-55 Axes Labeling

Problem 19 asks for understanding of axis labeling and slope interpretation. Switch students into random groups if you haven't done so yet. Ask students to work this problem in their new teams, and get volunteers to put the graphs on the board. Note that answers may vary, as the axis intercepts are not given. This problem is harder for students than it looks.

55-70 Summary

Summarize the material from today's lesson. Students should know what a linear function is, what general form their equations take, how to find a linear function from two points or a table of data, and how to make predictions or find certain information from a linear model. Stress that a linear function can be viewed graphically as a line, algebraically as an equation $y = b + mx$, and numerically as a table that exhibits a constant rate of change.

70-80 Discussion on Gateway

Suggest students prepare for the gateway exam by studying the Tools section of Chapter 1. If you have not discussed the gateway, explain that they should be taking the gateway exam in the computer lab soon. You may want to take some time now to work some difficult types of problems from a sample test.

1.4 LESSON 4

Getting Started

Announce Collection of Team Homework #1 on the front table at the start of class
Reading Assignment: Read Section 1.5
Homework Assignment: Section 1.4: 31, 34, 37, 38, 40, 43; include any of Exercises 1–30 as appropriate for your class
Team Homework Assignment #2 (due first class of 3rd week): 1.3#24, 1.4#44, 1.R#45, 1.R#42-43

0-25   Quiz

Pass out the quiz. Remind students that the seating is tight and to keep their eyes on their own papers. Allow 20 minutes for the quiz (or less, if it is a short quiz). Get in the habit of announcing the time allowed, and stick to that allotment.)

25-35   Homework

As you collect the quizzes, ask for questions from the homework and volunteers for solutions.

35-45   Graphing Calculator

This is a good time to make sure students can use a graphing calculator and determine a suitable window. Problems 27–29 from Section 1.3 can be used here. Again, allow for variability of answers to the second part of Problem 27.

45-60   Linear Formula

If you have talked about finding a linear formula from a table of data, finding a linear formula from a graph follows easily. Most students are familiar with ways to find an equation for a line given two points. Assign Problems 18 and 19 for in-class work. Have the formulas put on the board. This should not take long.

60-75   Alternate Linear Form - Budget Constraint

Example 3 on budget constraint is difficult for students. Ask students to work a similar but different example. For example-assume the stock of a company ZYX costs $28 per share and the stock of company ABC costs $20 per share. You have decided to buy a total of $600 worth of stock in the two companies. Let z be the amount of ZYX stock and a be the amount of ABC stock, and ask students to find a linear equation relating the values of z and a. It should not take students long to arrive at the equation $28z + 20a = 600$. Have them put their equation in slope intercept form and to interpret the meaning of the slope and the axis intercepts. There can be different answers depending on whether students solve for a in terms of z or vice-versa. If possible, discuss both interpretations. You do not have to impose the restriction that whole shares must be purchased, but you may introduce that idea if you wish. If you make up another example, try to choose variable names so that x and y are not used exclusively.

75-80   Three Linear Forms

A summary box on page 31 presents three versions of the equation of a line. This is sometimes confusing to students. Be sure to point out that all of these equations just boil down to the slope-intercept form and the three forms are equivalent. Sometimes one form is easier than another to find a formula from the given information (as in the above budget constraint example).

1.5   LESSON 5

Starting Class

Announce: Regrettably, we will skip Section 1-6
Reading Assignment: Section 2.1
Homework Assignment: Section 1.5: 17, 18, 22, 24, 31, 33; include any of Exercises 1–14 as appropriate for your class

0-10   Return Quizzes

Go over anything consistently missed. Ask for questions from the previous homework.

10-25   Parallel and Perpendicular Lines

Section 1.5 brings together geometric properties of lines, comparison of slopes, properties of parallel and perpendicular lines, and solving linear systems. You might start with an abstract example such as the following: Consider $y = P + Mx$ and $y = Q + Nx$, with $N < M < 0$ and $P < Q$. What are the relative positions of the lines (which line is above the other) as x tends toward positive infinity/negative infinity. Students sometimes have problems dealing with abstract or literal parameters. It is fine for them to plug in some numbers, but ask them to try to justify their conjectures using the letters M, N, P and Q, rather than numbers. Ask them if the lines will cross, and if so will the intersection be for $x > 0$, $x < 0$, or $x = 0$, and why. Ask if there are any conditions under which the lines will not cross. This will lead to a discussion of parallel lines, and you can lead from there to the conditions for perpendicular lines. Be sure they are clear on the terminology and meaning of negative reciprocal.

25-40   Group Work

Discuss, briefly, horizontal and vertical lines and their equations. Ask why a vertical line is not a function. Encourage students to use their knowledge of slope and intercept properties to work Exercises 2 and 6 without the aid of a calculator. Assign Exercises 1 or 7 for in-class group work and ask for reasons for their choices. To extend the practice with literal parameters, have them work Problem 35 in their teams. Make sure to include closure on each of these problems before going on.

40-60   Intersections

Finally, have the students work out a problem that requires them to correctly interpret the points of intersection of various pairs of lines. The text deals with a car rental problem, here is another good example: A power company offers residents the following options:
  1. flat fee of $180 per month regardless of how much power is used
  2. flat fee of $50 per month plus $0.12 per KWH
  3. fee of $0.21 per KWH with no flat fee imposed
Have students determine which option is best. (Of course, it depends on power usage, but the students should provide this in their answers.

60-75   Solving a Linear Systems

If you have time, draw and find the intersection of the two linear equations $y = 2x - 3.5$ and $y = -0.5x + 4$. This can be solved algebraically or graphically. Asking for both methods will give an opportunity for an algebra review and a demonstrations of the use of the solve routine on the calculator. Be sure that students have a good understanding of lines and their properties from the *Rule of Four* standpoint. We will move on to Chapter 2 in the next class.

75-80   Gateway Reminder

Ask students how they're doing on the gateway. Tell them that the deadline for passing the test is absolute, so if it has not been passed, they must work on this immediately.

PART V

SYLLABI

This section contains sample syllabi for four different general course configurations. These can be easily modified to meet other specific courses.

Syllabus for a Semester Course in Precalculus

(Based on a 14-week semester.)

Week	Activity
1	1.1, 1.2, 1.3
2	1.4, 1.5, 2.1
3	2.2, 2.3, 2.4, 2.5
4	2.6, Review, Exam 1
5	3.1, 3.2, 3.3
6	3.4, 3.5, 4.1, 4.2
7	4.3, 5.1, 5.2
8	5.3, 5.4, 5.5
9	Review, Exam 2, 6.1
10	6.2, 6.3, 6.4
11	6.5, 6.7, 8.1
12	8.2, 8.3, 9.1
13	9.2, 9.3, 9.4, 9.5
14	9.6, Review
15	Final Exam (Comprehensive)

Note: This syllabus does not use Chapter 7.

Syllabus for a Semester Course in Precalculus with Gateways and Labs

(Based on a 14-week semester, 4 meetings per week)

Week	Activity
1	1.1, 1.2, 1.3, Gateway: Equations
2	1.4, 1.5, Lab on 1.6, 2.1
3	2.2, 2.3, 2.4, 2.5
4	2.6, Review, Exam 1, 3.1
5	3.2, Gateway: Exponents, 3.3, 3.4
6	Lab: Excel, 4.1, 4.2, Gateway: Logs
7	4.3, Review, Exam 2, 5.1
8	5.2, 5.3, 5.4, 5.5
9	6.1, Lab, 6.2, 6.3
10	6.4, 6.5, 6.6, Gateway: Trig.
11	6.7, Review, Exam 3, 8.1
12	Lab, 8.2, 8.3, 9.1
13	9.2, 9.3, 9.4, 9.5
14	9.6, Lab on 9.7, Review, Exam 4
15	Final Exam (Comprehensive)

Note: This syllabus shows each day's schedule separated by a comma.

Syllabus for a Quarter System

(Based on a 10-week quarter.)

Week	Activity
1	1.1 – 1.5
2	Exam, 2.1– 2.4
3	2.5, 2.6, 3.1–3.3
4	3.4, 3.5, Review, Exam, 4.1, 4.2
5	4.3, 4.4, 5.1, 5.2, 5.3
6	5.4, 5.5, Review, Exam
7	6.1–6.5
8	6.6, 6.7, 7.1, 7.2, 7.3
9	8.1, 8.2, 8.3, Review, Exam
10	9.1–9.6
11	Final Exam (Comprehensive)

Syllabus for a Forty Week High School Course

Semester I	
Week	**Activity**
1	1.1, 1.2
2	1.3, 1.4
3	1.5, 1.6
4	Review, Exam, 2.1
5	2.2, 2.3
6	2.4, 2.5
7	2.6, Review, Exam
8	3.1, 3.2
9	3.3, 3.4
10	3.5, Review, Exam
11	4.1, 4.2
12	4.2, 4.3
13	4.3, 4.4
14	Review, Exam
15	5.1, 5.2
16	5.3, 5.4
17	5.5, Review
18	Exam, 6.1
19	6.2, 6.3
20	6.4, 6.5

Semester II	
Week	**Activity**
21	6.5, Exam
22	6.6, 6.7
23	Review, Exam
24	7.1, 7.2
25	7.3, 7.4
26	7.5, 7.6
27	Review, Exam, 8.1
28	8.2, 8.3
29	Review, Exam, 9.1
30	9.2, 9.3, 9.4
31	9.5, 9.6
32	9.7, Review, Exam
33	10.1, 10.2
34	10.3, 10.4
35	10.5, Review, Exam
36	11.1, 11.2
37	11.3, 11.4
38	Review, Exam, 12.1
39	12.2, 12.3, 12.4
40	12.5, 12.6, Review, Final Exam

Note: This syllabus assumes that students have a previous knowledge of trigonometry. If students do not have this knowledge, then Chapters 6 and 7 should be covered at a slower pace. Teachers might omit some topics in Chapters 10, 11, and 12 to compensate.

PART VI

WORKSHEETS AND TRANSPARENCIES

This section contains worksheets and transparencies that have been referenced this manual.

Section 1.1: Functions and Function Notation

Definition. A *function* is a rule that takes certain values as inputs and assigns to each input value exactly one output value.

1. Let $y = \dfrac{2}{1+x}$. Fill in the table below.

Table 1

x	0	1	2	3
y				

2. Which of the graphs below represent y as a function of x? Explain you reasoning.

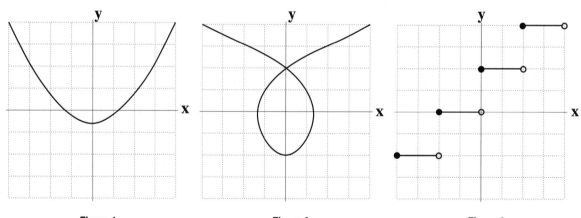

Figure 1   Figure 2   Figure 3

3. A woman drives from Aberdeen to Webster, South Dakota, going through Groton on the way, traveling at a constant speed for the whole trip. (See map below).

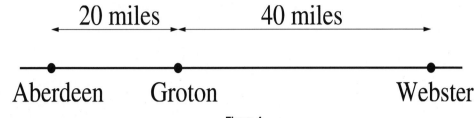

Figure 4

a. Sketch a graph of the woman's distance from Webster as a function of time.

b. Sketch a graph of the woman's distance from Groton as a function of time.

Section 1.2A: Rates of Change

1. Let $f(x) = 4 - x^2$. Find the average rate of change of $f(x)$ on each of the following intervals.
   (a) $0 \le x \le 2$ (b) $2 \le x \le 4$ (c) $b \le x \le 2b$

2. Below, you are given a graph of the amount, Q, of a radioactive substance remaining after t years. Only the t-axis has been labeled. Use the graph to give a **practical interpretation** of each of the three quantities that follow. A practical interpretation is an explanation of meaning using everyday language.

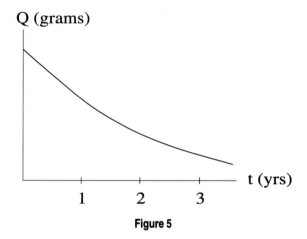

Figure 5

    a. $f(1)$

    b. $f(3)$

    c. $\dfrac{f(3) - f(1)}{3 - 1}$

3. Two cars travel for 5 hours along Interstate 5. Car A travels 300 miles, always at a constant speed. Car B travels 400 miles, but at varying speeds (see graph below).

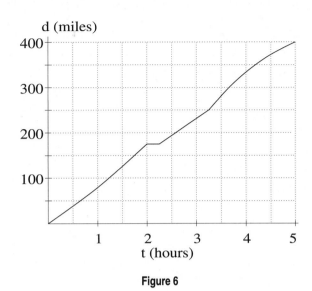

Figure 6

(a) On the axes above, sketch a graph of the distance traveled by Car A as a function of time.

(b) Compute the average velocity of each car over the 5-hour trip.

(c) Does Car B drive faster than Car A over the entire 5 hour interval? Justify your answer!

Section 1.2B: Rates of Change

Match each story with the table and graph which best represent it.

1. When you study a foreign language, the number of new verbs you learn increases rapidly at first, but slows almost to a halt as you approach your saturation level.

2. You board an airplane in Philadelphia heading west. Your distance from the Atlantic Ocean, in kilometers per minute, increases at a constant rate.

3. The interest on your savings plan is compounded annually. At first your balance grows slowly, but its rate of growth continues to increase.

(E)

x	0	5	10	15	20	25
y	20	275	360	390	395	399

(F)

x	0	5	10	15	20	25
y	20	36	66	120	220	400

(G)

x	0	5	10	15	20	25
y	20	95	170	245	320	395

(I)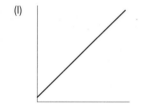

(II)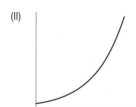

(III)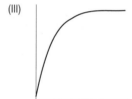

Section 1.3: Linear Functions

1. Let $C = 20 - 0.35t$, where C is the cost of a case of apples (in dollars) t days after they were picked.

   (a) Complete the table below:

   Table 2

t (days)	0	5	10	15
C (dollars)				

   (b) What was the initial cost of the case of apples?

   (c) Find the average rate of change of C with respect to t. Explain in practical terms (i.e., in terms of cost and apples) what this average rate of change means.

2. In parts (a) and (b) below, two different linear functions are described. Find a formula for each linear function, and write it in slope intercept form.

   (a) The line passing through the points $(1, 2)$ and $(-1, 5)$.

   (b)

   Table 3

C	10	15	20	25
F	50	59	68	77

3. According to one economic model, the demand for gasoline is a linear function of price. If the price of gasoline is $p = \$1.10$ per gallon, the quantity demanded in a fixed period of time is $q = 65$ gallons. If the price is $\$1.50$ per gallon, the quantity of gasoline demanded is 45 gallons for that period.

   (a) Find a formula for q (demand) in terms of p (price).

   (b) Explain the economic significance of the slope in the above formula. In other words, give a practical interpretation of the slope.

   (c) According to this model, at what price is the gas so expensive that there is no demand?

   (d) Explain the economic significance of the vertical intercept of your formula from part (a).

4. Look back at your answer to problem 2(b). You might recognize this answer as the formula for converting Celsius temperatures to Fahrenheit temperatures. Use your formula to answer the following questions.

   (a) Find C as a function of F.

   (b) What Celsius temperature corresponds to $90°F$?

   (c) Is there a number at which the two temperature scales agree?

ections 1.4 and 1.5: Formulas for and Geometric Properties of Linear Functions

1. You need to rent a car for one day and to compare the charges of 3 different companies. Company I charges $20 per day with an additional charge of $0.20 per mile. Company II charges $30 per day with an additional charge of $0.10 per mile. Company III charges $70 per day with no additional mileage charge.

   (a) For each company, find a formula for the cost, C, of driving a car m miles in one day. Then, graph the cost functions for each company for $0 \leq m \leq 500$. (Before you graph, try to choose a range of C values that would be appropriate.)

   (b) How many miles would you have to drive in order for Company II to be cheaper than Company I?

2. Consider the lines given in the figure below. Given that the slope of one of the lines is -2, find the **exact coordinates** of the point of intersection of the two lines. ("Exact" means to leave your answers in fractional form.)

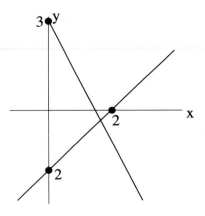

Figure 7

3. Parts (a) and (b) below each describe a linear function. Find a formula for the linear function described in each case.

(a) The line parallel to $2x - 3y = 2$ that goes through the point $(1, 1)$.

(b) The line perpendicular to $2x - 3y = 2$ that goes through the point $(1, 1)$.

Section 1.5: Geometric Properties of Linear Functions

Given below are the equations for five different lines. Match each formula with its graph.

- $f(x) = 20 + 2x$
- $g(x) = 20 + 4x$
- $h(x) = 2x - 30$
- $u(x) = 60 - x$
- $v(x) = 60 - 2x$

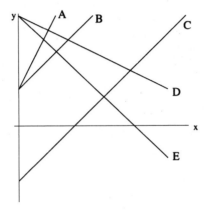

Figure 8

Worksheet 2.1: Input–Output

1. The circumference of a circle is a function of its radius: $c(r) = 2\pi r$.

   (a) $c(10) =$

   (b) Describe the expression in (a) using a complete sentence.

2. Let $f(x) = ax^2 - x + c$. Compute the following expressions:

   (a) $f(3) =$

   (b) $f(c) =$

   (c) $f(-2c) =$

   (d) $f(7t) =$

3. Let $h(x) = \dfrac{x+1}{x^2+3}$. Then

   (a) $h(1) =$

   (b) $h(2) =$

   (c) $h(b) =$

   (d) $h(a+3) =$

   (e) $h(2a) =$

   (f) $h(1) + 2 =$

4. The following table shows the amount of garbage produced in the US as reported by the EPA.

Table 4

t (years since 1900)	60	65	70	75	80	85	90
G (millions of tons of garbage per year)	90	105	120	130	150	165	180

Consider the amount of garbage G as a function of time $G = f(t)$. Include units with your answers.

(a) $f(60) =$

(b) $f(75) =$

(c) Solve $f(t) = 165$.

(d) Solve $f(t + 5) = 130$.

(e) Solve $f(t) + 15 = 105$.

5. Given is the graph of the function $v(t)$. It represents the velocity of a man riding his bike to the library and going back home after a little while. A negative velocity indicates that he is riding toward his house, away from the library.

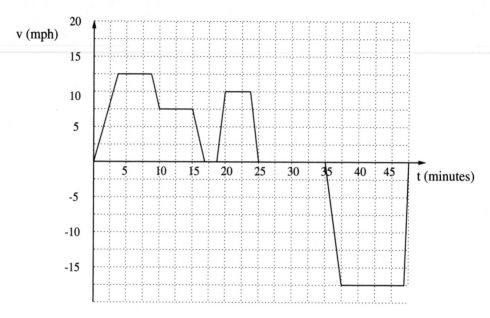

Figure 9

Evaluate and interpret:

(a) $v(5) =$

(b) $v(40) =$

(c) $v(12) - v(7) =$

(d) $v(-7) =$

Solve for t and interpret:

(e) $v(t) = 5$

(f) $v(t) = -10$

(g) $v(t) = v(10)$

Section 2.2: Domain and Range

1. For each of the following functions below, give the domain and the range.

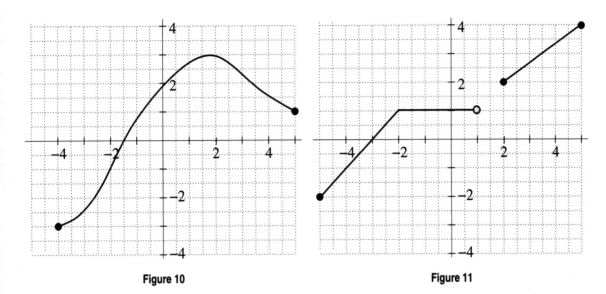

Figure 10   Figure 11

2. Oakland Coliseum is capable of seating 63,026 fans. For each game, the amount of money that the Raider's organization makes is a function of the number of people, n, in attendance. If each ticket costs \$30.00, find the domain and range of this function. Sketch its graph.

3. Find the domain and range of each of the following functions.

    (a) $f(x) = \sqrt{3x + 7}$

    (b) $g(x) = \dfrac{1}{(x - 1)^2}$

    (c) $h(x) = x^2 - x - 6$

    (d) $k(x) = \sqrt{x^2 - x - 6}$

Section 2.3: Piecewise Defined Functions

1. Consider the absolute value function

$$f(x) = |x| = \begin{cases} x, & \text{if } x \geq 0 \\ -x, & \text{if } x < 0 \end{cases}.$$

   (a) Draw a graph of $f(x)$.

   (b) Find $f(-2)$ and $f(2)$ algebraically and graphically.

   (c) Write $g(x) = |x - 2|$ as a piecewise defined function and graph it.

2. Let $h(x) = \begin{cases} x + 1, & \text{for } x \leq 2 \\ 1, & \text{for } x > 2 \end{cases}.$

   (a) Draw the graph of $h(x)$.

   (b) Compute $h(2)$, $h(1)$, $h(10)$, $h(-3)$.

   (c) Solve $h(x) = 0$ and $h(x) = 5$, if possible.

3. Find a formula for the function given below.

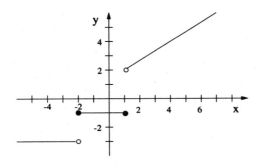

Figure 12

4. A private museum charges $40 for a group of 10 or fewer people. A group consisting of more than 10 people must, in addition to the $40, pay $2 per person for the number of people above 10. For example, a group of 12 pays $44. The maximum group size is 50.

   (a) Draw a graph that represents this situation.

   (b) How much does a group of 16 pay?

   (c) Find a formula for the cost function.

   (d) What are the domain and range of the cost function?

5. Give an example of another real life situation that can be modeled with a piecewise defined function.

Section 2.4: Inverse Functions

1. Use the two functions shown below to fill in the blanks. Note that the function shown in the graph is $f(x)$ and that the values of $g(x)$ are given in the table.

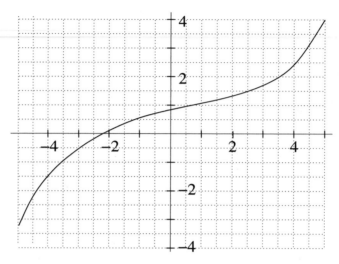

Figure 13

Table 5

x	-6	-4	-2	0	2	4	6
$g(x)$	2	0	3	7	6	1	5

(a) $f(2) =$ _____   (b) $f^{-1}(2) =$ _____   (c) $g(0) =$ _____   (d) $g^{-1}(0) =$ _____

(e) $f(3)+1 =$ _____   (f) $f^{-1}(3)+1 =$ _____   (g) $f(3+1) =$ _____   (h) $f^{-1}(3+1) =$ _____

(g) If $g^{-1}(x) = 0$, then $x =$ _____.

2. Let $A = f(n)$ be the amount of periwinkle blue paint, in gallons, needed to paint n square feet of a house. Explain in practical terms what each of the following quantities represents. Use a complete sentence in each case.

(a) $f(20)$

(b) $f^{-1}(20)$

3. If a cricket chirps R times per minute, then the outside temperature is given by $T = f(R) = \frac{1}{4}R + 40$ degrees Fahrenheit.

   (a) Find a formula for the inverse function $R = f^{-1}(T)$.

   (b) Calculate and interpret $f(50)$ and $f^{-1}(50)$.

2.5: Concavity

1. Consider the functions shown below. Fill in the accompanying tables and then decide whether each function is increasing or decreasing, and whether it is concave up or concave down.

(a) **Description.** This graph gives distance driven as a function of time for a fast driver.

t	0	2	3	5
d				
$\dfrac{\Delta d}{\Delta t}$				

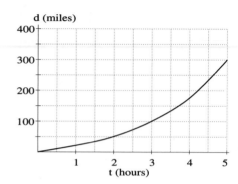

(b) **Description.** This graph gives distance driven as a function of time for a slow driver.

t	0	2	3	5
d				
$\dfrac{\Delta d}{\Delta t}$				

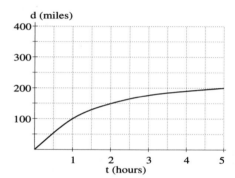

(c) **Description.** This graph gives the amount of a decaying twinkie as a function of time.

t	0	4	6	10
A				
$\dfrac{\Delta A}{\Delta t}$				

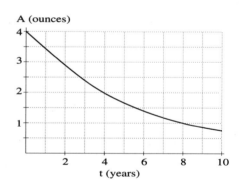

(d) **Description.** This graph gives the amount of ice remaining in a melting ice cube as a function of time.

t	0	4	6	10
A				
$\dfrac{\Delta A}{\Delta t}$				

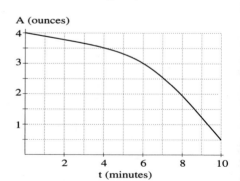

2. Decide whether each of the following functions are concave up, concave down, or neither.

x	0	1	2	3	4
$f(x)$	1	3	6	10	20

x	0	1	2	3	4
$g(x)$	10	9	7	4	0

$p(x) = 3x + 1$

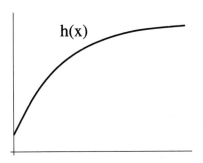

3. Read the following description of a function. Then, decide whether the function is increasing or decreasing. What does the scenario tell you about the concavity of the graph modeling it?

"When a new product is introduced, the number of people who use the product increases slowly at first, and then the rate of increase is faster (as more and more people learn about the product). Eventually, the rate of increase slows down again (when most people who are interested in the product are already using it)."

Section 2.6: Quadratic Functions

1. Find (if possible), the zeros of the following quadratic functions.

   (a) $f(x) = x^2 + 5x - 14$

   (b) $g(x) = x^2 + 1$

2. The height of a rock thrown into the air is given by $h(t) = 40t - 16t^2$ feet, where t is measured in seconds.

   (a) Calculate $h(1)$ and give a practical interpretation of your answer.

   (b) Calculate the zeros of $h(t)$ and explain their meaning in the context of this problem.

   (c) Solve the equation $h(t) = 10$ and explain the meaning of your solutions in the context of this problem.

   (d) Use a graph of $h(t)$ to estimate the maximum height reached by the stone. When, approximately, does the stone reach its maximum height? Is the function concave up or concave down?

Sections 3.1 – 3.3: Exponential Functions I

1. Suppose we start with 100 grams of a radioactive substance that decays by 20% per year. First, complete the table below. Then, find a formula for the amount of the substance as a function of t and sketch a graph of the function.

Table 6

t (years)	0	1	2	3	4
Q (grams)					

2. Suppose you invest $10000 in the year 2000 and that the investment earns 4.5% interest annually.

   (a) Find a formula for the value of your investment, V, as a function of time.

   (b) What will the investment be worth in 2010? in 2020? in 2030?

3. The population of the planet Vulcan and the planet Romulus are recorded in 1980 and in 1990 according to the table below. Also, assume that the population of Vulcan is growing exponentially and that the population of Romulus is growing linearly.

Table 7

Planet	1980 Population (billions)	1990 Population (billions)
Vulcan	8	12
Romulus	16	20

(a) Find two formulas; one for the population of Vulcan as a function of time and one for the population of Romulus as a function of time. Let $t = 0$ denote the year 1980.

(b) Use your formulas to predict the population of both planets in the year 2000.

(c) According to your formula, in what year will the population of Vulcan reach 50 billion? Explain how you got your answer.

(d) In what year does the population of Vulcan overtake the population of Romulus? Justify your answer with an accurate graph and an explanation.

Sections 3.1 – 3.3: Exponential Functions II

1. Find possible formulas for each of the two functions f and g described below.

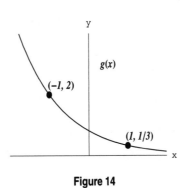

Figure 14

Table 8

x	0	2	4	6
$f(x)$	2	2.5	3.125	3.90625

2. Consider the exponential graphs pictured below and the six constants $a, b, c, d, p,$ and q.

   (a) Which of these constants are **definitely** positive?

   (b) What of these constants are **definitely** between 0 and 1?

   (c) Which two of these constants are **definitely** equal?

   (d) Which one of the following pairs of constants **could be** equal?

   a and p b and d b and q d and q

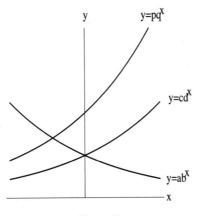

Figure 15

Section 3.4: Continuous Growth

1. Suppose that the population of an insect colony starts at 10000 and has a continuous growth rate of 4% per day.

   (a) Find a formula for the population of the insect colony after t days.

   (b) What is the population of the colony after 5 days?

   (c) By what percent does the colony grow each year?

Section 4.1: Logarithms and Their Properties

1. Solve each of the following equations for x.

(a) $5 \cdot 9^x = 10$

(d) $5x^9 = 10$

(b) $10e^{4x+1} = 20$

(e) $e^{2x} + e^{2x} = 1$

(c) $a \cdot b^t = c \cdot d^{2t}$

(f) $\ln(x + 5) = 10$

2. Simplify each of the following expressions.

   (a) $\log(2A) + \log(B) - \log(AB)$

   (b) $\ln(ab^t) - \ln((ab)^t) - \ln a$

3. Decide whether each of the following statements are true or false.

   (a) $\ln(x + y) = \ln x + \ln y$

   (b) $\ln(x + y) = (\ln x)(\ln y)$

   (c) $\ln(ab^2) = \ln a + 2\ln b$

   (d) $\ln(ab^x) = \ln a + x\ln b$

   (e) $\ln(1/a) = -\ln a$

Section 4.2: Logarithms and Exponential Models

1. Scientists observing owl and hawk populations collect the following data. Their initial count for the owl population is 245 owls, and the population grows by 3% per year. They initially observe 63 hawks, and this population doubles ever 10 years.

   (a) Find a formula for the size of the population of owls and hawks as functions of time.

   (b) When will the populations be equal?

2. Find the half-lives of each of the following substances.

   (a) Tritium, which decays at an annual rate of 5.471% per year.

   (b) Vikinium, which decays at a continuous rate of 10% per week.

3. If 17% of a radioactive substance decays in 5 hours, how long will it take until only 10% of a given sample of the substance remains?

Section 4.3: Logarithmic Functions

1. Consider the functions $f(x) = \ln x$ and $g(x) = \log x$.

   (a) Complete the table below.

   Table 9

x	0.1	0.5	1	2	4	6	8	10
$\ln x$								
$\log x$								

   (b) Plug a few very small numbers x into $\ln x$ and $\log x$ (like 0.01, 0.001, etc.) What happens to the output values of each function?

   (c) If you plug in $x = 0$ or negative numbers for x, are $\ln x$ and $\log x$ defined? Explain.

   (d) What is the domain of $f(x) = \ln x$? What is the domain of $g(x) = \log x$?

   (e) Sketch a graph of $f(x) = \ln x$ below, choosing a reasonable scale on the x and y axes. Does $f(x)$ have any vertical asymptotes? Any horizontal asymptotes?

2. What is the domain of the following four functions?

   (a) $y = \ln(x^2)$
   (b) $y = (\ln x)^2$
   (c) $y = \ln(\ln x)$
   (d) $y = \ln(x - 3)$

3. Consider the exponential functions $f(x) = e^x$ and $g(x) = e^{-x}$. What are the domains of these two functions? Do they have any horizontal asymptotes? any vertical asymptotes?

Sections 5.1 – 5.3: Function Transformations

1. Consider the function $f(x) = x^2 - 4x + 4$.

Transformation	Formula	Graph	Description
$y = f(x) + 2$			
$y = f(x) - 2$			
$y = f(x + 2)$			
$y = f(x - 2)$			
$y = f(-x)$			
$y = -f(x)$			

2. Let $y = f(x)$ be the function whose graph is given below. Fill in the entries in the table below, and then sketch a graph of the transformations $y = 2f(x)$ and $y = f(x - 2)$.

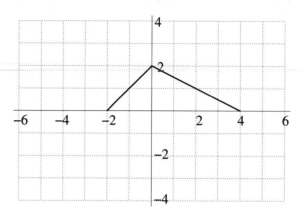

Figure 16

Table 10

x	-4	-2	0	2	4	6
$f(x)$						
$2f(x)$						
$f(x-2)$						

3. Let $y = f(x)$ be the function whose graph is given below. Fill in the entries in the table below, and then sketch a graph of the transformations $y = f(-x)$ and $y = 1 - 2f(x)$.

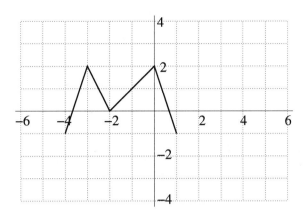

Figure 17

Table 11

x	-6	-5	-4	-3	-2	-1	0	1	2	3	4	5	6
$f(x)$			0	2	0	1	2	-1					
$f(-x)$						-1	2	1	0	2	0		
$1 - 2f(x)$			1	-3	1	-1	-3	3					

4. Given to the right is the graph of the function $y = \left(\frac{1}{2}\right)^x$. On the same set of axes, sketch the graph of $y = \left(\frac{1}{2}\right)^{x-2}$ and $y = \left(\frac{1}{2}\right)^x - 2$.

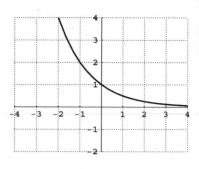

Figure 18

5. Let $H = f(t)$ be the temperature of a heated office building t hours after midnight. (See diagram to the right for a graph of f.) Write down a formula for a new function that matches each story below.

(a) The manager decides that the temperature should be lowered by 5 degrees throughout the day.

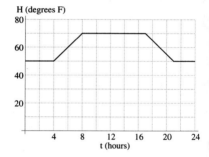

Figure 19

(b) The manager decides that employees should come to work 2 hours later and leave 2 hours later.

6. Use algebra to show that $f(x) = x^4 - 2x^2 + 1$ is an even function and that $g(x) = x^3 - 5x$ is an odd function.

7. Given the graph of $y = f(x)$ given below, sketch the graph of the following related functions:

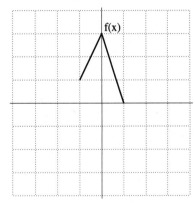

(a) $y = -f(2 - x) + 2$

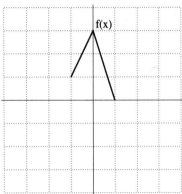

(b) $y = 2 - f(1 - x)$

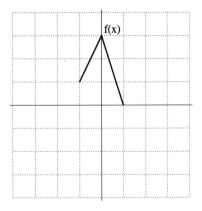

Section 5.5: The Family of Quadratic Functions

1. For each of the following, complete the square in order to find the vertex. In part (b), your answer will contain the constant "b."

     (a) $y = x^2 - 40x + 1$ (b) $y = 2x^2 + bx + 3$

2. Find a formula for the quadratic function shown below. Also find the vertex of the function.

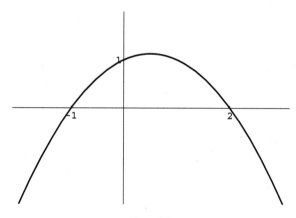

Figure 20

3. A parabola has its vertex at the point $(2, 3)$ and goes through the point $(6, 11)$. Find a formula for the parabola.

4. A tomato is thrown vertically into the air at time $t = 0$. Its height, $d(t)$ (in feet), above the ground at time t (in seconds) is given by $d(t) = -16t^2 + 48t$.

   (a) Find t when $d(t) = 0$. What is happening to the tomato the first time that $d(t) = 0$? The second time?

   (b) When does the tomato reach its maximum height? How high is the tomato's maximum height?

Section 6.1: Introduction to Periodic Functions

1. The Brown County Ferris Wheel has diameter 50 meters and completes one full revolution every two minutes. When you are at the lowest point on the wheel, you are still 5 meters above the ground. Assuming you board the ride at $t = 0$ seconds, sketch a graph of your height, $h = f(t)$, as a function of time.

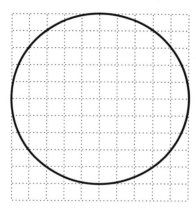

Figure 21

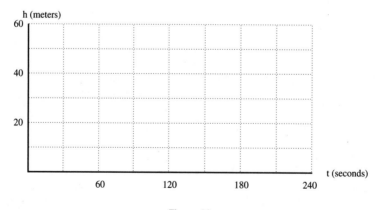

Figure 22

What are the amplitude, midline and period of the function?

2. The function given below models the height, h, in feet, of the tide above (or below) mean sea level t hours after 6:00 a.m.

   (a) Is the tide rising or falling at 7:00 a.m.?

   (b) When does low tide occur?

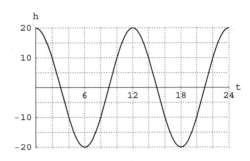

Figure 23

   (c) What is the amplitude of the function? Give a practical interpretation of your answer.

   (d) What is the midline of the function? Give a practical interpretation of your answer.

3. Which of the following functions are periodic? For those that are, what is the period?

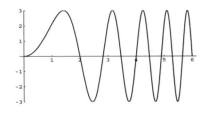

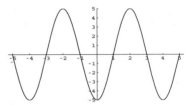

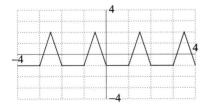

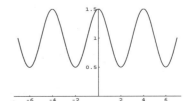

Section 6.2: The Sine and Cosine Function

1. Use the unit circle to the right to estimate each of the following quantities to the nearest 0.05 of a unit.

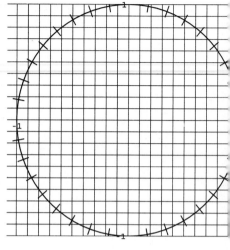

Figure 24

(a) $\sin(90°) = $ _____

(b) $\cos(90°) = $ _____

(c) $\sin(180°) = $ _____

(d) $\cos(180°) = $ _____

(e) $\cos(45°) = $ _____

(f) $\sin(-90°) = $ _____

(g) $\cos(70°) = $ _____

(h) $\sin(190°) = $ _____

(i) $\sin(100°) = $ _____

(j) $\cos(100°) = $ _____

2. For each of the following, fill in the blank with an angle between 0° and 360°, different from the first one, that makes the statement true.

(a) $\sin(20°) = \sin($ _____ $)$

(b) $\sin(70°) = \sin($ _____ $)$

(c) $\sin(225°) = \sin($ _____ $)$

(d) $\cos(20°) = \cos($ _____ $)$

(e) $\cos(70°) = \cos($ _____ $)$

(f) $\cos(225°) = \cos($ _____ $)$

3. Given to the right is a unit circle. Fill in the blanks with the correct answer in terms of a or b.

(a) $\sin(\theta + 360°) = $ _____

(b) $\sin(\theta + 180°) = $ _____

(c) $\cos(180° - \theta) = $ _____

(d) $\sin(180° - \theta) = $ _____

(e) $\cos(360° - \theta) = $ _____

(f) $\sin(360° - \theta) = $ _____

(g) $\sin(90° - \theta) = $ _____

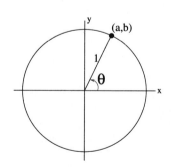

Figure 25

4. Use your calculator to find the coordinates of the point P at the given angle on a circle of radius 4 centered at the origin.

(a) 70°

(b) 255°

Section 6.3: Radian Measure

1. In the pictures below, you are given the radius of a circle and the length of a circular arc cut off by an angle θ. Find the degree and radian measure of θ.

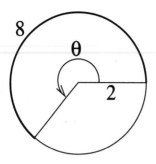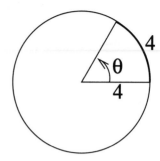

Figure 26

2. In the pictures below, find the length of the arc cut off by each angle.

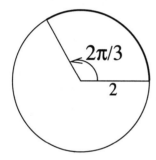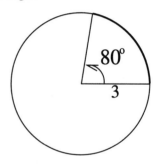

Figure 27

3. A satellite orbiting the earth in a circular path stays at a constant altitude of 100 kilometers throughout its orbit. Given that the radius of the earth is 6370 kilometers, find the distance that the satellite travels in completing 70% of one complete orbit.

4. An ant starts at the point (0,3) on a circle of radius 3 (centered at the origin) and walks 2 units counterclockwise along the arc of a circle. Find the x and the y coordinates of where the ant ends up.

Sections 6.4 and 6.5 – Graphs of Sinusoidal Functions

1. Find a possible formula for each of the following sinusoidal functions.

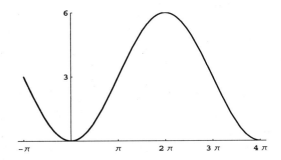

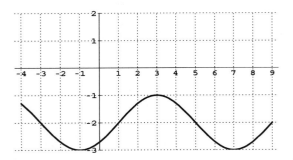

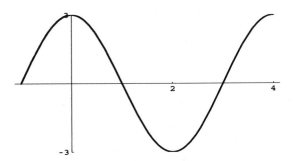

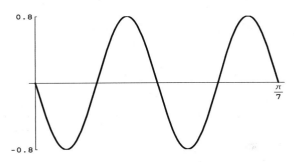

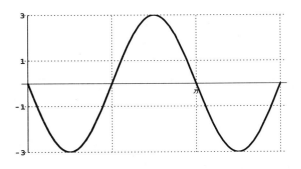

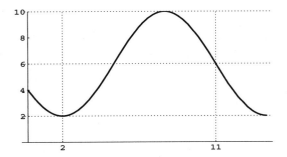

2. For each of the following, find the amplitude, the period, the phase shift, and the midline.

   (a) $y = 2\cos(\pi x + \frac{2\pi}{3}) - 1$

   (b) $y = 3 - \sin(2x - 7\pi)$

3. A population of animals oscillates annually from a low of 1300 on January 1st to a high of 2200 on July 1st, and back to a low of 1300 on the following January. Assume that the population is well-approximated by a sine or a cosine function.

   (a) Find a formula for the population, P, as a function of time, t. Let t represent the number of months after January 1st. (**Hint.** First, make a rough sketch of the population, and use the sketch to find the amplitude, period, and midline.)

   (b) Estimate the animal population on May 15th.

   (c) On what dates will the animal population be halfway between the maximum and the minimum populations?

Section 6.6: Other Trigonometric Functions

1. Suppose that $\sin \theta = -\frac{3}{4}$ and that $\frac{3\pi}{2} \leq \theta \leq 2\pi$. Find the **exact values** of $\cos \theta$ and $\sec \theta$.

2. Suppose that $\csc \theta = \frac{x}{2}$ and that θ lies in the 2nd quadrant. Find expressions for $\cos \theta$ and $\tan \theta$ in terms of x.

3. Given to the right is a circle of radius 2 feet (not drawn to scale). The length of the circular arc s is 2.6 feet. Find the lengths of the segments labeled $u, v,$ and w. Give all answers rounded to the nearest 0.001.

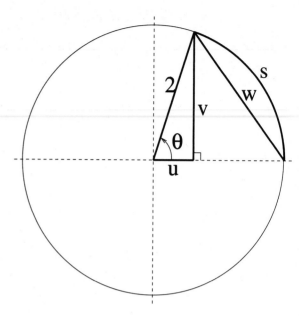

Figure 28

Section 6.7: Solving Trigonometric Equations

1. Solve each of the following trigonometric equations, giving all solutions between 0 and 2π. Give **exact** answers whenever possible.

(a) $\sin\theta = -\frac{\sqrt{3}}{2}$

(b) $\tan\theta = -\frac{1}{4}$

(c) $\cos\theta = \frac{1}{2}$

2. Find all solutions to $2 \sin x \cos x + \cos x = 0$ that lie between 0 and 2π. Give your answers **exactly**.

3. Use the graph to the right to estimate the solutions to the equation

$$\cos x = 0.8$$

that lie between 0 and 2π. Then, use reference angles to find more accurate estimates of your solutions.

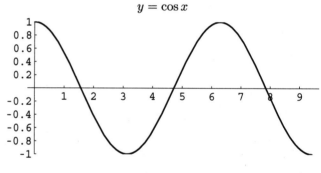

$y = \cos x$

Figure 29

Section 7.1: The Laws of Sines and Cosines

1. Two fire stations are located 25 miles apart, at points A and B. There is a forest fire at point C. If $\angle CAB = 54°$ and $\angle CBA = 58°$, which fire station is closer? How much closer?

2. A triangular park is bordered on the south by a 1.7-mile stretch of highway and on the northwest by a 4-mile stretch of railroad track, where $33°$ is the measure of the acute angle between the highway and the railroad tracks. As part of a community improvement project, the city wants to fence the third side of the park and seed the park with grass.

   (a) How much fence is needed for the third side of the park?

   (b) What is the degree measure of the angle on the southeast side of the park?

   (c) For how much total area will they need grass seed?

3. To measure the height of the Eiffel Tower in Paris, a person stands away from the base and measures the angle of elevation to the top of the tower to be 60°. Moving 210 feet closer, the angle of elevation to the top of the tower is 70°. How tall is the Eiffel Tower?

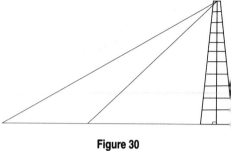

Figure 30

4. The two points P and T are on opposite sides of a canyon (see sketch to the right). From P to another point R on the same side is 200 feet. Angles PRT and RPT are found to be 25° and 120°, respectively.
   (a) What is the distance from P to T?

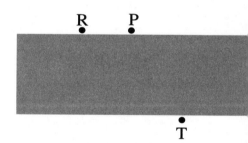

Figure 31

   (b) Suppose the canyon is reasonably straight, what is the shortest distance across the canyon?

Section 7.2: Trigonometric Identities

1. Given the right triangle to the right, write each of the following quantities in terms of h.

   Note. Asking you to "write something in terms of h" is NOT asking you to solve for h. It is asking you to rewrite the quantity that you are given so that h is the only unknown in your answer.

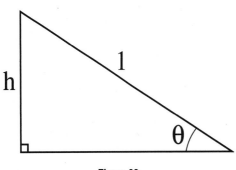

Figure 32

(a) $\sin\theta$

(b) $\cos\theta$

(c) $\cos\left(\frac{\pi}{2} - \theta\right)$

(d) $\sin(2\theta)$

(e) $\cos(\sin^{-1} h)$

2. By starting with one side and showing that it is equal to the other side, prove the following trigonometric identity:

$$\frac{\sin t}{1 - \cos t} = \frac{1 + \cos t}{\sin t}$$

Section 8.1: Function Composition

1. Given below are the graphs of two functions, f and g. Use the graphs to estimate each of the following.

    (a) $g(f(0)) =$ _____

    (b) $f(g(0)) =$ _____

    (c) $f(g(3)) =$ _____

    (d) $g(g(4)) =$ _____

    (e) $f(f(1)) =$ _____

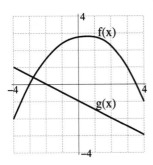

Figure 33

2. Let $f(x) = \dfrac{1}{1 + 2x}$.

    (a) Solve $f(x + 1) = 4$ for x.

    (b) Solve $f(x) + 1 = 4$ for x.

    (c) Calculate $f(f(x))$ and simplify your answer.

3. For each of the following functions $f(x)$, find functions $u(x)$ and $v(x)$ such that $f(x) = u(v(x))$.

(a) $\sqrt{1+x}$

(c) $\sin(x^3 + 1)\cos(x^3 + 1)$

(b) 3^{2x+1}

(d) $\dfrac{1}{1 + \frac{2}{x}}$

4. For each of the following functions, calculate

$$\frac{f(x+h) - f(x)}{h}$$

on a separate sheet of paper, if necessary, and simplify your answers.

(a) $f(x) = x^2 + 2x + 1$ (b) $f(x) = \frac{1}{x}$ (c) $f(x) = 3x + 1$

Section 8.2: Inverse Functions

1. Find a formula for the inverse function of each of the following functions.

   (a) $f(x) = \dfrac{x-1}{x+1}$

   (b) $g(x) = \ln(3-x)$

2. Given below is the graph of the functions $f(x)$ and $g(x)$. Use the functions to estimate each of the following.

   (a) $f(2) = $ _____

   (b) $f^{-1}(2) = $ _____

   (c) $f^{-1}(g(-1)) = $ _____

   (d) $g^{-1}(f(3)) = $ _____

   (e) Rank the following quantities in order from smallest to largest: $f(1)$, $f(-2)$, $f^{-1}(1)$, $f^{-1}(-2)$, 0

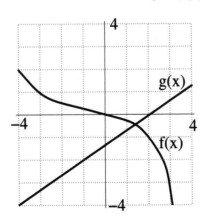

Figure 34

3. Let $f(x) = 10e^{(x-1)/2}$ and $g(x) = 2\ln x - 2\ln 10 + 1$. Show that $g(x)$ is the inverse function of $f(x)$.

4. Let $f(t)$ represent the amount of a radioactive substance, in grams, that remain after t hours have passed. Explain the difference between the quantities $f(8)$ and $f^{-1}(8)$ in the context of this problem.

Section 9.1: Power Functions

Definition. A *power function* is a function of the form $f(x) = kx^p$, where k and p are constants.

I. Positive Integer Powers. Match the following functions to the appropriate graphs below: $y = x^2, y = x^3, y = x^4, y = x^5$

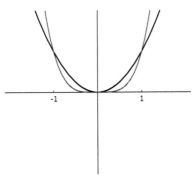

Figure 35

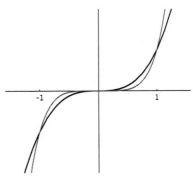

Figure 36

II. Negative Integer Powers. Match the following functions to the appropriate graphs below: $y = x^{-2}, y = x^{-3}, y = x^{-4}, y = x^{-5}$

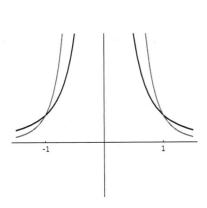

Figure 37

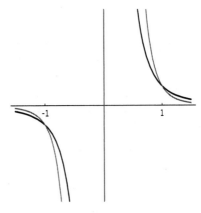

Figure 38

III. Positive Fractional Powers. Match the following functions to the appropriate graphs below: $y = x^{1/2}, y = x^{1/3}$

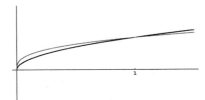

Figure 39

1. The blood circulation time (t) of a mammal is directly proportional to the 4th root of its mass (m). If a hippo having mass 2520 kilograms takes 123 seconds for its blood to circulate, how long will it take for the blood of a lion with body mass 180 kg to circulate?

2. Find a formula for the power function $g(x)$ described by the table of values below. Be as accurate as you can with your rounding.

Table 12

x	2	3	4	5
$g(x)$	4.5948	7.4744	10.5561	13.7973

Sections 9.2 and 9.3: Polynomials

1. Use your calculator to plot the following polynomials. Then answer questions (i)-(ii) below about each polynomial.

    (a) $y = 2x + 3$
    (b) $y = x^2 - x - 2$
    (c) $y = x^3 - 2x^2 - x + 2$
    (d) $y = 5x^2 + 4$

    (i) How often does each polynomial cross the x-axis?

    (ii) How many turning points does each polynomial have?

    (iii) How many roots can a 6th degree polynomial have at most? How many roots does it have at least?

    (iv) Find a quadratic polynomial that has no roots.

2. For the four polynomials from question (1), and for the three polynomials below, find out what happens to y as x goes to plus or minus infinity.

    (e) $y = -2x^3 + 6x - 2$
    (f) $y = 2x - x^2$
    (g) $y = -x^6 - x - 2$

    (i) Make a guess about the endpoint behavior of a polynomial in general.

    (ii) Plot a few more polynomials to test your guess.

3. Consider $p(x) = (x - 3)(x + 5)(x - 37)(2x + 4)x^2$

    (a) What is the degree of $p(x)$?

    (b) What is its leading coefficient?

    (c) What is the constant coefficient

    (d) How many roots does $p(x)$ have?

    (e) What are the roots?

4. Consider the graphs given below. For each graph, complete the following:

   (a) Make a guess about the degree of each polynomial.
   (b) What are the roots of each polynomial?
   (c) We know that a polynomial with single roots a, b, and c is given by $y = k(x - a)(x - b)(x - c)$, where k is a constant. Find possible equations for the polynomials.

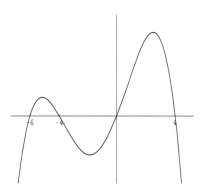

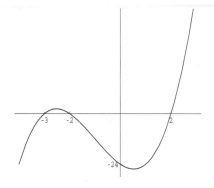

Figure 40

Figure 41

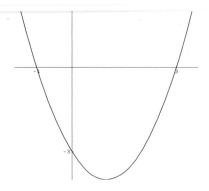

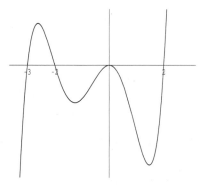

Figure 42

Figure 43

Sections 9.4 and 9.5: Rational Functions

For each of the following rational functions, find all horizontal and vertical asymptotes (if there are any), all x-intercepts (if there are any), and the y-intercept. Find exact and approximate values when possible. Then, give a rough sketch of the function.

1. $f(x) = \dfrac{3x - 4}{7x + 1}$

2. $f(x) = \dfrac{x^2 + 10x + 24}{x^2 - 2x + 1}$

3. $f(x) = \dfrac{2x^3 + 1}{x^2 + x}$

4. $f(x) = \dfrac{(x^2 - 4)(x^2 + 1)}{x^6}$

5. $f(x) = \dfrac{2x + 1}{6x^2 + 31x - 11}$

6. $f(x) = \dfrac{2x^2 - c}{(x - c)(3x + d)}$, where c and d are constants, and $c \neq 0$.

7. $f(x) = \dfrac{1}{x - 3} + \dfrac{1}{x - 5}$

   Hint: First, find a common denominator.

8. $f(x) = \dfrac{x^5 - 2x^4 - 9x + 18}{8x^3 + 2x^2 - 3x}$

   Hint: $x^5 - 2x^4 - 9x + 18 = x^4(x - 2) - 9(x - 2)$

9. $f(x) = \dfrac{1}{x - 1} + \dfrac{2}{x + 2} + 3$

   Hint: First, find a common denominator.

Section 9.5A: Asymptotes

For each of the following situations, sketch the graph of a function $f(x)$ which has all of the described properties. Your functions should be defined everywhere and have no jumps or breaks except where vertical asymptotes occur.

(1) As $x \to \infty$, $f(x) \to 2$.   (2) As $x \to -\infty$, $f(x) \to -2$.

(3) As $x \to -4^-$, $f(x) \to \infty$.   (4) As $x \to -4^+$, $f(x) \to -\infty$.

(5) As $x \to 3^-$, $f(x) \to -\infty$.   (6) As $x \to 3^+$, $f(x) \to -\infty$.

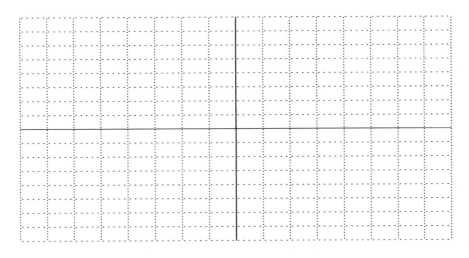

Figure 44

(1) $f(0) = 3$

(2) $f(x)$ has a vertical asymptote at $x = -3$.

(3) $f(x)$ is increasing on $-8 < x < -3$, on $-3 < x < 1$, and on $4 < x < 8$.

(4) $f(x)$ is decreasing on $1 < x < 4$.

(5) $f(x)$ is concave up on $-8 < x < -3$ and on $3 < x < 6$.

(6) $f(x)$ is concave down on $-3 < x < 3$ and on $6 < x < 8$.

(7) As $x \to \infty$, $f(x) \to -3$.

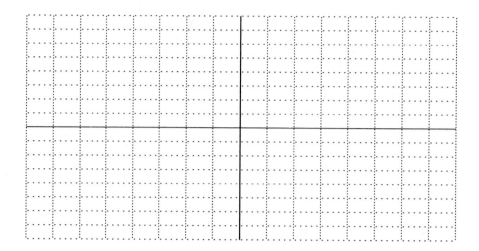

Figure 45

Section 9.5B: Rational Functions

1. For each of the following rational functions, find all horizontal and vertical asymptotes, all real zeros (exactly if possible), and the y-intercept. Do the computations on a separate sheet of paper.

(a) $f(x) = \dfrac{2x+1}{6x^2 + 31x - 11}$

(b) $f(x) = \dfrac{3x-4}{7x+1}$

(c) $f(x) = \dfrac{2x^2 - c}{(x-c)(3x+d)}$

(d) $f(x) = \dfrac{2x^3 + 1}{x^2 + x}$

(e) $f(x) = \dfrac{1}{x-3} + \dfrac{1}{x-5}$

(f) $f(x) = \dfrac{1}{x-1} + \dfrac{2}{x+2} + 3$

2. It costs a company \$30000 to begin production of a good, plus \$3 for every unit of the good produced. Let x be the number of units produced by the company.

(a) Find a formula for $C(x)$, the total cost for the production of x units of the good.

(b) Find a formula for the company's average cost per unit, $a(x)$.

(c) Graph $y = a(x)$ for $0 < x \le 50000$ and $0 \le y \le 10$. Label the horizontal asymptote.

(d) Explain in practical terms why the graph of a has the long-run behavior that it does.

(e) Explain in practical terms why the graph of a has the vertical asymptote that it does.

(f) Find a formula for $a^{-1}(y)$. Give an economic interpretation of $a^{-1}(y)$.

(g) The company makes a profit if the average cost of its good is less than \$5 per unit. Find the minimum number of units that the company can produce and make a profit.

PART VII

SAMPLE GATEWAY TESTS

This section contains sample gateway exam
Parallel forms are easily constructed from
them. Gateway exams are commonly used
insure that students have the prerequisite
particularly algebraic, to successfully mas
the precalculus material. The gateway exa
are normally given outside of class time, c
taken repeatedly, and are not part of grad
This signals to the student that prerequisi
are important but that valuable class time
not be spent on reviewing prerequisite ski

Precalculus
Gateway Exam: Equations

Name: _____

Solve the following equations for the variable shown next to the answer space.

1. $2 - 3(x - 1) = 5 - (x - 2)$ $\qquad$ $x =$ _____

2. $\dfrac{5 + y}{5 - y} = 3$ $\qquad$ $y =$ _____

3. $\dfrac{0.1}{7 - 2t} = \dfrac{2}{30 + 4t}$ $\qquad$ $t =$ _____

4. $ax + b = c - a(x - b)$ $\qquad$ $x =$ _____

5. $1 = \dfrac{At + B}{C - At}$ $\qquad$ $t =$ _____

6. $\dfrac{P}{q - rt} - \dfrac{r}{r + pt} = 0$ $\qquad$ $t =$ _____

7. $z^2 - 4z - 21 = 0$ $\qquad$ $z =$ _____

8. $x(x - 2a) = 3a(x - 2a)$ $\qquad$ $x =$ _____

9. $\begin{cases} 3x - 5y = 20 \\ -y = \frac{x}{5} \end{cases}$ $\qquad$ $x =$ _____

$\qquad$ $y =$ _____

10. $\begin{cases} x + by = 2b \\ x + y = b^2 + 1 \end{cases}$ $\qquad$ $x =$ _____

$\qquad$ $y =$ _____

Precalculus   Name: _____

Gateway Exam: Exponents

Simplify without using a calculator:

Evaluate or simplify without a calculator:

1. $4^{-\frac{1}{2}} + \sqrt{0.01}$ = _____

2. $\dfrac{(ab^2)^3}{a^0 b^5}$ = _____

3. $\dfrac{(AB)^2}{A^{-1}B^{-3}}$ = _____

4. $\dfrac{\sqrt{x^{-1}y^3}}{x^{\frac{1}{2}}y^{\frac{5}{2}}}$ = _____

5. $b^{-1}(b^2 + b) - 1$ = _____

6. $\dfrac{M + M^{-1}}{1 + M^{-2}}$ = _____

7. $3\sqrt{t^3} + 7(t^9)^{1/3}$ = _____

8. $\dfrac{2km^2 + k^2 m}{km^{-1}}$ = _____

Solve for x:

9. $32^x = 2$ $x =$ _____

10. $\dfrac{6}{3a^0} = 2$ $x =$ _____

Precalculus   Name: _____
Gateway Exam: Logs

Simplify without using a calculator:

1. $\log(0.01)$ = _____

2. $\ln(e\sqrt{e})$ = _____

3. $\log(2A) + \log(B) - \log(AB)$ = _____

4. $2\log M - \log(10M^2)$ = _____

5. $\ln(e^2 + e) - \ln(e + 1)$ = _____

Solve for the variable shown next to the answer space. Do not use a calculator.

6. $7^x - 31 = 0$ $x =$ _____

7. $5e^{2t} = 0.1$ $t =$ _____

8. $Ae^t = Be^{-t}$ $t =$ _____

9. $\log(x - 5) = 2$ $x =$ _____

10. $Pa^t = Qb^t$ $t =$ _____

Precalculus
Gateway Exam: Trigonometry

Name: _____

Evaluate or simplify without a calculator:

1. $\sin(-90°)$ _____

2. $\cos(3\pi/2)$ _____

3. $\tan(\pi/4)$ _____

4. $\cos(\pi/6)$ _____

5. $\sin(2\pi/3)$ _____

6. $\cos A \tan A$ _____

7. $\cos^2(A+B) + \sin^2(A+B)$ _____

8. $\left(1 - \dfrac{1}{\cos^2\theta}\right) \cdot \dfrac{\cos^2\theta}{\sin^2\theta}$ _____

9. $\sin^{-1}\left(\frac{1}{2}\right)$ _____

10. $\arccos\left(-\frac{1}{2}\right)$ _____

NOTES

NOTES

NOTES

NOTES

NOTES

NOTES

NOTES